Mathematics
for
Elementary
School
Teachers

MATHEMATICS
FOR
ELEMENTARY
SCHOOL
TEACHERS

Meridon Vestal Garner

Assistant Professor of Mathematics
North Texas State University

Goodyear Publishing Company, Inc.
Pacific Palisades, California

G-5849

Library of Congress Catalog Card Number 72–77903

Printed in the United States of America

Current Printing (last digit):

10   9   8   7   6   5   4   3   2   1

Preface

The mathematics of the elementary curriculum provides a teacher with one of the best opportunities to introduce his pupils to the elements of mathematical logic. Unfortunately, many of the present-day teachers have not studied under curricula that provide such opportunities. As an in-service or a preservice teacher, competence in mathematics consisting of the basic components of the "new" mathematics as well as those of the "old" mathematics will be expected.

This book presents a blend of the modern and of the traditional. Occasionally, reference is made to where a particular result might be useful to a teacher of elementary mathematics. This is in sharp contrast to some of the almost sterile developments within some current texts in this area.

The user of this text will also find that different levels of rigor in instruction may be used from class to class, depending upon the level desired and suitable to the students. For example, properties such as Commutativity and Associativity are simply stated within the context of the material, and are then rationalized in the form of proofs within the Problem Sets. Hence both the speed and the rigor of the course may vary without fear of "leaving something out".

One of the aims of this book is to introduce to the in-service or preservice teacher the nature of mathematics as a logical system. For this reason, precise definitions as well as important theorems derived from these definitions are stated and set apart.

Effort has been made to present an intuitive development for each new concept prior to a rigorous definition. For this reason, the formal definitions in many instances are simply a summation of prior discussion, with a Problem Set immediately following which allows a student to illustrate knowledge of the concept under discussion.

Another aim of this text is to provide the student with mathematical models encountered in the teaching of mathematics and to illustrate how these basic models are generalized in later courses of mathematics. Provision is made so that the student can get an overview of the elementary mathematics program as an entity.

The recommendations of the Committee on the Undergraduate Program in Mathematics of the Mathematical Association of America have greatly influenced the academic level of the text. Generally, the text follows the recommendations of this committee regarding a first-course for preservice or in-service teachers.

I wish to express my appreciation to all concerned with the preparation of the material of the text, particularly to Dr. Floyd Vest and Mrs. Karen Emmons.

M. V. G.
Denton, Texas

Contents

Mathematics
for
Elementary
School
Teachers

Basic Concepts

—the Whole Numbers

PART ONE

CHAPTER 1

Introduction to Sets
and Set Notation

1.1 SETS, A CONCEPT

Many times a dictionary will use a cyclic approach to define a particular word. For example, the word *polite* is defined by the words *polished, refined,* or *cultivated.* Further investigation reveals that *polished* is defined in terms of *refined, refined* is defined in terms of *cultivated* and *cultivated* is defined in terms of *polite.* Hence we have the endless cycle

This cyclic approach to defining terms can sometimes become confusing and frustrating, because no adequate definition may be given for these terms except by using another undefined term. Such expressions are called basic, or primitive terms.

3

In mathematics there are many terms for which no adequate definition may be given. These terms are considered to be basic, or primitive terms. Three examples of primitive terms are *point, number,* and *set.* Euclid, in his *Elements of Geometry,* attempted to define a point as "that which has no breadth, depth, or width." Modern geometers have found this definition superfluous, and now make no attempt to define a point. The term *point* is left as a primitive term.

Similarly, the term *number* is considered to be a primitive term. Using symbols, we may write the *numeral* that communicates the idea of number. For example, to convey the idea of four objects, we may write the numerals "4," "IV," "quatro (four in Spanish)," or "10_{four} (four in base four)." These numerals may be used to convey the *idea* of a set that contains a certain quantity of objects (cardinality) or as a numeral that designates a certain order (ordinality) of objects. Note that we write the communication symbols and not the number. A number is an abstract idea and is therefore relegated to being a primitive term.

Three ways to denote set membership. Each of us is familiar with the concept of a set. Synonymous with the term set are terms such as "team," "group," or "cluster." In mathematics we may use "a set of dishes," "a set of basketball players," or "a set of men from outer space." If three objects, such as the team containing Bill, Tom, and Jack are selected to be the members of a particular set, membership within this set is denoted by:

$$\{Bill, Tom, Jack\},$$

which means the set contains the members Bill, Tom, and Jack.

This method of denoting set membership is called listing the elements (or members) of the set. Other examples which illustrate the principle of listing the elements of the set are:

$$\{Mary, Mary's\ dog, Mary's\ hat\},$$
$$\{My\ car, your\ bicycle, Joe's\ second\ cousin\},$$
$$\{A\ triangle, a\ circle, a\ square\}.$$

Symbols such as "Bill, Tom, and Jack" are used to communicate an idea of certain objects that possess some common property. Therefore, the term *set* is a primitive term, and to indicate set membership, enclose in braces the *symbols* that convey to different people some common thought, idea, or property. For example, {A dog, a cat, a tiger}, may denote a set of animals with a common property that each animal within the set has four legs. This set may also denote one with a common property that each animal within the set has four paws; it may also denote a set with a common property that each animal within the set has fur.

Frequently, it becomes impossible or impractical to list the totality of elements within a set. When this situation occurs, a *description of the set* is preferable to listing the elements of the set. To describe the set, state in words the properties or characteristics that distinguish certain objects from other objects. This method is termed *describing the set*. For example:

{All grains of sand along the Mississippi River},
{All stars in the sky},
{All rocks in the Rio Grande River},
{All numbers greater than ten},

is each an example which describes the elements of a particular set.

Another method for denoting set membership is by the *set builder* or *set selector* method. This method makes use of a selector which indicates the pattern for denoting elements of a particular set:

{Pupils| pupils are in this class},

means "the set of elements, (pupils), such that these pupils belong to this class." Another example:

{Numbers| numbers are greater than ten},

means "the set of elements (numbers), such that these numbers are greater than ten." Note the selector, *numbers*, denotes which objects are to be considered as members of the set.

Instead of writing the word "numbers" to denote the selector, the selector is generally indicated by some alphabetical letter. For example

$\{n|\quad n\quad$ is less than 10$\}$,

means "the set of all numbers, n,   such that n is less than ten."

EXAMPLES

(a) $\{n|\quad n\quad$ is greater than 20$\}$.
(b) $\{n|\quad n + 4$ is less than 7$\}$.

The paragraphs above establish three methods to denote sets. These are (a) listing the elements of the set, (b) describing the set, and (c) denoting set membership by the set selector.

1.2 SET EQUALITY

Many of you are familiar with ideas of equality from prior study in mathematics. The sentence   "2 + 4 = 6"   means that   "2 + 4"   names a number, "6" names a number, and they both name the same number. In this sense, equality denoted identity. When dealing with sets, set equality need not be replaced with an idea that is completely different from that above:

$$A = \{\text{Bill, Tom, Jack}\}$$

means that "A" names a set, "$\{\text{Bill, Tom, Jack}\}$" names a set, and they both name the same set. We read the above as "A is the same set as the set Bill, Tom, and Jack," or more simply, "A equals $\{\text{Bill, Tom, Jack}\}$."

The symbol "$\in$" is used to indicate membership within, or to be an element of, a set:

EXAMPLE

(a) "Bill $\in$ $\{\text{Bill, Tom, Jack}\}$" means *Bill* is an element of $\{\text{Bill, Tom, Jack}\}$;

(b) "Your cow $\in$ $\{\text{Your cow, my dog, her cat}\}$" means *Your cow* is an element of $\{\text{Your cow, my dog, her cat}\}$;

(c) "$2 \in$ $\{n|$ $n + 2$ is less than $7\}$" means *2* is an element of $\{n|$ $n + 2$ is less than $7\}$.

To denote any element in set A, the symbols "$a \in A$" are used. These symbols mean that the elements represented by a are elements of (or belong to) set A. The negation of this statement, "$a \notin A$" means that the elements represented by a are not elements of (do not belong to), set A. Using this notation, we are able to define Equal Sets.

Definition 1.1 —Equal Sets For every set A and for every set B, "Set A equals set B" $(A = B)$, means that for each $a \in A$ then $a \in B$, and for each $b \in B$ then $b \in A$.

The symbols "$A = B$" mean the latter A names a set, the letter B names a set, and they both name the same set. To negate this statement, "$A \neq B$" means that letter A names a set, letter B names a set, and they both name *different* sets. This is referred to as the *inequality relation* for sets or more simply that "set A does not equal set B."

1.3   SPECIAL SETS OF NUMBERS

Within this text, reference will be made to special sets of numbers. When referring to these particular sets, it is sometimes impossible or impractical to list each element within the set. Devices have been developed so that certain established patterns can convey the idea that all elements are listed within a set. This is accomplished through the use of   "...". The set consisting of all Counting Numbers is defined as

$$C = \{1, 2, 3, 4, \ldots\},$$

where the three dots,   "..."   designate a continuation in the pattern that is established. Other special sets of numbers are defined as:

$$E = \{\text{Even Counting Numbers}\} = \{2, 4, 6, 8, \ldots\},$$
$$O = \{\text{Odd Counting Numbers}\} = \{1, 3, 5, 7, \ldots\},$$
$$W = \{\text{Whole Numbers}\} = \{0, 1, 2, 3, \ldots\}.$$

When indicating omissions as above, the student should be very certain that a pattern has been established that will not be misleading. For example, the set of Counting Numbers less than   2,000,000   may be listed as

$$\{1, 2, 3, 4, \ldots, 2,000,000\},$$

which established a definite pattern to follow before omissions are indicated. Other examples:

(a) $\{n|$ n is an odd Counting Number less than $100\} =$

$$\{1, 3, 5, 7, \ldots, 99\}.$$

(b) $\{n|$ $n + 7$ is less than 200, n is a Counting Number$\} =$

$$\{1, 2, 3, 4, \ldots, 192\}.$$

The listing of two or three successive elements will not be sufficient to establish a pattern before indicating omissions. For example,

$$\{2, 4, \ldots, 64\},$$

could mean

$$\{2, 4, 8, 16, 32, 64\},$$

or

$$\{2, 4, 6, 8, 10, \ldots, 64\}.$$

Similarly, $\{1, 2, 3, \ldots\}$ could mean

$$\{1, 2, 3, 4, 5, \ldots\},$$

or

$$\{1, 2, 3, 5, 8, 13, 21, \ldots\}.$$

From the above, careful consideration should be given to the particular situation before omissions are indicated. A definite pattern should be clearly established in each instance before indicating omissions.

PROBLEM SET 1.1

In the following, list the elements of the given set. You may use the three dots to indicate omissions.

1. $\{n|$ n is a Counting Number and n is less than 10$\}$ =

2. $\{x|$ x is a State of the United States and x borders the Gulf of Mexico$\}$ =

3. $\{g|$ g is one of the Great Lakes$\}$ =

4. $\{t|$ t was a President of the United States since Franklin Roosevelt$\}$ =

5. $\{p|$ p is a planet revolving about our sun$\}$ =

6. $\{x|$ $x + 3 = 5$, and x is a Counting Number$\}$ =

7. $\{x|$ x is the current President of the United States$\}$ =

8. $\{n|$ $n + 94$ is less than 100 and n is a Counting Number$\}$ =

9. $\{a|$ a is the largest State of the United States$\}$ =

10. $\{r|$ r is a woman and r was a President of the United States$\}$ = .

For each of the following, the elements of a particular set are listed. Write a description of each set.

1. $\{$Chevrolet, Ford, Plymouth, . . . , Valiant$\}$ =

2. $\{$Royal, Underwood, Smith, Olympia, . . . , I.B.M.$\}$ =

3. $\{$March, May$\}$ =

4. $\{1, 2, 3, 4, 5, 6, 7, 8, 9\}$ =

5. $\{$Mary, Margaret, Marilyn, . . . , Mable$\}$ =

6. $\{\frac{1}{7}, \frac{2}{7}, \frac{3}{7}, \frac{4}{7}, \frac{5}{7}, \frac{6}{7}, \ldots\}$ =

7. $\{6, 8, 10, 12, 14\}$ =

8. $\{$*Life, Newsweek, Time,* . . . , *U. S. News and World Report*$\}$ =

9. $\{$Brahman, Charlaise, Hereford, . . . , Shorthorn$\}$ = .

Answer the following   "True"   or   "False". Justify your answer.

1. Any collection of objects can be thought of as a set.

2. Any collection of symbols can be thought of as a set.

3. $\{$A dog, a cat, a mouse$\}$ = $\{$A mouse, a dog, a cat$\}$.

4. If $T = \{4, 7, 11, 13\}$, then   4 is an element of T.

5. If $T = \{4, 7, 11, 13\}$, then $4 \in T$.

6. $\{1, 2, 3,\} \neq \{2, 1, 3\} \neq \{3, 1, 2\}$.

7. In order for a collection of objects to be defined as a set, the objects have to be similar or alike in some manner.

8. If $M = \{2, 5, 8, 10\}$, then $5 \notin M$.

9. If each of A and B is a set and if for each $a \in A$, $a \in B$, then $A = B$.

10. $4 \in \{x |$ $x + 10$ is greater than 15$\}$.

1.4 ONE-TO-ONE CORRESPONDENCE

Each of us is familiar with the concepts of a complete one-to-one correspondence. We may think of a complete one-to-one correspondence between two sets as that of "matched pairs." Consider the following:

(a) For each U. S. State there is a State Governor and for each State Governor there is a U. S. State.

(b) For each stadium ticket there is a seat and for each stadium seat there is a ticket.

(c) For each name on the class roll there is a student and for each student in the class there is a name on the class roll.

(d) If $A = \{a, b, c, d\}$ and $B = \{4, dog, 2, cat\}$, then a complete one-to-one correspondence may be illustrated:

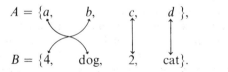

$$A = \{a, \quad b, \quad c, \quad d \},$$
$$B = \{4, \quad dog, \quad 2, \quad cat\}.$$

The idea of a one-for-one matching of objects in the pattern illustrated above is essential to the concepts of counting, a topic that will be discussed in a following section. For this reason, the following definition is given

Definition 1.2—One-to-One Correspondence The set A is said to be in complete one-to-one correspondence to the set B if, and only if, each element of A is matched (or paired) with one and only one element of B and each element of B is the mate of one and only one element of A.

The ideas of a complete one-to-one correspondence is used within the elementary curricula to aid in developing the properties for the set of Whole Numbers. For this reason, sets which may be placed into a complete one-to-one correspondence are defined as *Equivalent Sets*:

Definition 1.3—Equivalent Sets For every set A and for every set B, "Set A is equivalent to set B"; ($A \sim B$) means there exists a complete one-to-one correspondence between the sets.

For example, if $A = \{$My dog, your hat, Tom's car$\}$ and $B = \{$Mary's miniskirt, Tommy's tie, Gary's gorilla$\}$:

$$A = \{\text{My dog,} \qquad \text{Your hat,} \qquad \text{Tom's car,}\}$$

and

$$B = \{\text{Mary's miniskirt, Tommy's tie, Gary's gorilla}\}$$

we may conclude $A \sim B$ because there exists a complete one-to-one correspondence between set A and B.

PROBLEM SET 1.2

1. If $A = B$, then is $A \sim B$? Illustrate.

2. If $A \sim B$, then is $A = B$? Illustrate.

3. Illustrate that if $A \sim B$ and $B \sim C$, then $A \sim C$.

4. Is each of the following an illustration of a complete one-to-one correspondence?

(a) For each wrist there is a hand, and for each hand there is a wrist.
(b) For each elbow there is a wrist and for each wrist there is an elbow.
(c) For each theatre ticket there is a seat, and for each theatre seat there is a ticket.
(d) For each sheriff there is a criminal and for each criminal there is a sheriff.
(e) For each head there is an eye and for each eye there is a head.
(f) For each goat there are four legs and for each four legs there is a goat.

5. If $A = \{2, 4, 6, 8, \ldots\}$ and $B = \{4, 8, 12, 16, 20, \ldots\}$, is $A \sim B$?

6. If $A = \{1, 2, 3, 4, \ldots\}$, $B = \{2, 4, 6, 8, \ldots\}$ and $C = \{1, 3, 5, 7, \ldots\}$, is $A \sim B$ and $B \sim C$ and $A \sim C$?

1.5 SET UNION, SET INTERSECTION, THE NULL SET

If we could assign the set of students from this mathematics class to the auditorium and then assign a set of students from a history class to the same auditorium at the same hour for an assembly, the physical concept involved in Set Union would be illustrated. The physical interpretation of Set Union is one of *uniting* two or more sets into one set.

To illustrate this union, let $A = $ {Mary's duck, Tommy's turtle} and $B = $ {Bill's balloon, Anita's alligator}. Then the Union of set A B is the set

{Mary's duck, Tommy's turtle, Bill's balloon, Anita's alligator}.

However, physical situations do not adequately define set Union. This is so because the definition for Set Union pays particular attention to the word *or*:

Definition 1.4—Set Union For every set A and for every set B, the set of elements that are in set A or in set B is defined the Union of sets A and B. This is denoted "$A \cup B$".

When used in this sense, the word *or* is defined to be the *inclusive or*, i.e., $A \cup B$ is the set that contains all elements which are in set A *or* in set B, or in both sets A *and* B. For example, if $A = \{a, b, c, d, e, f\}$ and $B = \{d, e, f, g, h, i\}$, then $A \cup B = \{a, b, c, d, e, f, g, h, i\}$.

Note that $\{d, e, f\}$ is contained within set A and that $\{d, e, f\}$ is also within set B. Set $\{d, e, f\}$ is the set of elements that are in both sets A *and* B. The Union of sets A and B is illustrated by the shaded portion of Figure 1.1 below. (Pictures that are used to denote the relationship among sets are commonly called **Venn Diagrams**. Venn Diagrams are used extensively throughout the elementary curriculum).

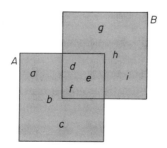

Figure 1.1

$$A \cup B = \{a, b, c, d, e, f, g, h, i\}.$$

Note that $\{d, e, f\}$ is within both sets A and B. This set is particularly important, for it is defined as the Intersection of sets A and B.

Definition 1.5—Set Intersection   For every set A and for every set B, the set of elements that are in set A *and* set B is defined as the *Intersection* of sets A and B. This is denoted "$A \cap B$".

For example, if $A = \{a, b, c, d, e, f\}$ and $B = \{d, e, f, g, h, i\}$, then the set $A \cap B$ is $\{d, e, f\}$. This set is represented by the shaded portion of Figure 1.2 below:

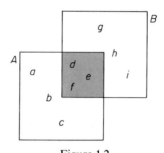

Figure 1.2

$$A \cap B = \{d, e, f\}.$$

But if set $A = \{2, 4, 6, 8\}$ and set $B = \{1, 3, 5, 7\}$, we see that set $A \cap B$ has no elements. This is illustrated as the shaded portion of Figure 1.3 below:

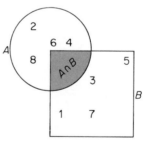

Figure 1.3

$A \cap B$ HAS NO ELEMENTS.

The above illustrates that there is no element a such that $a \in A$ and $a \in B$. When this occurs, we say that $A \cap B$ is the *Empty Set*. This set is sometimes referred to as the Null Set.

Definition 1.5—The Empty (Null) Set   The Empty Set is the set that contains no elements. This set is indicated by

$$\text{"}\{ \ \}\text{"}   \text{ or }   \text{"}\emptyset\text{".}$$

The set of Counting Numbers between   5   and   6, the set of all people with   4 feet   and   3 eyes, and the set $A \cap B$ if $A =$ {Boys}   and $B = \{Girls\}$ is each an example of the Empty Set.

Set A Union { }, $(A \cup \{ \})$, is A, since set Union defines the set which contains all elements that are in both A or   { }. Similarly, $A \cap \{ \} = \{ \}$, since the Intersection of two sets is the set of elements in both A and B.

PROBLEM SET 1.3

In Problems 1 and 2, a pictorial representation of sets A and B is given. Find, and list, the elements of $A \cup B$ and $A \cap B$.

1.

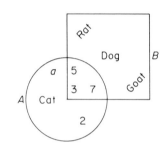

2.

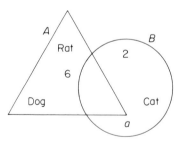

3. List $A \cup B$, $(A \cup B) \cup C$, $A \cap B$, $(A \cap B) \cap C$ below:

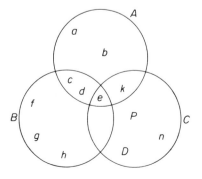

4. Describe set $A \cup B$ and set $A \cap B$ if $A = \{$All girls with blue eyes$\}$ and $B = \{$All girls with red hair$\}$.

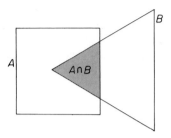

5. Describe sets D, E, F, and G if $A = \{$All students who take history$\}$, $B = \{$All students who take English$\}$, and $C = \{$All students who take art$\}$:

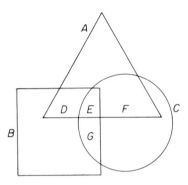

6. Find $A \cup B$ and $A \cap B$ if:

(a) $A = \{1, 2, 3, 4, 5, 6, 7\}$, $B = \{4, 5, 6, 7, 8\}$.

(b) $A = \{1, 2, 3, 4, 5, 6\}$, $B = \{3, 4, 5\}$.

(c) $A = \{2, 4, 6, 8, \ldots\}$, $B = \{1, 2, 3, 4, \ldots\}$.

(d) $A = \{2, 4, 6, 8, \ldots\}$, $B = \{4, 8, 12, 16, \ldots\}$.

(e) $A = \{x|$ $x + 10$ is greater than 15, $x \in C$ $\}$.

   $B = \{n|$ $n + 20$ is less than 75, $n \in C$ $\}$.

7. Illustrate, as in Problems 1–5, set $A \cup B$ and set $A \cap B$. List or describe, the elements $A \cup B$ and $A \cap B$.

(a) $A = \{$All counting numbers greater than 7$\}$; $B = \{$All even counting numbers greater than 13$\}$.

(b) $A = \{3, 6, 9, 13, \ldots\}$; $B = \{5, 10, 15, 20, \ldots\}$.

(c) $A = \{0, 1, 2, 3, \ldots\}$; $B = \{2, 4, 6, 8, \ldots\}$.

(d) $A = \{$All animals with four paws$\}$; $B = \{$All animals with four legs$\}$.

(e) $A = \{$All parents of boys$\}$; $B = \{$All parents of girls$\}$.

(f) $A = \{n|$ $n + 6$ is   less   than   14, $n \in C$ $\}$; $B = \{n|$ $n + 1$ is greater than 21, $n \in C$ $\}$,

8. Answer "True" or "False" in (a)–(e). Give an example to justify your answer.

(a) If set $A \cap$ set $B =$ set A, then $A = B$.

(b) If A is the set of Counting Numbers divisible by 4 and B is the set of Counting Numbers less than 20 which are divisible by 6, then $A \cap B = \{12\}$.

(c) If each of A and B is a set and if $A \sim B$, then $A \cap B = \{\ \}$.

(d) If each of A and B is a set, then $A \cap B$ represents one set.

(e) If A is a set and if B is a set and if $A \cap B = A$ and $A \cup B = B$, then $B = \{\ \}$.

1.6 A UNIVERSAL SET AND SUBSETS

In almost every problem that deals with sets, some set is used to specify a totality of elements which may be considered during this particular discussion. Such a set is called a Universal Set.

Definition 1.7—A Universal Set Any set that defines a totality of elements for a particular discussion is defined as a *Universal Set* or simply as the *Universe*. This set is denoted by the symbol "$\mathcal{U}$".

Frequently, problems require that a sub-collection of elements from a Universe be denoted. For example, let $\mathcal{U}$ be the set of Counting Numbers:

$$A = \{n \mid n + 2 \text{ is less than } 21, \quad n \in C\}$$

requires that $\mathcal{U}$ be the set of Counting Numbers and that the particular sub-collection of $\mathcal{U}$ be $\{1, 2, 3, 4, \ldots, 18\}$.

The sub-collection denoted by A above is defined to be a *subset* of the set of Counting Numbers. This is so because *each element of* A *is also an element of* C.

Definition 1.8—Subset of a Given Set For every set A and for every set B, if every element of A is also an element of B, then A is a *subset* of B. This is denoted "$A \subset B$".

For example, we may state in each case below that $A \subset B$:

Set A	Set B
$\{4, 6, 8\}$	$\{2, 4, 6, 8, \ldots\}$.
$\{2, 4, 6, 8, \ldots\}$	$\{1, 2, 3, 4, \ldots\}$.
$\{4, 8, 12, 16, \ldots\}$	$\{2, 4, 6, 8, \ldots\}$.

One immediate consequence of this illustration is to conclude that if set A is a subset B, then $A \cup B = B$. From this, we can also define the Empty Set to be a subset of every set A, since

$$\{ \ \} \cup A = A.$$

Definition 1.7 does not clearly define every classification of subsets. Subsets may be classified into two distinct categories—*proper subsets* and *improper subsets*.

Definition 1.9—A Proper Subset/An Improper Subset   For every set A and for every set B, set A is a *Proper Subset* of set B if set A is a subset of set B, $A \neq \{ \ \}$ and if set B contains at least one element not contained in set A.

If set A is a subset of set B and if A is not a Proper Subset of B, then A is an Improper subset of B.

From Definition 1.8, we conclude that if set $A = $ set B, then A is an Improper Subset of B and that B is an Improper Subset of A. Similarly, $\{ \}$ is also an Improper Subset of every set.

Using the ideas of Proper Subsets and Improper Subsets, any set may be classified as a Finite Set or as an Infinite Set.

Definition 1.10—An Infinite Set   For every set A, A is an Infinite Set if A is equivalent to one of its proper subsets.

For example, $A = \{1, 2, 3, 4, 5, \ldots\}$ is an Infinite set, for set A can be placed in a complete one-to-one correspondence with $B = \{5, 10, 15, 20, \ldots\}$, which is a proper subset of $\{1, 2, 3, 4, 5, \ldots\}$:

$$
\begin{array}{cccccc}
A = \{1, & 2, & 3, & 4, & 5, & \ldots\} \\
\updownarrow & \updownarrow & \updownarrow & \updownarrow & \updownarrow & \cdots \\
B = \{5, & 10, & 15, & 20, & 25, & \ldots\}
\end{array}
$$

PROBLEM SET 1.4

1. Answer "True" or "False" in (a) through (c) below. Give an example to justify your answer.

(a) If set $A \cap$ set $B = $ set A, then $A \subset B$.
(b) If set $A \subset$ set B and $A \cap B = B$, then $A = B$.
(c) If set $A \subset$ set B and $A \cap B = \{ \ \}$, then $A = \{ \ \}$.

(d) If set $A \cup$ set $B = A \cap B = \{\ \}$, then $A = B$.
(e) If set $A \subset$ set B, then $A \cap B = A$.

2. List each subset of $A = \{a, b, c\}$. How many subsets does A have?

3. In the illustration below, is $(A \cap B) \subset A$?

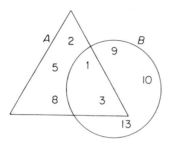

4. In the illustration below, let $A = \{$All men$\}$ and $B = \{$All men students$\}$. Describe $A \cap B$:

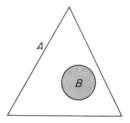

5. List all subsets of $A = \{1, 2, 3\}$. Illustrate that A contains no proper subsets which are equivalent to A, thereby illustrating that A is a finite set.

6. Given $C = \{1, 2, 3, 4, 5, \ldots\}$. Find four proper subsets of C that are equivalent to C, thereby illustrating that C is an infinite set.

7. If set $A \subset$ set B and set $B \subset$ set A can you conclude $A = B$? Illustrate.

8. List, or describe, the sets $A \cup B$ and $A \cap B$ if:

(a) $A = \{1, 2, 3, 4, 5, 6, 7\}$; $B = \{4, 5, 6, 7, 8, 9\}$.
(b) $A = \{$Chevrolet, Ford, Dodge$\}$; $B = \{$Plymouth, Chevrolet, Cadillac$\}$.
(c) $A = \{$Counting numbers greater than 7$\}$;
    $B = \{$Even counting numbers greater than 13$\}$.
(d) $A = \{$Counting numbers$\}$; $B = \{$Even counting numbers$\}$.
(e) Let $\mathcal{U} = \{$All teachers$\}$; $A = \{$Men teachers$\}$; and $B = \{$Women teachers$\}$.

9. List (a) the elements within the Intersection and (b) the elements within the Union, of the given sets. Use correct set notation.

(a) $A = \{1, 2, 3, 4, 5, 6, 7\}$; $B = \{6, 7, 8, 9, 10\}$.
(b) $A = \{x|$ x is a counting number between 1 and 8$\}$.
    $B = \{x|$ x is a counting number greater than 7$\}$.

10. List the sets (a) $(A \cup B) \cap C$ and (b) $(A \cap B) \cup C$ if:

(a) $A = \{1, 2, 3, 4, 5\}$; $B = \{4, 5, 6, 7, 8\}$; $C = \{1, 3, 5\}$.
(b) Let $\mathscr{U} = \{$Counting numbers$\}$.
    $A = \{x|$ x is an even counting number$\}$.
    $B = \{x|$ x is a multiple of 4$\}$.
    $C = \{x|$ x is evenly divisible by 8$\}$.

11. In the following, assume you are given a Universe $\mathscr{U}$, and subsets of $\mathscr{U}$ that satisfy the pictorial relationships. Copy these frames and then shade the desired portion.

(a) Shade $A \cup B$; shade $A \cap B$;

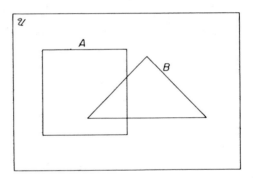

(b) Shade $A \cup B$; shade $A \cap B$;

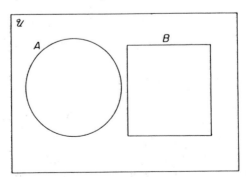

(c) Shade $A \cap B$; shade $B \cap C$; shade $(A \cap B) \cup (B \cap C)$:

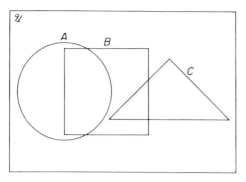

(d) Shade $A \cap B$; shade $A \cap C$; shade $B \cap C$; shade $(A \cap B) \cup (A \cap C)$;
shade $[(A \cap B) \cup (A \cap C)] \cup (B \cap C)$:

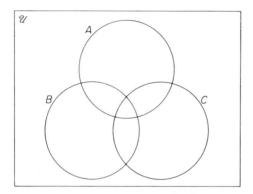

12. Pictorially represent the Universe, $\mathscr{U}$, by a rectangle. Complete the diagram by illustrating the subsets within $\mathscr{U}$. Shade the desired portions.

(a) $\mathscr{U} = \{\text{Men}\}$.
   $A = \{\text{Men over 6 feet tall}\}$.
   $B = \{\text{Fat men}\}$.
   Shade $A \cap B$.
(b) $\mathscr{U} = \{\text{Counting numbers}\}$.
   $A = \{\ \}$.
   $B = \{\text{Even counting numbers}\}$.
   Shade $A \cap B$.

1.7. SET COMPLEMENT

Almost all elementary textbooks develop the idea of "opposite" when dealing with "negatives" or "negative numbers." To establish a foundation for this study, it will be beneficial for the student to investigate the set of elements, denoted $\bar{A}$, which are contained in a Universal Set, and are not contained within a subset of $\mathscr{U}$.

Definition 1.11—Set Complement If A is a subset of a Universal set, $\mathscr{U}$, then the "complement of A with respect to $\mathscr{U}$" is the set of elements not in A. The complement of set A is designated by $\bar{A}$.

The following examples illustrate the principles of set complement.

EXAMPLE 1

Find $\bar{A}$ if $\mathscr{U} = \{\text{counting numbers}\}$ and $A = \{2, 4, 6, 8, \ldots\}$.
Solution: $\bar{A} = \{1, 3, 5, 7, \ldots\}$.

EXAMPLE 2

Find $\bar{B}$ if $\mathscr{U} = \{\text{All animals}\}$ and $B = \{\text{All horses}\}$.
Solution: $\bar{B} = \{\text{All animals that are not horses}\}$.

Set complement is easily demonstrated using diagrams. These diagrams are referred to as "Venn Diagrams." In Example 3 assume you are given $\mathscr{U}$ and subsets of $\mathscr{U}$ that satisfy the pictured relationships.

EXAMPLE 3

Given $\mathscr{U}$ and a particular subset, A of $\mathscr{U}$, that satisfies the conditions exhibited in the figure below.
Shade A; shade $\bar{A}$.

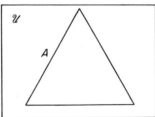

Solution: Shade A:

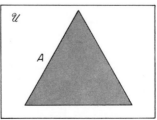

Shade $\bar{A}$:

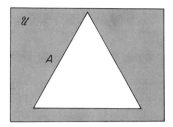

PROBLEM SET 1.5

1. Describe, or list, the set complement of A, $\bar{A}$, with respect to the given Universal Set, $\mathscr{U}$, in each of (a)–(f) below:

(a) $\mathscr{U} = \{22, 23, 24, 25, 26\}$; $A = \{22, 23\}$.
(b) $\mathscr{U} = \{\text{All women}\}$; $A = \{\text{All blonde women}\}$.
(c) $\mathscr{U} = \{\text{All fish}\}$; $A = \{\text{All catfish}\}$.
(d) $\mathscr{U} = \{0, 1, 2, 3, \ldots)$; $A = \{\text{Counting numbers}\}$.
(e) $\mathscr{U} = \{1, 2, 3, 4, \ldots\}$; $A = \{\text{Counting numbers}\}$.
(f) $\mathscr{U} = \{1, 2, 3, 4, \ldots\}$; $A = \{\ \}$.

2. In the following, assume you are given a Universal set and subsets of $\mathscr{U}$ that satisfy the pictured conditions. Copy these frames and then shade the desired portion.

(a) Shade $A \cup B$; in a separate frame shade $\overline{(A \cup B)}$:

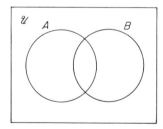

(b) Shade $A \cap B$; in a separate frame shade $\overline{(A \cap B)}$:

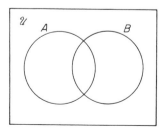

(c) Shade $A \cup B$; in a separate frame shade $(A \cup B) \cup C$; in a separate frame
shade $[\overline{(A \cup B) \cup C}]$:

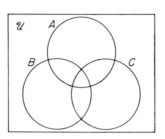

(d) Shade $A \cup B$; in a separate frame shade $(\overline{A \cup B})$:

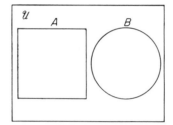

(e) Shade $\overline{A}$, in a separate frame shade B; in a separate frame shade $\overline{A} \cup B$:

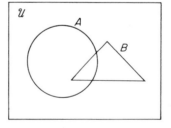

(f) Shade $\overline{A}$, in a separate frame shade $\overline{B}$; in a separate frame shade $\overline{A} \cup \overline{B}$:

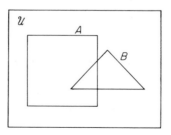

(g) Shade $\bar{A}$; in a separate frame shade $\bar{B}$; in a separate frame shade $\bar{A} \cap \bar{B}$:

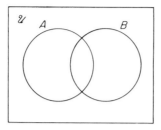

(h) Shade $A \cap B$; in a separate frame shade $(A \cap B) \cup C$; in a separate frame shade $\overline{[(A \cap B) \cup C]}$:

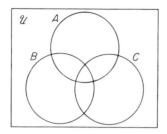

3. Answer the following true or false. Give an example or write a sentence to justify your answer.

(a) If $A \subset \mathcal{U}$, then $A \cup \bar{A} = \mathcal{U}$.

(b) If $A \subset \mathcal{U}$, then $A \cap \bar{A} = \mathcal{U}$.

(c) $\{\ \} \subset \{$Pencil, pen, pen's pal$\}$.

(d) If $A \subset \mathcal{U}$ and $A = \mathcal{U}$, then $\bar{A} = \mathcal{U}$.

(e) If $A \subset \mathcal{U}$ and $A = \{\ \}$, then $\bar{A} = \{\ \}$.

(f) If $A \subset \mathcal{U}$, $B \subset \mathcal{U}$, and $A \cup \bar{B} = \mathcal{U}$, then $B = \{\ \}$.

1.8 VARIOUS PROPERTIES OF SET UNION AND SET INTERSECTION

In the following, it is desired that the student become acquainted with the patterns of a few commonly used properties and to develop an understanding of the patterns established by these properties. Since Venn Diagrams clearly indicate (if done correctly) relationships between sets, these diagrams are the principal tools in each discussion. A summary of these is presented below:

For every set A, for every set B, and for every set C, except as noted below,
The Commutative Properties:

$$A \cup B = B \cup A \quad \text{and} \quad A \cap B = B \cap A.$$

The Associative Properties:

$$A \cup (B \cup C) = (A \cup B) \cup C \quad \text{and} \quad A \cap (B \cap C) = (A \cap B) \cap C.$$

The Distributive Properties:

$$A \cap (B \cup C) = (A \cap B) \cup (A \cap C) \quad \text{and} \quad A \cup (B \cap C) = (A \cup B) \cap (A \cup C).$$

Identity Properties:

$$A \cup \emptyset = A \quad \text{and} \quad A \cap \emptyset = \emptyset.$$

To illustrate the method that will reveal these various patterns, a step-by-step construction is shown below. This particular set of figures illustrate that "set $A \cup$ set $B =$ set $B \cup$ set A."

Property I: *The Commutative Property of Set Union* If A is a set and if B is a set, then $A \cup B = B \cup A$:
Solution:

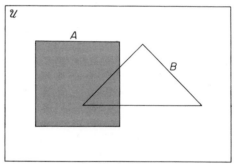

$A =$ Shaded Area
Figure 1.4

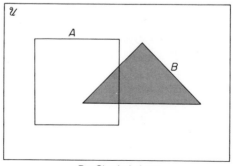

$B =$ Shaded Area
Figure 1.5

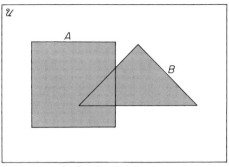

$A \cup B$ = Shaded Area
Figure 1.6

Solution:
In Figure 1.4, the area represented by set   *A*   is shaded; in Figure 1.5, the area represented by set   *B*   is shaded. Lastly, in Figure 1.6, the set $A \cup B$ is represented by the shaded area.

If set $A \cup B$ equals set $B \cup A$, then the pictorial representation of $B \cup A$ should be identical to that of Figure 1.6. This is illustrated in Figures 1.7–1.9:

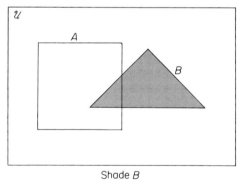

Shade *B*
Figure 1.7

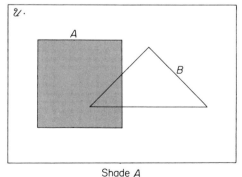

Shade *A*
Figure 1.8

Since the shaded area of Figure 1.6 is the same as that of Figure 1.9, it follows that $A \cup B = B \cup A$. Illustrate the various properties (II–VIII) in a manner similar to that above. These set properties form the basis for many parallel number properties.

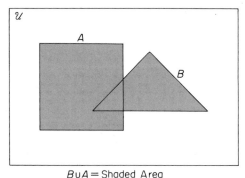

$B \cup A =$ Shaded Area

Figure 1.9

Property II: *The Commutative Property of Set Intersection.* If A is a set and B is a set, then $A \cap B = B \cap A$.

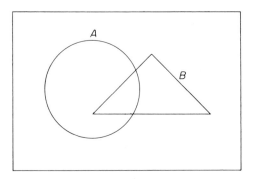

Figure 1.10

Property III: *The Associative Property of Set Union.* If each of A, B, and C is a set, then $(A \cup B) \cup C = A \cup (B \cup C)$.

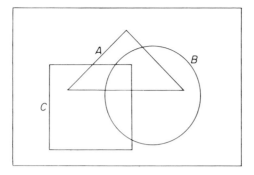

Figure 1.11

Property IV: *The Associative Property of Set Intersection.* If each of *A*, *B*, and *C* is a set, then $(A \cap B) \cap C = A \cap (B \cap C)$.

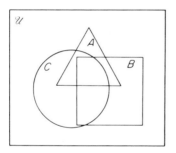

Figure 1.12

Property V: *The Distributive Property of Set Intersection over Set Union.* If each of *A*, *B*, and *C* is a set, then $A \cap (B \cup C) = (A \cap B)$ $\cup (A \cap C)$.

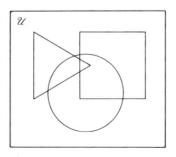

Figure 1.13

Property VI: *The Distributive Property of Set Union over Set Intersection.*
If each of   *A,*   *B,* and   *C*   is a set, then $A \cup (B \cap C) = (A \cup B) \cap (A \cup C)$.

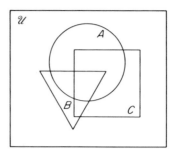

Figure 1.14

Property VII: *The Intersection of the Complement of two sets is equal to the Complement of the Union of two sets.*   In set notation, if each of   *A*   and   *B*   is a set, then $\overline{A} \cap \overline{B} = \overline{(A \cup B)}$.

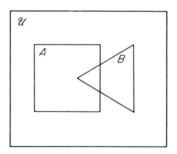

Figure 1.15

Property VIII: *The Complement of the Complement of a set.*   If   *A*   is a set, then $\overline{(\overline{A})} = A$.

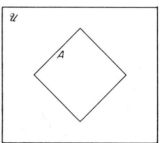

Figure 1.16

PROBLEM SET 1.6

1. Given sets A, B, and C. Find and list the elements of the set desired in (a)–(g) below if:

$$\text{Set} \quad A = \{1, 2, 3, 4, \ldots\}.$$
$$\text{Set} \quad B = \{4, 8, 12, 16, \ldots\}.$$
$$\text{Set} \quad C = \{2, 4, 6, 8, \ldots\}.$$

(a) $A \cup B$; $A \cap C$; $B \cap C$.
(b) $A \cap (B \cup C)$.
(c) $(A \cap B) \cup (A \cap C)$.
(d) $A \cup (B \cap C)$.
(e) $(A \cup B) \cap (A \cup C)$.
(f) $A \cap (A \cup B)$.
(g) $A \cap (A \cup B)$.

2. Let the Universal set be $\{0, 1, 2, 3, \ldots\}$, and set $A = \{0, 2, 4, 6, \ldots\}$. Find $\bar{A}$; find $(\bar{\bar{A}})$.

3. In a certain university, several students were interviewed in a campus poll. The following tabulations were made regarding the courses they were taking:

(a) 4 students were taking mathematics, history, and art.
(b) 7 students were taking only history and art.
(c) 6 students were taking only mathematics and history.
(d) 5 students were taking only mathematics and art.
(e) 27 students were taking only history.
(f) 25 students were taking only art.
(g) 23 students were taking only mathematics.
How many students were interviewed in the poll?

(*Hint:* Use a Venn Diagram. Let $A = \{$students taking history$\}$; $B = \{$students taking art$\}$; and $C = \{$students taking mathematics$\}$.)

4. Answer the following true or false. Give an example or write a sentence to justify your answer. In each case, each of A, B, and C represents a set.

(a) If $A = \{1, 2, 3,\}$ and if $B = \{a, b, c, d, 2, 3, 4\}$,   then $A \cup B = \{a, b, 1, 2, 3\}$.
(b) If $A \cap B = B$, then B is a subset of A.
(c) If $A \cup B = B$, then A is a subset of B.
(d) If $A \cup B = A \cap B$, then $A = B$.
(e) $A \cup B = A \cap B$.
(f) $A \cup (B \cap C) = (A \cap B) \cup C$.
(g) $A \cup (B \cap C)$ represents one set.
(h) If $A \subset \mathscr{U}$, $\mathscr{U}$ is the Universal set, then $(\bar{\bar{A}}) = \mathscr{U}$.
(i) The "Commutative Property of set Union" is a property that deals with the grouping of the various sets.

1.9 THE CARTESIAN PRODUCT SET

The prior sections of this chapter have revealed that certain sets operations parallel operations you will encounter when dealing with numbers. For this reason, an attempt has been made to show some of the more closely related operations within the preceding pages. The remainder of this chapter is devoted to a set operation that parallels the number operation multiplication.

Many of you are familiar with the game of Monopoly, in which two dice are tossed to begin the game. Then a selected token is advanced so many spaces from "go". The number of spaces the token is advanced is determined by the sum of the two "up" faces of the die.

Assume that we toss a red die and a white die simultaneously. The "up" number of the Red die is paired with the "up" number of the White die. The sum of these two numbers will determine the number of spaces to advance the token. The totality of pairings (36) of the "up" faces is illustrated below:

RED DIE

	1	2	3	4	5	6
1	(1, 1)	(1, 2)	(1, 3)	(1, 4)	(1, 5)	(1, 6)
2	(2, 1)	(2, 2)	(2, 3)	(2, 4)	(2, 5)	(2, 6)
3	(3, 1)	(3, 2)	(3, 3)	(3, 4)	(3, 5)	(3, 6)
4	(4, 1)	(4, 2)	(4, 3)	(4, 4)	(4, 5)	(4, 6)
5	(5, 1)	(5, 2)	(5, 3)	(5, 4)	(5, 5)	(5, 6)
6	(6, 1)	(6, 2)	(6, 3)	(6, 4)	(6, 5)	(6, 6)

WHITE DIE

Figure 1.17

These thirty-six pairings illustrate the totality of pairs of numbers available from the toss of two dice. From pairing of elements, we obtain *Ordered Pairs*, and we can list such a set of ordered pairs as:

$$\{(1, 1), \quad (1, 2), \ldots, (2, 1), \quad (2, 2), \ldots, (6, 6)\}.$$

A set of ordered pairs such as the above is defined to be a *Relation*. The elements of this relation are the ordered pairs, (x, y), where x denotes the first element and y denotes the second element of the ordered pairs. The set selection notation for these ordered pairs is:

$$\{(x, y)| \ldots \},$$

and means "the set of all ordered pairs, (x, y) such that ...."
Consider the relation $A = \{(1, 2),$ $(3, 4),$ $(5, 6)\}$. The set of first
elements of A is $\{1, 3, 5\}$. This set is defined as the *Domain* of the
relation. The set of second elements, $\{2, 4, 6\}$ is called the *Range* of
the relation.

Definition 1.12 —The Domain/Range of a Relation   If R is a relation,
then

1. The Domain of R is the set of first elements of the ordered pairs in R,
   and
2. The Range of R is the set of second elements of the ordered pairs of R.

We can use the ideas of *Domain* and *Range* to build a special type relation
called the Cartesian Product Set. Consider the example of tossing a penny
and then throwing a single die. If we then record the result of tossing the
penny and then the result of tossing the die, we have the following possibilities:

(a) The "up face" of the coin may be a "heads" (H) or a "tails" (T) and
(b) The "up face" of the die may be a 1 or 2 or 3 or 4 or 5 or 6.

The total possibilities for the "up faces" of the penny and the die are
pictured below:
The coin may fall as either a "heads" or a "tails":

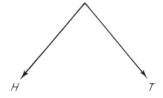

The die may fall as either a 1 or 2 or 3 or 4 or 5 or 6:

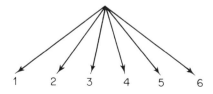

The total outcomes for tossing a penny and throwing a die is then represented by:

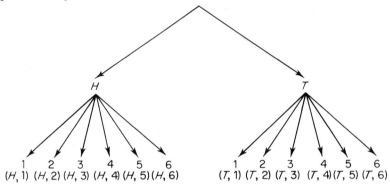

Figure 1.18

By recording the toss of the penny first, we generate the ordered pairs $\{(H, 1)(H, 2)\ldots, (T, 6)\}$, from which we can determine that H may be paired with a 1 or 2 or 3 or 4 or 5 or 6, or T may be associated with a 1 or 2 or 3 or 4 or 5 or 6. The totality of pairings is represented by the set $P = \{(H, 1),\quad (H, 2),\quad (H, 3),\ldots, (T, 5),\quad (T, 6)\}$.

The set P above is defined as the Cartesian Product Set of the two sets $D = \{H, T\}$ and $R = \{1, 2, 3, 4, 5, 6\}$, in which the set D is the Domain of the relation and the set R is the Range of the relation. This set product is written $A \times B$ and is generally read "A cross B."

The Cartesian Product Set is generally used as the basis for multiplication, in the study of probability, and in defining the *Cartesian Plane* for study in geometry. The following is a representation of the ordered pairs of the previous example. Note that each *pair* is associated with a *single* point:

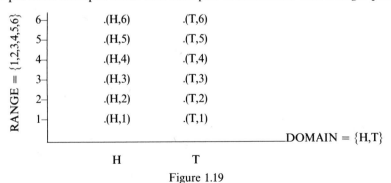

Figure 1.19

The previous example illustrates the *pairings* to generate the ordered pairs of the Cartesian Product of two sets, X and Y:

Definition 1.13—The Cartesian Product Set If each of X and Y is a set, then the set of all ordered pairs, (x, y), where $x \in X$ and $y \in Y$ is defined as the Cartesian Product set of X and Y.

PROBLEM SET 1.7

1. John has a white coat and a red coat. He also has a red tie, a green tie, and a black tie. (a) What are the different pairings of tie colors and coat colors John may have, and (b) how many different combinations of colors of ties and colors of coats may John have when dressing for the party?

Hint: Using the set of ties as the Domain and the set of coats as the Range, illustrate the pairings of colors in the following manner:

COATS	White			(Black, White)
	Red	(Red, Red)		
		Red	Green	Black

TIES

2. List the set that constitutes the Cartesian Product Set in Problem 1. List the set that constitutes the (a) Domain and (b) the Range of this Cartesian Product Set.

3. Mary and Jane can interchange sweaters. Between the two girls, there is a red sweater, a white sweater, and a blue sweater. Let

$$G = \{\text{Mary, Jane}\} \text{ and}$$
$$S = \{\text{Red, white, blue}\}.$$

(a) Using a chart similar to that in Problem 1, find, and list, the Cartesian Product Set $G \times S$.
(b) In how many ways can the girls and the sweaters be paired?

4. Below is a picture that illustrates the Cartesian Product Set of $X = \{0, 1, 2, 3, 4\}$ and $Y = \{1, 2, 3\}$. Complete this picture and then list $X \times Y$.

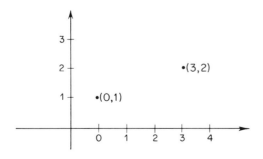

5. Form the Cartesian Product Set and then picture this set as in Problem 4 if:

(a) $A = \{a, b\}$ and $B = \{\text{Dog}, \text{cat}\}$. Form $A \times B$ and $B \times A$.
(b) $A = \{1, 2, 3\}$ and $B = \{a, b\}$. Form $A \times B$ and $B \times A$.
(c) $A = \{a, b, c, d, e, f\}$ and $B = \{1, 2, 3\}$. Form $A \times B$ and $B \times A$.
(d) $A = \{0, 1, 2, \ldots\}$ and $B = \{0, 1, 2, \ldots\}$. Form $A \times B$.

6. Illustrate, as in Problem 4, (a) the Cartesian Product Set $X \times Y$ if $X = \{a, b, c\}$ and $Y = \{1, 2\}$ and (b) the Cartesian Product Set $Y \times X$. One of the following is true. Select the correct answer and justify your selection in terms of *Domain* and *Range*.

(a) $A \times B = B \times A$.
(b) $A \times B \neq B \times A$.

7. If each of A and B is a set, is $A \times B \sim B \times A$ or is $A \times B = B \times A$? Justify your answer by using an illustration.

8. Assume you (a) throw a die and then (b) toss a penny. Represent the total possible outcomes as done in the example of the preceding section. Is the Cartesian Product Set $\{1, 2, 3, 4, 5, 6\} \times \{H, T\}$ identically   the   same   as $\{H, T\} \times \{1, 2, 3, 4, 5, 6\}$? If you considered only the *outcome* of tossing a die and flipping a coin, would it matter which set forms the Domain or Range of the Cartesian Product Set?

1.10   VARIOUS PROPERTIES OF CARTESIAN PRODUCT SETS

Heretofore, various patterns have been established for Set Union and Set Intersection. Two of these established patterns were the Commutative pattern and the Associative pattern for sets A, B, and C:

$$A \cup B = B \cup A,$$

$$A \cap B = B \cap A,$$

$$A \cup (B \cup C) = (A \cup B) \cup C,$$

$$A \cap (B \cap C) = (A \cap B) \cap C.$$

The patterns of Set Union parallel the patterns established for the number operation addition and some patterns established by the Cartesian Product parallel the number operation multiplication. The first of these is the Commutative Property of the Cartesian Set Product.

EXAMPLE

Form $A \times B$ and $B \times A$ if $A = \{1, 2\}$ and $B = \{3, 4\}$.

$A \times B = \{(1, 3),$ $(1, 4),$ $(2, 3),$ $(2, 4)\}$.

$B \times A = \{(3, 1),$ $(3, 2),$ $(4, 1),$ $(4, 2)\}$.

The student should note that the Domain of $A \times B$ is the Range of $B \times A$ and the Range of $A \times B$ is the Domain of $B \times A$. Hence $A \times B \neq B \times A$. However, sets $A \times B$ and $B \times A$ are equivalent sets, since a complete one-to-one correspondence can be established between the two sets. We can then conclude that the Commutative Property for the Cartesian Set is not true, but that

$$A \times B \sim B \times A.$$

The Associative pattern is a pattern that involves three or more sets. The patterns established previously were

$$A \cup (B \cup C) = (A \cup B) \cup C,$$

$$A \cap (B \cap C) = (A \cap B) \cap C,$$

and we wish to determine if $(A \times B) \times C = A \times (B \times C)$. If $A = \{a, b\}$, $B = \{c, d\}$, and $C = \{e, f\}$, then

$$A \times B = \{(a, c), \quad (a, d), \quad (b, c), \quad (b, d)\},$$

and

$$(A \times B) \times C = \{[(a, c), e], \quad [(a, c), f], \quad [(a, d), e], \ldots, \quad [(b, d), f]\}.$$

Similarly, we can determine:

$$A \times (B \times C) = \{[a, (c, e)], \quad [a, (c, f)], \quad [a, (d, e)], \ldots, \quad [b, (d, f)]\}.$$

Again, we see that $A \times (B \times C) \neq (A \times B) \times C$, but that a complete one-to-one correspondence between the two sets can be established. We conclude that

$$A \times (B \times C) \sim (A \times B) \times C.$$

Distributive patterns are encountered in many instances within the study of mathematics. The patterns under discussion reveal that (a) The *Cartesian Set Product* may be expressed in terms of *Set Union* and (b) Set *Union* be expressed in terms of Cartesian Set Product.

EXAMPLE

Show that $A \times (B \cup C) = (A \times B) \cup (A \times C)$.

Let $A = \{1, 2\}$, $B = \{3, 4\}$, $C = \{5, 6\}$. Then the ordered pairs of $A \times (B \cup C)$ may be illustrated as $\{1, 2\} \times \{3, 4, 5, 6\}$:

$B \cup C$

		3	4	5	6
A	1	(1, 3)	(1, 4)	(1, 5)	(1, 6)
	2	(2, 3)	(2, 4)	(2, 5)	(2, 6)

$A \times (B \cup C)$

Figure 1.20

Similarly, the sets $(A \times B)$, $(A \times C)$, and $(A \times B) \cup (A \times C)$
are illustrated as follows:

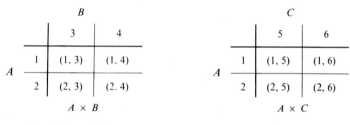

		3	4
A	1	(1, 3)	(1, 4)
	2	(2, 3)	(2. 4)

$A \times B$

Figure 1.21

		5	6
A	1	(1, 5)	(1, 6)
	2	(2, 5)	(2, 6)

$A \times C$

Figure 1.22

The set $(A \times B) \cup (A \times C)$ is illustrated in Figure 1.23:

		3	4	5	6
A	1	(1, 3)	(1, 4)	(1, 5)	(1, 6)
	2	(2, 3)	(2, 4)	(2, 5)	(2, 6)

$(A \times B) \cup (A \times C)$

Figure 1.23

Thus we see that in $A \times (B \cup C)$, illustrated in Figure 1.20, is the
same set as that illustrated in Figure 1.23. Thus we illustrate the *distributive
pattern*, and state that "Cartesian Set Product distributes over Set Union:"

$$A \times (B \cup C) = (A \times B) \cup (A \times C).$$

Note that the set $A \times (B \cup C)$ is expressed in terms of *Cartesian
Set Product* and that the set $(A \times B) \cup (A \times C)$ is expressed in terms
of *Set Union*. This pattern parallels that of expressing the product of two

numbers as the sum of two numbers which is used in the teaching of addition and multiplication in elementary grades.

To form the Cartesian Product Set of any non-empty set A and the Empty Set $\varnothing$,

$$A \times \varnothing,$$

recall that to generate the Cartesian Product Set we must pair each $a \in A$ with each $b \in \varnothing$ to form the set of ordered pairs, $(a, b) \in A \times \varnothing$. However, $\varnothing$ is the set that contains no elements, hence there are no second elements to form the set of ordered pairs. Since by definition the Cartesian Product Set is a set containing ordered pairs, the Cartesian Product contains no elements. Therefore

$$A \times \varnothing = \varnothing.$$

Similarly, $\varnothing \times A = \varnothing$, for it is impossible to generate the set of ordered pairs since $\varnothing$ contains no elements.

PROBLEM SET 1.8

1. Form the Cartesian Product Set $A \times B$ and $B \times A$. Illustrate, on perpendicular axes, the graph of $A \times B$ and $B \times A$ as in Figure 1.19 to show equivalence.

(a) Let $A = \{0, 1, 2\}$ and $B = \{\text{John, Mary}\}$.
(b) Let $A = \{x\}$ and $B = \{1, \text{Daniel}\}$.
(c) Let $A = \{1, b\}$ and $B = \{a, b, \text{dog}\}$.

2. Find $A \times (B \times C)$ and $(A \times B) \times C$ and illustrate equivalence between the two sets if:

(a) $A = \{0, 1\}$, $B = \{\text{Dog}\}$, $C = \{2, 3\}$.
(b) $A = \{1\}$, $B = \{2, 3\}$, $C = \{a, b, c\}$.

3. Illustrate, as in Figures 1.20–1.23 that $A \times (B \cup C) = (A \times B) \cup (A \times C)$ if:

(a) $A = \{a, b, c\}$, $B = \{1, 2\}$, $C = \{d, e, f\}$.
(b) $A = \{4, 5\}$, $B = \{1, 2, 3\}$, $C = \{a, b, c, d\}$.

4. Show that $A \times (B \cup C) = (A \times B) \cup (A \times C)$ by (1) finding $A \times (B \cup C)$, (2) finding $(A \times B) \cup (A \times C)$, and (3) comparing the results of (1) and (2) if:

(a) $A = \{1, 2\}$, $B = \{a, b, c\}$, $C = \{5\}$.
(b) $A = \{3, 4, 5\}$, $B = \{2\}$, $C = \{4, 7\}$.

5. If $A = \{a, b\}$, $B = \{b, c\}$, $C = \{c, d\}$, illustrate that $A \times (B \cap C) = (A \times B) \cap (A \times C)$. (Cartesian Set Product distributes over Set Intersection).

6. If $A = \{a, b\}$, $B = \{c, d\}$, $C = \{e, f\}$, illustrate that $A \times (B \cap C) = (A \times B) \cap (A \times C)$.

CHAPTER 2

Introduction to
the Whole Numbers

2.1 INTRODUCTION

The purpose of this chapter is to develop the concept of *Number* and then to
study properties related to numbers. In order to develop the idea of number,
we must use the ideas of set, set equivalence, and set membership. The
properties of such numbers will be studied by using the above ideas and other
ideas studied in Chapter 1.

2.2 THE CONCEPT OF NUMBER

Mathematical historians emphasize the fact that a basic concept of number
is that of one-to-one correspondence, or that the elements of one set could
be matched, one-to-one, with a given set of objects, as in the case of the well-
known herder who was losing sheep to the wolves:

Assume that as each sheep left the pen in the morning, the herder placed a rock in
his pocket, thereby establishing a one-to-one matching between the elements of the

set of sheep and the elements of the set of rocks. In the evening, as each sheep entered the pen, the herder removed a rock from his pocket. If his pocket was empty when the herd was in the pen, he knew that no sheep were eaten that day. However, if he found one or more rocks in his pocket, he knew some sheep were missing.

The herder was able to keep track of his sheep by using the ideas of a complete one-to-one correspondence. Through the centuries, the idea of a "Representative Set" developed, a set that showed the various groupings of the objects used in a one-to-one correspondence, Figure 2.1 :

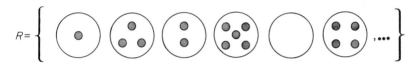

Figure 2.1

In order to distinguish one element of R from another element of R, each element was given a name, Figure 2.2 :

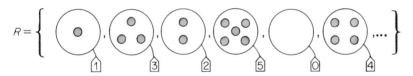

Figure 2.2

By using this set, names to other sets could be assigned by establishing a complete one-to-one correspondence with a particular element of R. The name "2" would be assigned to every set whose elements could be matched, one-to-one, with elements of

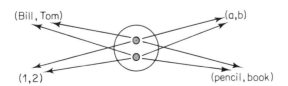

Figure 2.3

By using one-to-one correspondence, we generate a *set of sets*, the elements of this set having one common property—there is a complete one-to-one correspondence between the elements of these sets. For example:

(a) {{Bill, Tom},   {1, 2},   {a, b},   {Pencil, book},...}.
(b) {{Tom, a, Bill},   {1, 2, 3},   {a, b, c},   {Cow, dog, cat},...}.
(c) {{126},   {Joe},   {Ball},   {Pencil},   {Church},...}.

We define that

(a) 2   is   {{Bill, Tom},   {1, 2},   {a, b},...}   since each element of this set can be matched in a one-to-one correspondence with

(b) 3   is   {{Tom, a, Bill},   {1, 2, 3},   {d, e, f},...} since each element of this set can be matched with the elements of

(c) 1   is   {{126},   {Joe},   {Ball},   {Pencil},   {Church},...} since each element of this set can be matched with the elements of

(d) etc.

As noted in Chapter 1, a number has many names. Names for numbers are called numerals. Some names for the number three are "3," "III," "tres (three in Spanish)," "11_{two} (three in base two)," "$12 \div 4$," "$n\{1, 2, 3\}$." When referring to the numeral that names a number, we are referring to the symbols themselves, and will indicate this by using the double quotation marks.

Of particular interest to the elementary teacher are numerals such as "$n\{a, b, c\}$," "$n\{1, 2, 3\}$," "$n\{4, 5, 6\}$," for these numerals are used to indicate that there is a complete one-to-one correspondence between $\{a, b, c\}$, $\{1, 2, 3\}$, $\{4, 5, 6\}$, and   , thereby establishing that each

of these sets is an element of the set   3.

Definition 2.1   "$n\{a, b, c\} = 3$" means that there exists a complete one-to-one correspondence between $\{a, b, c\}$ and   .
Similarly, we can define   "$n\{a\} = 1$"   to mean that there exists a complete   one-to-one   correspondence   between $\{a\}$ and   ; "$n\{a, b\} = 2$"   to mean that there exists a complete one-to-one correspondence between $\{a, b\}$ and   ; and so on.

If $A = \{a\}$, then   "$n(A) = 1$"   means identically the same as $n\{a\} = 1$; if $B = \{a, b\}$, then   "$n(B) = 2$"   means the same as "$n\{a, b\} = 2$,"   etc.

In order that no misunderstandings arise when discussing the Natural, or Counting Numbers, this set is defined.

Definition 2.2—The Set of Natural, or Counting Numbers   The set of Natural, or Counting Numbers is defined as

$$C = \{1, 2, 3, 4, \ldots\}.$$

The above definition reveals that zero is not a Natural Number. The numeral for zero is   "0." The set of Whole Numbers, W , is the set of Natural Numbers and the number   0.

Definition 2.3—The Set of Whole Numbers   The set of Whole Numbers is defined as

$$W = \{0, 1, 2, 3, 4, \ldots\}.$$

The two sets C and W above are the sets of numbers generally studied in the early elementary school curriculum (W is sometimes referred to as the Numbers of Arithmetic). The remainder of this chapter is devoted to the properties concerning the set W.

2.3   INEQUALITY RELATIONS

By placing the elements of $\bigodot$ and $\bigodot$ in a "one-to-one" matching, we see that there is an element of   3   that is left unpaired. Hence we say that if $n(A) = 2$ and $n(B) = 3$, then set A has fewer elements than set B, or that B has more elements than A. From this one-to-one matching, the ideas of Inequality are developed.

Definition 2.4—The Inequality Relations   The number of elements contained in set A is greater than the number of elements in set B, $n(A) > n(B)$, means with every attempt to match the elements of set A one-to-one with the elements of set B there is at least one element of set A which cannot be matched with an element of set B.

Furthermore, if the number of elements contained in set B is greater than the number of elements contained in set A, then the number of elements contained in set A is less than the number of elements contained in set B, or $n(A) < n(B)$.

The expression $"n(A) > n(B)"$ is read "the cardinal number of set A is greater than the cardinal number of set B," or "the number of elements in set A is greater than the number of elements in set B." The expression $"n(A) < n(B)"$ is read "the cardinal number of set A is less than the cardinal number of set B," or "the number of elements in set A is less than the number of elements in set B."

PROBLEM SET 2.1

1. Punctuate the following statements correctly, so that they will be true statements by placing double quotation marks in the appropriate places:

(a) Boston is a big city but Boston is a six-letter word.

(b) 2   is smaller than   2.

(c) One-half of   8   is   ᵌ.

(d) 2   from   42   is   4.

(e) 76   is a number but   76   is a numeral.

(f) Mary has four letters but Mary is a girl.

(g) One-half of   21   is   11   because one-half of   XXI
    is   VVI

(h) 2345   is smaller than   2345.

(i) The elevation of Alpine is 5000 feet but Alpine is a six letter word.

For problems 2–14, supply (a) the missing numeral, or (b) the missing sign of equality or inequality, or (c) the missing sign of equivalence.

2. $n\{0\} = $ _____.

3. $n\{1\} = $ _____.

4. $n\{1,2\} = $ _____.

5. $n\{\ \} = $ _____.

6. If $A = \{a, b, c, d, e, f\}$ then $n(A) = $ _____.

7. If $A = \{r, t, q\}$ and $B = \{s, r, t\}$, then
      $\{r, t, q\}$ _____ $\{s, r, t\}$,
      $n\{r, t, q\}$ _____ $n\{s, r, t\}$,
      $\underline{\quad 3 \quad} = $ _____.

8.   4 _____ $n\{1, 2, 3, 4\}$.

9.   If $A = \{r, w, t, v\}$ and $B = \{v, \%, *, \$\}$, then

     A _____ B,

    $n(A)$ _____ $n(B)$,

      $4 =$ _____.

10.   If $A = \{a, b\}$ and $B = \{a, b, c, d\}$, then

     $\{a, b\}$ _____ $\{a, b, c, d\}$.

    $n\{a, b\}$ _____ $n\{a, b, c, d\}$,

     _____ $<$ _____.

11. $n\{1, 2, 3, 5, 7\}$ _____   4.

12. $\{x, y, z, h\}$ _____ $\{x, y, z\}$.

   $n\{x, y, z, h\}$ _____ $n\{x, y, z\}$,

   _____   _____   _____.

13. $n\{1, 2\}$ _____   6,

   _____ $<$ _____.

2.4   THE NUMBER LINE

One of the most powerful tools used in the teaching of arithmetic is the concept of a Number Line, and the representation of sets of numbers using this line. For this reason, we shall investigate the pictorial representation for the set of Whole Numbers and their relation to a number line. An introduction to addition and subtraction using a number line is undertaken in Chapter 10.

First, a line segment may be defined as two distinct points, A and B and every point lying on the most direct path between A and B. To picture a line segment, first select two particular points in space, and assign to these points letters A and B as shown in Figure 2.4:

     •
     A •
                        B

Figure 2.4

Next, follow the most direct path from A to B. The path described by a straight-edge is used to designate every point between A and B, Figure 2.5:

     A B

Figure 2.5

The set of points pictured above has two end points, A and B. These end-points and every point between A and B are called a "line segment." The symbol for the line segment AB is $\overline{AB}$.

One of the most familiar of all sets of points is that of "line," and in particular a "straight line." If a line segment is extended indefinitely without change of direction, we define a line that contains a particular line segment as shown in Figure 2.6:

Figure 2.6

A straight line has no end points. However, we can designate the line above as $\overleftrightarrow{AB}$, where each of A and B is a point within this line.

To picture a *number line*, first establish a particular set of points using a pencil and ruler. Match some particular point of this number line with the number zero, Figure 2.7:

Figure 2.7

Next advance any convenient distance to the right of the point labeled zero. Associate with this point the number one. Again, associate this number and this particular point by placing the symbol "1" directly beneath the point, Figure 2.8:

Figure 2.8

A unit of measure (length) has been established by this process. Using this length, start at the point labeled zero and lay successive distances to the right of zero. The point that terminates each of these equal distances describes a particular subset of points on the number line, Figure 2.9:

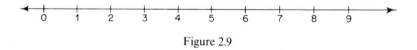

Figure 2.9

It should be noted that every Whole Number, no matter how large, can be matched by a one-to-one correspondence with a particular subset of points on the number line.

Is the converse of the above statement true, i.e., is there a number that can be mated with every point? In the future, we shall show this to be true, but for now it will suffice to say that a one-to-one correspondence between the Whole Numbers and a subset of points on a line can be established.

2.5 ORDERING THE WHOLE NUMBERS

From Definitions 2.4 and 2.5 (the Definitions for Inequality), we use the idea of "one greater than," and "one less than" to arrange in ascending order the set of Whole Numbers. This is illustrated through the matching of elements from the Representative Class. The related number inequalities are shown in Figure 2.10:

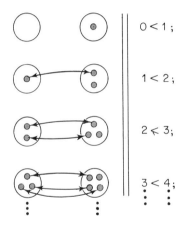

Figure 2.10

From the above illustration, the Representative Class may be depicted as

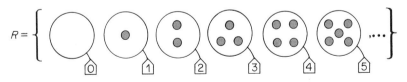

Figure 2.11

and the ordering of the Whole Numbers is:

$$W = \{0, 1, 2, 3, 4, \ldots\},$$

in which $0 < 1 < 2 < 3 < \ldots$.

Since the set of Counting Numbers, C, is a subset of the set of Whole Numbers, we also establish an order among the Counting Numbers,

$$C = \{1, 2, 3, 4, \ldots\},$$

2.6 THE NATURE OF COUNTING

The process of counting depends totally upon the ordering of the set of Counting Numbers. To count a set of objects, we first match the number 1 with one of the elements of the set. Next, we pair the number 2 with another, different element of the set; then the number 3 with still another, different element of the set, etc. We continue this process until no element of the set is left unpaired. If 4 is the last counting number paired with an element in the set, we can state that the set has 4 elements. This is illustrated below:

$$C = \{\underset{\downarrow}{1}, \underset{\downarrow}{2}, \underset{\downarrow}{3}, \underset{\downarrow}{4}, 5, 6, 7, 8, \ldots\},$$

$$D = \{\$, \%, +, *\},$$

$$n(D) = 4.$$

Hence counting is essentially a pairing, or matching process. A one-to-one correspondence between the set consisting of the first four counting numbers and the given set was established in which one, and only one, counting number is matched with each object of the given set.

2.7 EQUIVALENCE

In Chapter 1, we defined two sets to be Equivalent Sets, if there existed a complete one-to-one correspondence between the sets:

$$A = \{1, 2, 3, 4, 5\}, \quad n(A) = 5,$$

$$B = \{a, b, c, d, e\}, \quad n(B) = 5,$$

$$A \sim B \qquad n(A) = n(B).$$

From the above, we see that $n(A) = 5$ and $n(B) = 5$. Since $n(A)$ is identically the same as $n(B)$, it intuitively follows that for any two sets A and B, if $n(A) = n(B)$, then $A \sim B$. This forms the basis for redefining Equivalent Sets.

Definition 2.5—Equivalence   If each of A and B is a set and if $n(A) = n(B)$, then $A \sim B$. Conversely, if $A \sim B$, then $n(A) = n(B)$.

2.8   ADDITION

The addition process is a process that is parallel to, but not the same as, the set Union of two disjoint sets. Set A is disjoint from set B if $A \cap B = \{\ \}$. Similarly, if $A \cap B = \{\ \}$, then set B is disjoint from set A.

The student should realize that "set Union" involves an operation of sets, while "addition" involves numbers. It is important that the two distinct operations be separated. For example:

EXAMPLE

Let $A = \{1, 2, 3\}$ and $B = \{4, 5, 6, 7\}$. Then

$$\{1, 2, 3\} \cup \{4, 5, 6, 7\} = \{1, 2, 3, 4, 5, 6, 7\}$$
$$A \quad \cup \quad B \quad = \quad (A \cup B)$$

Using the sets A, B, and $(A \cup B)$ as shown above, consider the number properties, $n(A)$, $n(B)$, and $n(A \cup B)$ associated with these sets:

$$\{1, 2, 3\} \cup \{4, 5, 6, 7\} = \{1, 2, 3, 4, 5, 6, 7\},$$
$$A \quad \cup \quad B \quad = \quad (A \cup B),$$
$$n(A) \quad + \quad n(B) \quad = \quad n(A \cup B),$$
$$3 \quad + \quad 4 \quad = \quad 7.$$

Note that a parallel has been established between the set operation Union, and the number operation, addition. This forms the basis for the definition of addition for Whole Numbers.

Definition 2.6—Addition for Whole Numbers   If A and B are finite, disjoint sets with Cardinal Numbers $n(A)$ and $n(B)$, respectively, then

$$n(A) + n(B) = n(A \cup B).$$

From this definition, we may say that the statement   "$3 + 2 = 5$" means that   "$3 + 2$"   denotes a number,   "5"   denotes a number, and they both denote the same number. This is generally referred to as an Addition Fact and abbreviated "af". The reader should note again that the operation addition cannot be thought of as the operation set Union, for the first operation deals with numbers and the other one deals with sets.

PROBLEM SET 2.2

1. Illustrate the process of counting, as done above, for each set below. Determine the number of objects in each set by using this method.

(a) $D = \{a, b, c, d, e\}$.
(b) $D = \{1, 2, 3, \%, \$, \Delta\}$.
(c) $D = \{1, 2, \pi, \Delta, \$, \%, +, 9\}$.

2. Answer the following   "True"   or   "False". Justify your answer by citing an example or definition.

(a) If $A = \{1, 2, 3\}$ and $B = \{+, \Delta, \pi\}$, is $n(A) \sim n(B)$?
(b) If each of A and B is a set, $n(A) = n(B)$, is $A = B$?
(c) If each of A and B is a set, $n(A) < n(B)$, is $A \subset B$?
(d) If set $A = $ set B, is $n(A) + 0 = n(B)$?
(e) If $A = \{\emptyset\}$ and $B = \{\ \}$, is $n(A) = n(B)$?

3. If set A and set B are not disjoint sets, is $n(A) + n(B) = n(A \cup B)$? Justify your answer by citing an example.

4. An elementary text illustrates a set of kittens joining a set of puppies in a playpen. Can you add the set of kittens to the set of puppies? Why?

5. If A and B are sets, does $n(A) + n(B)$ denote one number?

Complete each sentence in Problems 6–12 below:

6. If $\{c, r\} \cup \{s, b, h\} = \{c, r, s, b, h\}$, then
$$n\{c, r\} + \underline{\hspace{1cm}} = \underline{\hspace{1cm}},$$
$$2 + \underline{\hspace{1cm}} = \underline{\hspace{1cm}}.$$

7. If x is a Whole Number and $x + n\{a, b, c\} = 13$, then $x = \underline{\hspace{1cm}}$.

8. If x is a Whole Number and $n\{c, h\} + x = n\{a, 1, 5, 7, 9\}$, then $x = \underline{\hspace{1cm}}$.

9. Fill in the blank spaces with the appropriate number:
$$\underline{\hspace{1cm}} + n\{s, p, b, r\} = n\{5, 6, +, \Delta, \pi\},$$
$$\underline{\hspace{1cm}} + \underline{\hspace{1cm}} = \underline{\hspace{1cm}}.$$

10. If x is a Whole Number and $2 + x = n\{s, 2, 4, \text{dog}, \text{man}\}$, then $x = \underline{\hspace{1cm}}$.

11. If each of x and y is a Whole Number and $n\{r, p, q\} + x = y + n\{s, m\}$, then $x = \underline{\hspace{1cm}}$ and $y = \underline{\hspace{1cm}}$.

12. If y is a Whole Number and $n\{x, 5\} + y = 6 + 3$, then $y = \underline{\hspace{1cm}}$.

In Problems 13–15, answer   "True"   or   "False". Justify your answer by citing an example.

13. If each of A and B is a set and if $n(A) = 3$ and $n(B) = 4$, then $n(A \cup B) = 7$.

14. If A and B represent sets and if $n(A \cup B) = n(A) + n(B)$, then it is certain that $n(A \cap B) = 0$.

15. If A and B represent sets and if $n(A) = 5$ and if $n(A \cup B)$ $= 9$ and if $n(A \cap B) = 2$, then $n(B) = 7$.

2.9 MULTIPLICATION

In the preceding section, addition was defined for Whole Numbers. In this section, a second fundamental operation, multiplication, is defined for this set. To illustrate multiplication, assume we are given the   4   disjoint sets A, B, C,   and D:

$$A = \{a, b\}; \quad B = \{c, d\}; \quad C = \{e, f\}; \quad D = \{g, h\}.$$
$$n(A) = 2; \quad n(B) = 2; \quad n(C) = 2; \quad n(D) = 2.$$

By counting, we determine (a) there are ___4___ sets and (b) each set contains ___2___ elements. By investigating:

$$A \cup B \cup C \cup D,$$

multiplication is then defined (in elementary texts) as:

$$4(2) = n(A \cup B \cup C \cup D),$$
$$4(2) = n(A) + n(B) + n(C) + n(D),$$
$$4(2) = 2 + 2 + 2 + 2.$$

In this intuitive development for multiplication, the operation is considered to be a systematic regrouping procedure, or a regrouping of like quantities a given number of times. This method is generally referred to as "Multiplication defined in terms of repeated Addition." Using this development, the product of the counting number p, and the whole number q would be expressed as:

$$p \text{ times } q = p \times q = p(q) = pq = p \cdot q = \underbrace{q + q + q + \ldots + q.}_{p \text{ summands}}$$

The product   4(3)   would mean

$$4(3) = \underbrace{3 + 3 + 3 + 3}_{\text{4 summands}} = 12,$$

and would be distinguished from the product   3(4):

$$3(4) = \underbrace{4 + 4 + 4}_{\text{3 summands}} = 12.$$

However, this definition for multiplication has no meaning if $p = 0$, i.e., $0(q)$ is undefined.

Multiplication is also defined from the Cartesian Product Set. Consider the sets $A = \{1, 2\}$ and $B = \{3, 4, 5\}$:

$$A \times B = \{(1, 3), \quad (1, 4), \quad (1, 5), \quad (2, 3), \quad (2, 4), \quad (2, 5)\},$$

$$n(A) \text{ times } n(B) = n\{(1, 3), \quad (1, 4), \quad (1, 5), \quad (2, 3), \quad (2, 4), \quad (2, 5)\},$$

$$n(A) \cdot n(B) = n(A \times B),$$

$$2(3) = 6.$$

Note that in the Cartesian Product Set, each $a \in A$ was associated, one at a time, with $b \in B$. Similarly, for each $b \in B$, B was associated, one at a time with each $a \in A$. The total number of associations formed in this manner is then defined as the product $n(A) \cdot n(B)$.

We need not restrict $n(A)$ to be a nonzero number, if multiplication is defined in this manner. For example, let $A = \{ \ \}$ and B be any finite set. Then

$$A \times B = \{ \ \},$$

$$n(A) \cdot n(B) = n\{ \ \},$$

$$0 \cdot n(B) = 0.$$

Note that this intuitive development established a parallel between the Cartesian Product Set and the number operation multiplication. This forms the basis for the definition of multiplication:

Definition 2.7—Multiplication for Whole Numbers   If A and B are finite sets with Cardinal Numbers $n(A)$ and $n(B)$,   respectively, then

$$n(A) \cdot n(B) = n(A \times B).$$

From this definition, we can say that the statement   "$3 \times 4 = 12$"

means that   "3 × 4"   names a number,   "12"   names a number, and they both name the same number. This is generally referred to as a *Multiplication Fact* (mf).

PROBLEM SET 2.3

Problems 1–4 illustrate multiplication when defined in terms of repeated addition. Fill in the spaces with their proper values.

1. Let $X = \{x, s, b, t\}$ and $Y = \{h, i, c, t\}$.

There are _____ sets.
There are _____ elements in each set.
There are _____ total elements.
_____(4) = 8.

2. $\{a, b\ c, d\ e, f\} = \{a, b, c, d, e, f\}$,
   $n\{a, b\} + n\{c, d\} + n\{e, f\} = n\{a, b, c, d, e, f\}$
   _____ + _____ + _____ = _____,
   _____ twos = 6,
   _____ times _____ = _____.

3. $n\{r, c, k, n\} + n\{k, d, s, f\} + n\{k, t, s, f\} =$ _____,
   _____ + _____ + _____ = _____,
   _____ fours = _____,
   _____ times _____ = _____.

4. $\{\ \} \cup \{\ \} \cup \{\ \} \cup \{\ \} \cup \{\ \} =$ _____.
   $n\{\ \} + n\{\ \} + n\{\ \} + n\{\ \} + n\{\ \} =$ _____,
   _____ + _____ + _____ + _____ + _____ = _____,
   _____ zeros = _____,
   _____ times   = _____.

5. If $A = \{1, 2, 3\}$ and $B = \{a, b\}$, their Cartesian Product Set, $A \times B$, is pictured below. This diagram suggests what multiplication fact?

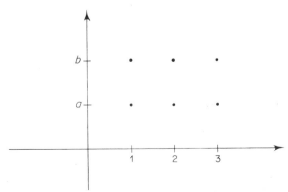

Illustrate $n(A) \cdot n(B)$ from $n(A \times B)$ in Problems 6–7 on next page.

6. The menu at a school cafeteria offered either chicken or turkey. A choice of milk or tea was also offered. How many different lunches may be obtained between choices of meats and drinks?

7. Jimmy must take Algebra or English or History. Two teachers in his school teach all three subjects. In how many ways can Jimmy arrange a schedule?

8. In the last section of Chapter 1, it was illustrated that if A is any finite set, $A \times \{\ \} = \{\ \} \times A = \{\ \}$. What multiplication fact does this illustrate when considering $n(A) \cdot n(B) = n(A \times B)$?

9. If $p(q) = \underbrace{q + q + q + \ldots + q}_{p \text{ summands}}$, briefly describe why $0(4)$ has no meaning.

2.10 THE CLOSURE, COMMUTATIVE, ASSOCIATIVE, AND DISTRIBUTIVE PROPERTIES FOR WHOLE NUMBERS

In the following sections, a study of several properties pertaining to the addition and multiplication of Whole Numbers is undertaken.

The prior study of sets revealed certain *patterns* for Set Union and Set Intersection. These patterns from set study directly parallel certain patterns established by addition and multiplication.

The reader should be able to state and should also understand the patterns established by the properties of addition and multiplication, for these will be referred to in almost every section of the text. They are listed below. A rationalization for these properties, based on prior study of sets, is presented in Problem Set 2.3.

For every Whole Number a, for every Whole Number b, and for every Whole Number c (except as denoted below) there are:

P1: *Closure Properties.*

$$a + b \in W; \quad a(b) \in W.$$

P2: *Commutative Properties.*

$$a + b = b + a; \quad a(b) = b(a).$$

P3: *Associative Properties.*

$$a + (b + c) = (a + b) + c; \quad a(bc) = (ab)c.$$

The Closure Property for Addition and the Closure Property for Multiplication, abbreviated cla and clm, respectively, provide an answer to the question "If A is a set of numbers and if $a \in A$ and if $b \in A$, then is $a + b \in A$ and is $a(b) \in A$?" If $a + b \in A$, then we state "set A is closed under addition;" if $a(b) \in A$, then we state "set A is closed under multiplication." If $a + b \notin A$, then we state "set A is *not* closed under addition;" if $a(b) \notin A$, then we state "set A is not closed under multiplication."

EXAMPLE

Let $A = \{1, 3, 5, 7, 9, \ldots\}$.

A.	M.
$1 + 3 = 4$. Therefore, we conclude "set A is not closed under addition." (This is so because the number 4 is not in A).	$1 \times 3 = 3$, $3 \times 5 = 15$, $7 \times 9 = 63$, etc. Since the product of every pair of numbers is an element of A, we conclude (intuitively) that "set A is closed under multiplication."

Property P1 assures us that the set of Whole Numbers is closed under Addition and Multiplication.

The Commutative Properties for Addition and for Multiplication (cpa and cpm, respectively,) are the properties that deal with the *order* of the summands and the *order* of the factors. These properties allow a restatement in the *order* of summands and factors:

EXAMPLE

$$3 + 4 = 4 + 3; \quad \text{(cpa)}.$$
$$a + 6 = 6 + a; \quad \text{(cpa)}.$$
$$3(4) = 4(3); \quad \text{(cpm)}.$$
$$a \times 6 = 6 \times a; \quad \text{(cpm)}.$$

The Associative Properties for Addition and for Multiplication (cpa and cpm, respectively) are the properties that deal with the *grouping* of summands and the *grouping* of factors. Applied in a straightforward manner, the following can be stated:

EXAMPLE

$$1 + (2 + 3) = (1 + 2) + 3; \quad \text{(apa)}.$$
$$a + (4 + 5) = (a + 4) + 5; \quad \text{(apa)}.$$
$$1 \times (2 \times 3) = (1 \times 2) \times 3; \quad \text{(apm)}.$$
$$a \times (4 \times 5) = (a \times 4) \times 5; \quad \text{(apm)}.$$

By using the Commutative Properties and the Associative Properties:

EXAMPLE

$$(1 + 2) + 3 = (2 + 1) + 3; \quad \text{(cpa)}.$$
$$= 3 + (2 + 1); \quad \text{(cpa)}.$$
$$= 3 + (1 + 2). \quad \text{(cpa)}.$$

One immediate consequence of the Commutative and Associative Properties illustrated by the Example immediately above, is in "column" addition. This property allows us to group any two summands together without affecting the sum of the numbers:

$$\begin{array}{r} 1 \\ 2 \\ +3 \\ \hline 6 \end{array}$$

To add this column of numbers, pupils always (a) group two summands together and represent their sum as a single number, and then (b) regroup the remaining summand and the summand from (a), find their sum which in turn is the sum of the column.

P4:   Distributivity.

$$a(b + c) = a(b) + a(c).$$

The Distributive Property of Multiplication over Addition (dpma) is that property which unites the two separate operations, multiplication and addition. Heretofore, the distributive pattern has been studied within sets as

$$A \cup (B \cap C) = (A \cup B) \cap (A \cup C),$$
$$A \cap (B \cup C) = (A \cap B) \cup (A \cap C),$$
$$A \times (B \cup C) = (A \times B) \cup (A \times C).$$

The importance of this pattern cannot be overemphasized, for this pattern is used extensively in the teaching of topics such as

(a) Algorithms that involve addition of Whole Numbers,
(b) Algorithms that involve multiplication of Whole Numbers,
(c) Algorithms that involve factoring, addition, and multiplication in elementary algebra.

The student should note that the equality $a(b + c) = a(b) + a(c)$ involves the product of a and $(b + c)$ which in turn is expressed as the sum $a(b) + a(c)$. This is generally referred to as "expressing a product as a sum."

EXAMPLES

(a) Find the product $3(5 + 4)$ by first expressing the product as a sum:

$$3(5 + 4) = 3(5) + 3(4),$$
$$= 15 + 12,$$
$$= 27.$$

(b) Find the product $30(43)$ by first expressing the product $30(40 + 3)$ as a sum:

$$30(40 + 3) = 30(40) + 30(3),$$
$$= 1200 + 90,$$
$$= 1290.$$

(c) Find the sum of $3(4) + 3(5)$ by first expressing the sum as a product:

$$3(4) + 3(5) = 3(4 + 5)$$
$$= 3(9),$$
$$= 27.$$

(d) If a is any whole number, find the sum of $3a + 4a$ by first expressing the product as a sum:

$$3a + 4a = a(3) + a(4),$$
$$= a(3 + 4),$$
$$= a(7),$$
$$= 7a.$$

In addition to the properties noted above, there are two elements referred to as Identity Elements.

$A1$: *Additive Identity.* There exists within the set of Whole Numbers an element called   0, such that if n is any Whole Number

$$n + 0 = 0 + n = n.$$

$A2$: *Multiplicative Identity.* There exists within the set of Whole Numbers an element called   1, such that if n is any Whole Number,

$$1(n) = n(1) = n.$$

The numbers   0   and   1   are rather "special" numbers within the set of Whole Numbers. Note that when considering addition,

$$1 + 0 = 1,$$

$$2 + 0 = 2,$$

$$3 + 0 = 3,$$

and if n is any Whole Number, we can conclude that

$$n + 0 = n.$$

The sum of any whole number, n, and   0   is the whole number, n. We can intuitively see that   0   is the only number that has this property, and for this reason, the number zero is called the Additive Identity Element.

Parallel to the case of addition,   1   *times* any whole number, n, is

$$1(0) = 0,$$

$$1(1) = 1,$$

$$1(2) = 2,$$

$$1(3) = 3,$$

and if n is any Whole Number, we conclude that

$$1(n) = n.$$

The number   1   is referred to as the Multiplicative Identity Element.

The problems of Problem Set 2.4, immediately following, deal with the properties listed above. There are also problems presented in the form of "proofs" to rationalize these properties.

PROBLEM SET 2.4

Justify your answer for Problems 1–6 below by citing examples.

1. Is $0 = \{3, 6, 9, 12, \ldots\}$ closed under addition? Multiplication?

2. If $S = \{x| \quad x > 20, x$ a counting number$\}$, is S closed under addition? Multiplication?

3. If $T = \{x| \quad x > 20$ and $x < 40$, x a counting number$\}$, is T closed under addition? Multiplication?

4. If $X = \{n| \quad n < 20, n$ a counting number$\}$, is X closed under addition? Multiplication?

5. If $V = \{0, 1, 2, 3, 4\}$, is V closed under addition? Multiplication?

6. If $W = \{0, 1, 2, 3, \ldots\}$, is W closed under addition? Multiplication?

7. (a) Let $A =$ put on shoes and $B =$ put on socks. Is the result "A and then B" the same result as "B and then A"?

(b) Let $A =$ study for the test and $B =$ take the test. Would you expect the result "A and then B" to be the same result as "B and then A"?

(c) Let $a|b$ mean "divide the first number by the second number." Would you expect the result $a|b$ to be the same result as $b|a$?

8. The following table is read in identically the same manner as any addition or multiplication table. Is the operation $\oplus$ (circle plus) commutative for the set $\{0, 1, 2, 3, 4\}$? Associative? What element of $\{0, 1, 2, 3, 4\}$ acts as an Identity Element for $\oplus$?

$\oplus$	0	1	2	3	4
0	0	0	0	0	0
1	0	1	2	3	4
2	0	2	4	0	2
3	0	3	0	3	0
4	0	4	2	0	4

Example:
$3 \oplus 2 = 0.$
$2 \oplus 3 = 0.$

9. The following problem illustrates, using sets, how the Associative Property for Addition is developed within an elementary school program. Fill in the appropriate spaces provided:

EXAMPLE

$$\{s\} \cup [\{b, k\} \cup \{h, d, v\}] = [\{s\} \cup \{b, k\}] \cup \{h, d, v\},$$
$$\{s\} \cup \{b, k, h, d, v\} = \{s, b, k\} \cup \{h, d, v\},$$
$$\{s, b, k, h, d, v\} = \{s, b, k, h, b, v\},$$
$$n\{s, b, k, h, d, v\} = n\{s, b, h, h, b, v\}.$$

(a) $[n\{\ \} + n\{f, b\}] + 6 = n\{\ \} + [n\{f, b\} + 6],$

     $[\underline{\hspace{1cm}} + \underline{\hspace{1cm}}] + 6 + \underline{\hspace{1cm}} + [\underline{\hspace{1cm}} + 6],$

     $\underline{\hspace{1cm}} + 6 = \underline{\hspace{1cm}} + \underline{\hspace{1cm}},$

     $\underline{\hspace{1cm}} = \underline{\hspace{1cm}}.$

(b) $4 + [1 + n\{\$, \%, \pi\}] = [4 + 1] + 3,$

     $\underline{\hspace{1cm}} + [\underline{\hspace{1cm}} + \underline{\hspace{1cm}}] = \underline{\hspace{1cm}} + \underline{\hspace{1cm}},$

     $\underline{\hspace{1cm}} + \underline{\hspace{1cm}} = \underline{\hspace{1cm}} + \underline{\hspace{1cm}},$

     $\underline{\hspace{1cm}} = \underline{\hspace{1cm}}.$

10. Assume each of a, b, and c is a Whole Number. Prove, as in the example below, each of (a), (b), and (c) by justifying each step in the following with (a) the Commutative Property for Addition (cpa), or (b) the Associative Property for Addition (apa):

Proof:

STEP	JUSTIFICATION
1. $(a + b) + c = a + (b + c)$	1. cpa.
2. $c + (a + b) = c + (b + a)$.	2. cpa.
(a) $(a + b) + c = a + (c + b)$.	
(b) $(a + b) + c = (c + b) + a$.	
(c) $(2 + a) + 8 = (8 + 2) + a$.	

11. Justify each step in the following which shows that $(20 + 4) + (40 + 3) = 67$.

STEP	JUSTIFICATION
1. $(20 + 4) + (40 + 3) = (4 + 20) + (3 + 40)$,	1.
2. $(4 + 20) + (3 + 40) = (4 + 20) + 43$,	2. Addition Fact (af).
3. $(4 + 20) + 43 = 4 + (20 + 43)$,	3.
4. $4 + (20 + 43) = 4 + (43 + 20)$,	4.
5. $4 + (43 + 20) = 4 + 63$,	5.
6. $4 + 63 = 67$.	6.

12. The following table is a table of multiplication taken from Lower Slovakia. All numbers are from the set $\{\triangle, \square, \odot, \pi\}$ and the multiplication facts under $\otimes$ (circle multiplication) are given below. The table is read as an ordinary multiplication table.

$\otimes$	$\triangle$	$\square$	$\odot$	π
$\triangle$	$\odot$	π	$\triangle$	$\square$
$\square$	π	$\triangle$	$\square$	$\odot$
$\odot$	$\triangle$	$\square$	$\odot$	π
π	$\square$	$\odot$	π	$\triangle$

Example:
$\square \otimes \pi = \odot$.
$\pi \otimes \odot = \pi$.

Find the value of

(a) $\triangle \otimes \pi = $ _____.
(b) $\square \otimes (\triangle \otimes \pi) = $ _____.
(c) $(\square \otimes \triangle) \otimes \pi = $ _____.
(d) $(\odot \otimes \triangle) \otimes \square = $ _____.
(e) $\odot \otimes (\triangle \otimes \square) = $ _____.

13. Is the set $A = \{\triangle, \square, \odot, \pi\}$, above, closed under $\otimes$? (i.e., If $a \in A$ and $b \in A$ is $a \otimes b \in A$?) Commutative? Associative? What element is the Identity?

14. The following problem illustrates, using sets, how the Commutative Property for Multiplication is developed in an elementary school program. Fill in the appropriate blank spaces.

(a) $\{a, b, c, d, e, f\} = \{a, b, c, d, e, f\}$,

   $\{a, b\} \cup \{c, d\} \cup \{e, f\} = \{a, b, c\} \cup \{d, e, f\}$,

$n\{a, b\} + n\{c, d\} + n\{e, f\} = n\{a, b, c\} + n\{d, e, f\}$,

_____ + _____ + _____ = _____ + _____

_____ twos = _____ threes,

3(2) = _____ (3).

(b) $\{a, b, c, d\} \cup \{e, f, g, h\} = \{a, b\} \cup \{c, d\} \cup \{e, f\} \cup \{f, h\}$

$n\{a, b, c, d\} + n\{e, f, g, h\} = n\{a, b\} + n\{c, d\} + n\{e, f\} + n\{g, h\}$

_____ + _____ = _____ + _____ + _____ + _____,

_____ fours = _____ twos,

_____ (4) = _____ (2).

15. If $A = \{1, 2)$ and $B = \{a, b\}$, illustrate, using Definition 2.7, that $n(A) \cdot n(B) = n(B) \cdot n(A)$. *Hint:* Find $A \times B$ and $B \times A$.

16. If $A = \{1, 2\}$, $B = \{a\}$, and $C = \{d\}$, verify that $n(A)[n(B) \cdot n(C)] = [n(A) \cdot n(B)]n(C)$. *Hint:* Find $A \times (B \times C)$ and $(A \times B) \times C$.

17. Assume each of $a, b,$ and c is a Whole Number. Prove, as in the example below each of (a), (b), and (c) Justify each step within the proof with (a) the Commutative Property for Multiplication (cpm); or (b) the Associative Property for Multiplication (apm):

EXAMPLE

Prove $(1 \times 2) \times 3 = 1 \times (3 \times 2)$.

STEP	JUSTIFICATION
1. $(1 \times 2) \times 3 = 1 \times (2 \times 3)$,	1. apm.
2. $1 \times (2 \times 3) = 1 \times (3 \times 2)$.	2. cpm.
(a) $(a \times b) \times c = a \times (c \times b)$.	
(b) $(a \times b) \times c = (c \times b) \times c$.	
(c) $(a \times b) \times c = (c \times a) \times b$.	

18. Since the Associative Property for Multiplication reveals that $a(b \cdot c) = (a \cdot b)c$, a, b, c Whole Numbers, is it necessary to insert the grouping symbols in the product $2 \times 3 \times 4 \times 5 \times 6 = 720$? Why?

19. Find the products in a–j, below, by first expressing each product as a sum. All letters represent whole numbers.

(a) $3(4 + 8) =$ (b) $6(1 + 4) =$

(c) $5(x + y) =$ (d) $(4 + 5)x =$

(e) $(3 + n)(5) =$ (f) $4a(3 + t) =$

(g) $x(a + b) =$ (h) $t(2w + 4w) =$

(i) $3a(1 + 1) =$ (j) $(a + a)(3) =$

20. Find the sum of each of the following by first expressing each sum as a product. All letters represent Whole Numbers.

(a) $5(2) + 5(3) =$

(b) $4(6) + 4(8) =$

(c) $x(y) + x(w) =$

(d) $4a(w) + 4a(t) =$

(e) $5(4) + 5(3z) =$

(f) $3a + 3z =$

(g) $(x + 1)(5) + (x + 1)(7) =$

(h) $(3 + w)z + (3 + w)t =$

(i) $(x - 1)a + (x + 1)(7) =$

(j) $(4 + x)(t + 7) + (4 + x)(w + 8) =$

21. Prove, if x is a Whole Number, using the Distributive Property of Multiplication over Addition, that (a) $7x + 8x = 15x$. (b) Prove also that $3x + 3x = 6x$. (c) If $x = 1x$, prove $x + x = 2x$.

22. Show that $3[(a + b) + (x + d)] = 3a + 3b + 3c + 3d$.

23. From Problem 22, can you intuitively generalize the Distributive Property of Multiplication over Addition, i.e., does $n(a + b + c + \ldots + k) = n(a) + n(b) + n(c) + \ldots + n(k)$? Why?

24. Find the sum of the two given numbers by applying the Distributive Property of Multiplication over addition:

EXAMPLE

$[2(100) + 3(10) + 4(1)] + [3(100) + 6(10) + 5(1)]$,

$= [2(100) + 3(100)] + [3(10) + 6(10)] + [4(1) + 5(1)]$,   (cpa and apa).

$= (2 + 3)100 + (3 + 6)10 + (4 + 5)1$,   (dpma).

$= 5(100) + 9(10) + 9(1)$.   (af).

$= 500 + 90 + 9$,   (mf).

$= 599$.   (af).

(a) $[6(100) + 0(10) + 8(1)] + [2(100) + 8(10) + 1(1)] =$

(b) $[0(100) + 7(10) + 5(1)] + [9(100) + 0(10) + 0(1)] =$

25. If x is any Whole Number, show that

(a) $(3 + 5)x + (4 + 7)x = 7x + 12x = 19x$.

(b) $3x + (6x + 5x) = 14x$.

26. The following illustrate processes contained within the multiplication algorithm. By using the Distributive Property of Multiplication over addition, find the product of the following by converting each product to a sum. Each letter represents a Whole Number.

EXAMPLE

$$36 \times 43 = (30 + 6)(40 + 3)$$
$$= 30(40 + 3) + 6(40 + 3),$$
$$= 30(40) + 30(3) + 6(40) + 6(3),$$
$$= 1200 + 90 + 240 + 18,$$
$$= 1,548.$$

(a) $21 \times 17 =$
(b) $54 \times 23 =$
(c) $(3 + 5)(a + b) =$
(d) $(7 + 6)(2a + a) =$
(e) $(t + 2)(a + b) =$
(f) $(x + y)(2a + 4) =$

27. The following illustrate, using sets, an intuitive development for $1(n) = n$ and $0 + n = n$, n any Whole Number. Fill in the blanks to make true sentences.

(a) $\{f\} \cup \{d\} = \{f, d\}$,
         $n\{f\} + n\{d\} = n\{f, d\}$,
         _____ + _____ = _____,
         _____ ones = 2,
         _____ (1) = 2.

(b) $\{f\} \cup \{b\} \cup \{k\} = \{f, b, k\}$,
         $n\{f\} + n\{b\} + n\{k\} = n\{f, b, d\}$,
         _____ + _____ + _____ = _____,
                  _____ ones = _____,
                  _____ (1) = _____.

(c) $\{a\} \cup \{\ \} = a$,
         $n\{a\} + n\{\ \} = n\{a\}$,
         _____ + _____ = _____,

(d) $\{x\,y\} \cup \{\ \} = \{x, y\}$,
         $n\{x, y\} + n\{\ \} = n\{x, y\}$,
         _____ + _____ = _____.

28. The following table is a table of "circle addition, $\oplus$." The table is read as common addition tables are read. Which element within $\{a, b, c\}$ serves as the "Additive Identity Element"?

$\oplus$	a	b	c
a	b	c	a
b	c	a	b
c	a	b	c

Example:
$a \oplus b = c$.
$b \oplus c = b$.

29. The following table is that for "Circle Multiplication." Which element within $\{a, b, c\}$ serves as the "Multiplicative Identity Element"?

$\otimes$	a	b	c
a	a	a	a
b	a	b	c
c	a	c	b

Example:
$c \otimes b = c$.
$a \otimes c = a$.

30–36. Problems 30–36 illustrate how the Commutative, Associative, and Distributive Properties may be rationalized using sets. Copy these statements on a separate sheet of paper and supply the justifications for each step by citing a definition or property previously studied.

30. P2: Assume A and B are finite, disjoint sets with Cardinal Numbers $n(A)$ and $n(B)$, respectively, then

STATEMENT	JUSTIFICATION
1. $A \cup B = B \cup A$	1. Set Union is Commutative.
2. $n(A \cup B) = n(B \cup A)$	2.
Therefore,	
3. $n(A) + n(B) = n(B) + n(A)$	3.

31. P3: Let each of A, B, and C be finite, disjoint sets with Cardinal Numbers $n(A)$, $n(B)$, and $n(C)$, respectively. Then

STATEMENT	JUSTIFICATION
1. $A \cup (B \cup C) = (A \cup B) \cup C$,	1. Set Union is Associative.
2. $n[A \cup (B \cup C)] = n[(A \cup B) \cup C]$,	2.
3. $n(A) + n(B \cup C) = n(A \cup B) + n(C)$,	3.
4. $n(A) + [n(B) + n(C)] = [n(A) + n(B)] + n(C)$	4.

32. P2: Assume each of A and B is a finite set with Cardinal Numbers $n(A)$ and $n(B)$, respectively. Then

STATEMENT	JUSTIFICATION
1. $A \times B \sim B \times A$.	1. Cartesian Product Sets are equivalent.
2. $n(A \times B) = n(B \times A)$.	2.
3. Therefore,	
$n(A) \cdot n(B) = n(B) \cdot n(A)$	3.

33. P3: Assume each of A, B, and C is a finite set with Cardinal Numbers $n(A)$, $n(B)$, and $n(C)$, respectively. Then

STATEMENT	JUSTIFICATION
1. $A \times (B \times C) \sim (A \times B) \times C$,	1. Cartesian Product Sets are equivalent.
2. $n[A \times (B \times C)] = n[(A \times B) \times C]$,	2.
3. $n(A) \cdot n(B \times C) = n(A \times B) \cdot n(C)$,	3.
4. $n(A) \cdot [n(B) \cdot n(C)] = [n(A) \cdot n(B)] \cdot n(C)$.	4.

34. P4: Assume A is a finite set with Cardinal Number $n(A)$, B and C to be finite, disjoint sets with Cardinal Numbers $n(B)$ and $n(C)$, respectively:

STEPS	JUSTIFICATION
1. $A \times (B \cup C) = (A \times B) \cup (A \times C)$,	1. Cartesian Product is distributive over set union.
2. $n[A \times (B \cup C)] = n[(A \times B) \cup (A \cup C)]$,	2.
3. $n[A \times (B \cup C)] = n(A \times B) + n(A \times C)$,	3.
4. $n(A) \cdot n(B \cup C) = n(A) \cdot n(B) + n(A) \cdot n(C)$,	4.
5. $n(A)[n(B) + n(C)] = n(A) \cdot n(B) + n(A) \cdot n(C)$.	5.

35–36. P4, above, is sometimes referred to as the "left" Distributive Property for obvious reasons. However, we can prove the Distributive Property of Multiplication over Addition to be a "right" distributive property. This is done is two parts, Problems 35 and 36. The reader should justify each step within the proof.

35. If each of a, b, and c is a Whole Number, then

$$a(b + c) = (b + c)a.$$

Assumption: Assume each of a, b, and c is a Whole Number. Then

STEP	JUSTIFICATION
1. $a(b + c) = (b + c)a$	1.

36. If each of a, b, and c is a Whole Number, then

$$(b + c)a = b(a) + c(a).$$

Assumptions: Assume each of a, b, and c is a Whole Number. Then

STEPS	JUSTIFICATION
1. $(b + c)a = a(b + c)$,	1.
2. $a(b + c) = a(b) + a(c)$,	2.
3. $a(b) + a(c) = b(a) + c(a)$	3.
Conclusion:	
4. $(b + c)a = b(a) + c(a)$	4.

CHAPTER 3

Additional Properties
for Whole Numbers

3.1 INTRODUCTION

An investigation of the properties of equality and the properties of order
shall be made within this chapter, along with an introduction to subtraction
and division. It is appropriate to list those properties investigated in
Chapter 2.

$P1$: *The Closure Properties.* For all Whole Numbers a and b,
$a + b \in W$ and $a(b) \in W$.

$P2$: *The Commutative Properties.* For all Whole Numbers a and
b, $a + b = b + a$ and $a(b) = b(a)$.

$P3$: *The Associative Properties.* For all Whole Numbers a, b, and
c, $a + (b + c) = (a + b) + c$ and $a(bc) = (ab)c$.

$P4$: *The Distributive Property of Multiplication Over Addition.* For all
Whole Numbers a, b, and c, $a(b + c) = ab + ac$.

64

In addition to the properties above, there are the two identity elements:

*A*1: *The Additive Identity Element.* There is Whole Number, 0, such that if   *a*   is any Whole Number,   *a* + 0 = *a*.

*A*2: *The Multiplicative Identity Element.* There is a Whole Number, 1, such that if   *a*   is any Whole Number,   *a*(1) = *a*.

3.2 EQUIVALENCE RELATIONS

We shall continue the study of Whole Numbers by investigating additional properties associated with equality and inequality by first defining an Equivalence Relation.

Definition 3.1—An Equivalence Relation If any relation,   *R*, satisfies each of the following properties, then   *R*   is defined as an Equivalence Relation.

1. Reflexivity: *a R a*.
2. Symmetry: If   *a R b*   then   *b R a*.
3. Transitivity: If   *a R b*   and   *b R c*, then   *a R c*.

For example, let   *R*   be the relation "is the mother of." In order to determine if the relation "is the mother of," is an Equivalence Relation, we must investigate each of 1, 2, and 3 above. In order to do this, let each of *x*,   *y*, and   *z*   be a person:

1. Reflexivity: *x* is the mother of   *x*.   (*False*)
2. Symmetry: If   *x*   is the mother of   *y*, then   *y*   is the mother of   *x*.   (*False*)
3. Transitivity: If   *x*   is the mother of   *y*   and   *y*   is the mother of   *z*, then   *x*   is the mother of *z*.   (*False*)

From this, we can conclude that the relation "is the mother of" is not an Equivalence Relation.

Similarly, the relation "is less than (<)" does not satisfy each of the three conditions established in Definition 3.1. For this reason, the relation "is less than" is *not* an Equivalence Relation. For all Whole Numbers *x*,   *y*, and   *z*:

1. Reflexivity: *x* < *x*.   (*False*)
2. Symmetry: If   *x* < *y*   then   *y* < *x*.   (*False*)
3. Transitivity: If   *x* < *y*   and   *y* < *z*, then   *x* < *a*. (*True*)

We define the relation $=$ to be an Equivalence Relation. For all Whole Numbers a, b, and c:

1. Reflexivity: $a = a$.
2. Symmetry: If $a = b$ then $b = a$.
3. Transitivity: If $a = b$ and $b = c$, then $a = c$.

The relation $=$ and the associated properties of reflexivity, symmetry, and transitivity form a basis for solving equations. Similarly, the following properties are also used in the same manner.

3.3 FOUR ADDITIONAL PROPERTIES FOR ADDITION AND MULTIPLICATION AND ORDER PROPERTIES

The following properties for Whole Numbers are listed and an illustrative example is given to show how these properties are used in mathematical situations. A rationalization, using sets, for these properties is included in Problem Set 3.1.

For every Whole Number a, for every Whole Number b, and for every Whole Number c, (except as denoted below):

P5–6: *Uniqueness Properties.*
    P5: If $a = b$, then $a + c = b + c$.
    P6: If $a = b$, then $a(c) = b(c)$.

EXAMPLES

    P5: If $3a = 6$, then $3a + 5 = 6 + 5$.
    P6: If $4a = 7$, then $24a = 42$.

P7–8: *Cancellation Properties.*
    P7: If $a + c = b + c$, then $a = b$.
    P8: If $a(c) = b(c)$, then $a = b$, $(c \neq 0)$.

EXAMPLES

    P7: If $a + 7 = 42$, then $a = 35$.
    P8: If $7(a) = 42$, then $a = 6$.

PROBLEM SET 3.1

1. Which of the following relations is an equivalence relation?

(a) Is a sister of.

(b) Is perpendicular to.
(c) Is a divisor of.
(d) Is parallel to.
(e) Is on the same page as.
(f) Is greater than.
(g) Is the same area as.

2. Give an illustration to show that if $a \neq b$ and $c = 0$, then $a(c) = b(c)$.

3. What property (P1–P8) is illustrated in the following statements?

(a) $ab = ab$.
(b) $ab = ba$.
(c) If $t = 10$, then $10t = 100$.
(d) If $t = 10$, then $10 = t$.
(e) If $a = b + c$ and $b = d$, then $a = d + c$.
(f) If $6 = 4y$ and $4y = 10t$, then $6 = 10t$.
(g) If $2y = 20$ then $y = 10$.
(h) If $y = x + 2$ then $6y = 6x + 12$.
(i) If $x + 12 = y + 24$ then $x = y + 12$.
(j) If $12 = y + 24$ then $y + 24 = 12$.
(k) If $x + 20 = 24$ then $x = 5$.
(l) If $xy = x$ then $y = 1$.

4. Justify each step in the following. Each letter represents a Whole Number:

(a) If $2x + 5x = 14$, then
$$(2 + 5)x = 14,$$
$$7x = 14,$$
$$7x = 7(2),$$
$$x = 2.$$
(b) If $22x + 14 = 58$, then
$$22x + 14 = 44 + 14,$$
$$22x = 44,$$
$$22x = 22(2),$$
$$x = 2.$$

5. Find the value of x as in Problem 4 above. Justify each step.

(a) $10x + 12 = 66$.
(b) $10x + 30 = 20x$ (*Hint*: $20x = 10x + 10x$).

6. If $x = b + 2$ and $x + 4 = 6 + z$, prove $b = z$.

7. If $z = y + 1$ and $x + 10 = 10z$, prove $x = 10y$.

8–11. In Problems 8–11, which give a rationalization for properties P5–P6, justify each statement by citing a previously studied definition or property. Further discussion of P7 and P8 will follow in sections following the definition of subtraction.

8. P5: For all Whole Numbers a, b, and c, if $a = b$, then $a + c = b + c$.

Assumptions. Assume each of A, B, and C is a finite set, $A \sim B$, $A \cap C = \emptyset$ and $B \cap C = \emptyset$.

STEPS	JUSTIFICATION
1. $A \sim B$.	1. Given, or assumed.
2. $\therefore$ $n(A) = n(B)$.	2.
3. If $A \sim B$, then $A \cup C \sim B \cup C$.	3.
4. $n(A \cup C) = n(B \cup C)$.	4.
5. $n(A) + n(C) = n(B) + n(C)$.	5.

9. P6: For all Whole Numbers a, b, and c, if $a = b$, then $a(c) = b(c)$.

Assumptions. Assume each of A, B, and C is a finite set, $A \sim B$.

STEPS	JUSTIFICATION
1. $A \sim B$.	1. Given, or assumed.
2. $\therefore$ $n(A) = n(B)$.	2.
3. If $A \sim B$, then $A \times C \sim B \times C$.	3.
4. $n(A \times C) = n(B \times C)$.	4.
5. $\therefore$ $n(A) \cdot n(C) = n(B) \cdot n(C)$	5.

10. Using P5 and P6, we may generalize according to the following: If $a = b$ and $c = d$, then $a + c = b + d$. This is proven in the following manner:

Assume each of a, b, c, and d is a Whole Number, $a = b$ and $c = d$.

STEPS	JUSTIFICATION
1. $a = b$ and $c = d$.	1. Assumed, or given.
2. If $a = b$, then $a + c = b + c$.	2. P5.
3. If $c = d$, then $b + c = b + d$.	3.
4. $\therefore$ $a + c = b + c$.	4.

11. Prove the more general form for P6, i.e., if $a = b$ and $c = d$, then $a(c) = b(d)$, where each of a, b, c, and d is a Whole Number. The proof parallels that encountered in Problem 10.

3.4 THE ORDER PROPERTIES

From Chapter 2, the Inequality Relations were defined in terms of matching the elements of set A one-to-one with the elements of set B.

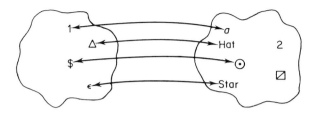

Figure 3.1

If one or more element of set　B　was left unpaired, then　$n(A) <$ $n(B)$ or　$n(B) > n(A)$.

However, by studying sets, the Inequality Relations may be illustrated in a more precise manner.

If each of　A　and　B　is a *representative set*, then　$n(A) <$ $n(B)$　means　A　is a subset of　B　and　$A \neq B$.

EXAMPLES

(a) If　$n(A) = 3$　and　$n(B) = 5$, then　$3 < 5$　means $\{1, 2, 3\} \subset \{1, 2, 3, 4, 5\}$.

(b) If　$n(A) = 1$　and　$n(B) = 7$, then　$1 < 7$　means $\{1\} \subset \{1, 2, 3, 4, 5, 6, 7\}$.

When studying sets such as the above, it is found that there exists a set C, such that　$A \cap C = \varnothing$　and　$A \cup C = B$:

(a) Let　$A = \{1, 2, 3\}$,　$B = \{1, 2, 3, 4, 5\}$. Then the set　C, such that　$A \cap C = \varnothing$　and　$A \cup C = B$　is the set　$\{4, 5\}$.

(b) Let　$A = \{1\}$,　$B = \{1, 2, 3, 4, 5, 6, 7\}$. Then the set　C, such that　$A \cap C = \varnothing$　and　$A \cup C = B$　is the set　$\{2, 3, 4, 5, 6, 7\}$.

Using the parallel number properties of sets　A,　B, and　C and the Definition for Addition leads to the conclusion that for the numbers $n(A)$,　$n(B)$, there is a Counting Number,　$n(C)$　such that

$$n(A) + n(C) = n(B).$$

EXAMPLES

(a) Let　$A = \{1, 2, 3\}$,　$B = \{1, 2, 3, 4, 5\}$, and　$C = \{4, 5\}$:

$$\{1, 2, 3\} \cup \{4, 5\} = \{1, 2, 3, 4, 5\},$$

$$n\{1, 2, 3\} + n\{4, 5\} = n\{1, 2, 3, 4, 5\},$$

$$3 + 2 = 5.$$

(b) Let $A = \{1\}$, $B = \{1, 2, 3, 4, 5, 6\}$, and $C = \{2, 3, 4, 5, 6\}$:

$$\{1\} \cup \{2, 3, 4, 5, 6\} = \{1, 2, 3, 4, 5, 6\},$$

$$n\{1\} + n\{2, 3, 4, 5, 6\} = n\{1, 2, 3, 4, 5, 6\},$$

$$1 + 4 = 5.$$

Note that in each case, set $A \subset$ set B, $A \neq B$. There is a set C, $A \cap C = \varnothing$, so that $A \cup C = B$. Under these conditions, it is always true that

$$n(A) + (\text{some Counting Number}) = n(B).$$

As another example, for the pair of numbers 6 and 10, there is the counting number, 4, such that $6 + 4 = 10$, and for the pair (8, 12) there is the counting number 4 such that $8 + 4 = 12$. This is the basis for an alternate definition for the Inequality Relations.

Definition 3.2—The Inequality Relations   If each of a and b is a Whole Number, then a is less than b $(a < b)$, if and only if there is a Counting Number, c,   such that $a + c = b$. Similarly, $b > a$ if and only if $a < b$.

The statement "if and only if" of Definition 3.2 combines the two distinct sentences:

(a) If $a < b$, then there is a number $c > 0$, such that $a + c = b$,

and

(b) If $a + c = b$, $c > 0$, then $a < b$.

3.5 PROPERTIES OF INEQUALITY

With Definitions 3.1 and 3.2 we are now able to prove various inequality properties within the set of Whole Numbers. To build a logical order for these properties, we must first prove that zero is less than any other Whole Number.

$I1$:   *The Whole Number   0   is Less Than Any Counting Number   X.* Let x be any counting number. Since $x \neq 0$, there is a nonempty set X, such that $n(X) = x$. Then $\varnothing \subset X$, $\varnothing \neq X$ and $n\{ \} < n(X)$. Therefore, since $n\{ \} = 0$ and $n(X) = x$, $0 < x$.

$I2$:   *The Trichotomy Property.*   In the above, we have shown that $0 < x$, $x \in C$. In order to show that one and only one of the following is true, $a = b$ or $a < b$ or $a > b$, we must state the following Axiom concerning sets:

AXIOM

Given Representative Set A and Representative Set B, set A and set B not empty, then one and only one of the following is true:

  (a) $A = B$.
  (b) A is a proper subset of B.
  (c) B is a proper subset of A.

Using the above, we can show that if each of a and b is a Whole Number, $a \neq b$, then $a < b$ or $b < a$, but not both, in the following manner:

Let each of a and b be a Whole Number, $a \neq b$. If $a = 0$, then $b \neq 0$, since $a \neq b$. Then $a < b$ by I1. If $b = 0$, then $a \neq 0$, since $a \neq b$. Then $b < a$ by I1. If $a \neq 0$ and $b \neq 0$, then consider the two sets A and B; $n(A) = a$ and $n(B) = b$, respectively.

$$A = \{1, 2, 3, 4, \ldots, a\}, \qquad B = \{1, 2, 3, 4, \ldots, b\}.$$

But $\{1, 2, 3, 4, \ldots, a\} \subset \{1, 2, 3, 4, \ldots, b\}$ or $\{1, 2, 3, 4, \ldots, b\} \subset \{1, 2, 3, 4, \ldots, a\}$, but not both. If A is a proper subset of B, then $a < b$. If B is a proper subset of A, then $b < a$. Therefore, if $a \neq b$, $a < b$ or $b > a$, but not both.

We can now state the *Trichotomy Property for Whole Numbers*: If each of a and b is a Whole Number, then exactly one of the following is true:

$$a = b \quad \text{or} \quad a < b \quad \text{or} \quad b < a.$$

I3: *Transitive Property of the Inequality Relation.* Recall that the equals relation was defined to be reflexive ($a = a$), symmetric (If $a = b$, then $b = a$), and transitive (If $a = b$ and $b = c$, then $a = c$). Many properties of inequality parallel those of equality, and one of these is that of *transitivity*. The Inequality relation is not an Equivalence Relation, for $a \not< a$ (not reflexive), if $a < b$, then $b \not< a$ (not symmetric), but if $a < b$ and $b < c$, then $a < c$. This is proven in the following manner:

If $a < b$ then there is a counting number x such that $a + x = b$, and if $b < c$, then there is a counting number y such that $b + y = c$. By substituting the number $a + x = b$,

$$(a + x) + y = c,$$

$$a + (x + y) = c.$$

We may conclude that $a < c$ because the number $(x + y)$ is a counting number and from the definition for inequality.

14: *The Order Property for Addition.* The order property for addition parallels one for the equals relation:
  If $a < b$ then $a + c < b + d$, for all Whole Numbers, a, b, and c. This is proven in the following manner:
  Let each of a, b, and c be a Whole Number, $a < b$. If $a < b$, then there is a counting number, x, such that $a + x = b$.

$$a + x = b,$$

$$(a + x) + c = b + c,$$

$$a + (x + c) = b + c,$$

$$a + (c + x) = b + c,$$

$$(a + c) + x = b + c.$$

Therefore, $a + c < b + c$ because x is a counting number and the definition for inequality.

Using the definition for the inequality relation and the properties of equality, the remaining properties can be proved in a manner similar to the above. These proofs are left as exercises in Problem Set 3.2.

15: *The Order Property for Multiplication.* For all Whole Numbers a, b, and c, $c > 0$, and $a < b$, then $ac < bc$.

16: *The Cancellation Property for Addition.* For all Whole Numbers a, b, and c, if $a + c < b + c$, then $a < b$.

17: *The Cancellation Property for Multiplication.* For all Whole Numbers a, b, and c, $(c > 0)$ if $ac < bc$, then $a < c$.

PROBLEM SET 3.2

1. What property of Whole Numbers is illustrated in the following?

(a) If $a < b + c$ and $b < d$, then $a < d + c$.
(b) If $2y < 30$, then $y < 15$.
(c) If $6 < 4y$ and $4y < 10z$, then $6 < 10z$.
(d) If $y < x + 2$ then $6y < 6x + 12$.
(e) If $x + 12 < y + 24$, then $x < y + 12$.
(f) If $x + 20 < 30$, then $x < 10$.

2. For all Counting Numbers n, a, b, and c, if $na + (a + b) = c$, is $na < c$? Is $(a + b) < c$? Why?

3. Find:

(a) $\{x|\quad x + 7 < 10, x \in C\}$.

(b) $\{x|\quad 7x < 5x, x \in W\}$.

(c) $\{x|\quad 5x < 7x, x \in C\}$.

(d) $\{x|\quad 5x + 10 < 7x, x \in C\}$.

(e) $\{x|\quad 10 + 2x < 20, x \in C\}$.

4. Prove that for all Whole Numbers a, b, and c if $a < b$, then $a + c < b + c$.

5. Prove that for all Whole Numbers a, b, and c if $a + c < b + c$, then $a < b$.

6. Prove that for all Whole Numbers a, b, and c, $c \neq 0$, if $ac < bc$, then $a < b$.

3.6 GRAPHING SETS OF WHOLE NUMBERS

Elementary programs use the study of sets and the picture of the number line to introduce inequalities. This is accomplished by using the primitive terms "to the left of," and "to the right of," by stating that "the number x is less than the number y because x lies to the left of y," or "the number y is greater than the number x because y lies to the right of x on the picture of the number line:"

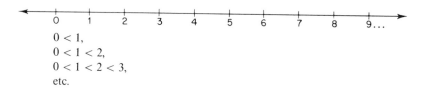

$$0 < 1,$$
$$0 < 1 < 2,$$
$$0 < 1 < 2 < 3,$$

etc.

Figure 3.2

To graph sets of numbers on the picture of the number line, solid dots are used to represent members of the solution set.

EXAMPLE

Graph $\{x|\quad x < 6,\quad x \in W\}$. The solution set is $\{0, 1, 2, 3, 4, 5\}$ and the graph of this set is:

Figure 3.3

EXAMPLE

Graph $\{x|\quad x < 6$ ‹ and $x > 3,\quad x \in W\}$. The solution set is $\{4, 5\}$:

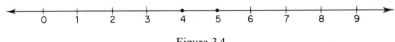

Figure 3.4

EXAMPLE

If $x \in W$, graph

$$\{x|\quad x < 10\} \cap \{x|\quad x > 5\} = \{0, 1, 2, \ldots, 9\} \cap \{6, 7, 8, 9, \ldots\}$$
$$= \{6, 7, 8, 9\}.$$

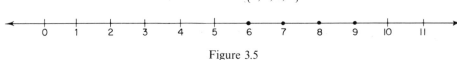

Figure 3.5

EXAMPLE

Graph $\{x|\quad x + 5 < 10,\quad x \in W\} = \{0, 1, 2, 3, 4\}$.

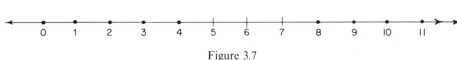

Figure 3.6

EXAMPLE

If $x \in W$, graph

$$\{x|\quad x < 4\} \cup \{x|\quad x > 7\} = \{0, 1, 2, 3, 4\} \cup \{8, 9, 10, \ldots\}$$
$$= \{0, 1, 2, 3, 4, 8, 9, 10, \ldots\}:$$

Figure 3.7

The examples above illustrate methods to graph sets of numbers involving inequalities and set operations, where the solid dots indicate that the number corresponding to this dot is a member of the solution set.

Since inequality is defined in terms of equality, many parallels exist between the two relations. For example, the relation $\leq$ (less than or equal to), means $a \leq b$ if and only if $a \not> b$. Similarly, $a \geq b$ (a is greater than or equal to b) if and only if $a \not< b$.

Frequently, the student will encounter statements such as $\{n|$ $5 \leq n \leq 20\}$, which is the set of all numbers, n, such that n is greater than or equal to 5 and n is less than or equal to 20. This same set may be restated $\{n|$ $5 \leq n\} \cup \{n| n \leq 20\} = \{5, 6, 7, \ldots, 20\}$.

PROBLEM SET 3.3

1. The following problems involve inequalities. Find the solution set to each of these and then graph the solution set. All letters represent Whole Numbers.

(a) $\{n|$ $4n < 20\}$.

(b) $\{n|$ $n + 4 \leq 24\}$.

(c) $\{n|$ $n < 10\} \cap \{n|$ $n \geq 2\}$.

(d) $\{n|$ $n \geq 10\} \cap \{n|$ $n < 16\}$.

(e) $\{n|$ $5 < n < 12\} \cup \{n|$ $9 < n \leq 13\}$.

(f) $\{n|$ $6 \leq n \leq 13\} \cap \{n|$ $10 \leq n\}$.

(g) $\{n|$ $0 \leq n \leq 8\} \cup \{n|$ $9 < n \leq 14\}$.

3.7   UNIQUENESS OF IDENTITY ELEMENTS

Is it possible that within the set of Whole Numbers, there is another number x that has the same properties as 0, and is there another number y that has the same properties as 1?

Let us investigate the possibility that there is another Additive Identity, x, within the set of Whole Numbers.

If x is an Additive Identity, then for all Whole Numbers c, $c + x = c$. But $c + 0 = c$, since 0 is also the Additive Identity. By substitution, $c + x = c + 0$, and therefore $x = 0$ by P7. Thus there is no number within the set of Whole Numbers, other than zero, that serves as an Additive Identity. For this reason, we say that 0 is unique.

Similarly, we can prove that 1 is unique. The proof is left as an exercise for the reader.

CHAPTER 4

Subtraction
—Introduction to Integers

4.1 INTRODUCTION

As in the case of addition, the subtraction of Whole Numbers will be introduced through the use of sets. To aid in the development of this concept, it
becomes necessary to introduce a new set operation, ——. This heavy
bar will define a set operation that is the inverse operation for set Union.
From this, we can define subtraction as the inverse of addition.

Definition 4.1 —The Remainder Set If each of A and B is
a set, $B \subset A$, then $A —— B$ means a set C such that C
contains every element of A which is not an element of B.

"$A —— B$" is read "A take away B," and the set C is called "the
remainder set."
For the set operation —— to have meaning, B must be a
subset of A. Consider the following:

76

EXAMPLE

If $A = \{a, b, c, d, e, f\}$ and $B = \{a, b, c\}$, then $A \longrightarrow B = \{d, e, f\}$.

The set $\{d, e, f\}$ is the set C referred to in Definition 4.1. This set is the Remainder Set.

The set operation $\longrightarrow$ is the inverse operation of set Union, that is to say that one operation "undoes" the other. This is stated as Axiom 3.

Axiom 3: If each of A and B is a set, $B \subset A$, then $(A \longrightarrow B) \cup B = A$.

EXAMPLE

If $A = \{1, 2, 3, 4, 5\}$ and $B = \{1, 2\}$, then

$$(A \longrightarrow B) \cup B = (\{1, 2, 3, 4, 5\} \longrightarrow \{1, 2\}) \cup \{1, 2\}$$

$$= \{3, 4, 5\} \cup \{1, 2\} = \{1, 2, 3, 4, 5\} = A.$$

The above examples illustrate the idea of "take away subtraction" and subtraction is introduced in the elementary school in this manner. For this reason a definition is given.

Definition 4.2—Remainder Subtraction If each of A and B is a set, $B \subset A$, then $n(A) - n(B) = n(A \longrightarrow B)$.

If $n(A) = a$, $n(B) = b$, and $n(A \longrightarrow B) = c$, then a is defined as the minuend, b is defined the subtrahend, and c is defined as the difference.

However, Definition 4.1 assures that $B \cup C = A$ and $B \cap C = \varnothing$. From this, we can conclude that $n(A) = n(B) + n(C)$. Hence the statements $a - b = c$ and $a = b + c$ are identical statements for all Whole Numbers a, b, and c. To illustrate this, $10 - 6 = 4$ because $10 = 6 + 4$; $5 - 3 = 2$ because $5 = 3 + 2$. From examples such as these two, the second definition for subtraction is made.

Definition 4.3—Subtraction in Terms of Addition For all Whole Numbers a, b, and c, $c = a - b$ if and only if $c + b = a$.

Therefore subtraction is defined in terms of addition, and the statements $a - b = c$ and $a = b + c$ mean exactly the same for all Whole Numbers a, b, and c.

PROBLEM SET 4.1

1. Form the Remainder Set. Fill in each blank to make true sentences.

(a) $\{d, c, t, p, q\} \!-\! \{d, c\} = $ _____.

$n\{d, c, t, p, q\} - n\{d, c\} = $ _____.

_____ $-$ _____ $=$ _____.

(b) $\{2, 3, 4, 5\} \!-\! \{2, 3, 4, 5\} = $ _____.

$n\{2, 3, 4, 5\} - n\{2, 3, 4, 5\} = $ _____.

_____ $-$ _____ $=$ _____.

(c) $\{a, b, c\} \!-\! \{ \ \} = $ _____.

$n\{a, b, c\} - n\{ \ \} = $ _____.

_____ $-$ _____ $=$ _____.

2. Illustrate that $(A \!-\! B) \cup B = A$ is *not* true for all sets A and B.

3. Complete the following statement: If $a = 20$ and $b = 7$, then $20 - 7 = x$ if and only if $20 = 7 + x$. The value of x is   13   because _____.

4. Is the set of Whole Numbers closed under subtraction? Give two examples to justify your answer.

5. Is subtraction commutative? Is subtraction associative? Give two examples of each to justify your answer.

4.2   SPECIAL PROPERTIES FOR SUBTRACTION

Since subtraction was defined in terms of addition and subtraction was also defined in terms of the Remainder Set, it is possible to prove certain properties of subtraction that will be used in later study. Several of these are stated below. Following these statements, proofs are given within the following pages.

For every Counting Number a, for every Counting Number b, and for every Counting Number c, except as noted below

$S1:$ $a = (a - b) + b,$ $a > b.$

EXAMPLE

(a) $17 = (17 - 10) + 10.$
(b) $25 = (25 - 17) + 17.$

$S2:$ $(a + b) - b = a.$

EXAMPLE

(a) $(7 + 3) - 3 = 7.$

(b) $(12 + 17) - 17 = 12$.

S3: $(a - b) + (c - d) = (a + c) - (b + d)$, $a > b$ and $c > d$.

EXAMPLE

(a) $(10 - 7) + (13 - 6) = (10 + 13) - (7 + 6) = 23 - 13 = 10$.
(b) $(7 - 4) + (20 - 14) = (7 + 20) - (4 + 14) = 27 - 18 = 9$.

S4:   *Multiplication Distributes Over Subtraction* $a(b - c) = a(b) - a(c)$,
$b > c$.

EXAMPLE

(a) $7(8 - 5) = 7(8) - 7(5) = 56 - 35 = 21$.
(b) $9(7 - 2) = 9(7) - 9(2) = 63 - 18 = 45$.

The proofs of each of these is presented below.

S1: $a = (a - b) + b$. From Definition 4.2, $c = a - b$ means
$c + b = a$. It follows $a = (a - b) + b$ by substitution and the statement is proven. This can also be proven using sets. Let each of A and
B be a finite set, $B \subset A$. Then

$$(A \rule[0.5ex]{1.5em}{0.4pt} B) \cup B = A,$$

$$n(A \rule[0.5ex]{1.5em}{0.4pt} B) + n(B) = n(A),$$

$$[n(A) - n(B)] + n(B) = n(A).$$

S2: $(a + b) - b = a$. Similarly by using sets, it can be shown that
$(a + b) - b = a$. Let   each   of A and B be   a   finite   set,
$A \cap B = \varnothing$. Then

$$(A \cup B) \rule[0.5ex]{1.5em}{0.4pt} B = A,$$

$$n(A \cup B) - n(B) = n(A),$$

$$[n(A) + n(B)] - n(B) = n(A).$$

S3: $(a - b) + (c - d) = (a + c) - (b + d)$, $a > b$ and $c > d$.
This Theorem pertaining to subtraction is very important because it is used in the teaching of the subtraction algorithm:

If each of a, b, and d is a Whole Number, $a > b$ and
$c > d$, then

$$(a - b) + (c - d) = (a + c) - (b + d).$$

Let each of a, b, c, and d be a Whole Number, $a > b$
and $c > d$. Then

$$a = (a - b) + b,$$
$$c = (c - d) + d,$$
$$a + c = [(a - b) + b] + [(c - d) + d],$$
$$a + c = (a - b) + (c - d) + (b + d).$$

Since $a > b$ and $c > d$, $a - b$ and $c - d$ is each a Whole Number. Similarly, their sum is a Whole Number. We may then conclude, from the definition of subtraction in terms of addition, that

$$(a + c) - (b + d) = (a - b) + (c - d).$$

The importance of S3 cannot be overemphasized, for this property is used extensively in the teaching of the subtraction algorithm. Particularly, this property would be used in finding the remainder, x, in $\quad 87 - 45 = x$.

EXAMPLE

$$87 - 45 = (80 + 7) - (40 + 5)$$

and by S3 we can now state that

$$87 - 45 = (80 - 40) + (7 - 5)$$
$$= 40 + 2$$
$$= 42.$$

The generalization of this property is:

$$(a_1 + a_2 + a_3 + \cdots + a_n) - (b_1 + b_2 + b_3 + \cdots + b_n) =$$
$$(a_1 - b_1) + (a_2 - b_2) + (a_3 - b_3) + \cdots + (a_n - b_n),$$

where $n = 1, 2, 3, 4, \ldots$, and each $a_n > b_n$.

To illustrate this:

EXAMPLE

$$879 - 453 = (800 + 70 + 9) - (400 + 50 + 3),$$
$$= (800 - 400) + (70 - 50) + (9 - 3),$$
$$= 400 + 20 + 6$$
$$= 426$$

S4: *Multiplication Distributes Over Subtraction.* The Distributive Property of Multiplication over Subtraction is parallel to that for addition:

  (a) $a(b + c) = a(b) + a(c)$,
  (b) $a(b - c) = a(b) - a(c)$, $b > c$.

In order to show (b) above, let each of a, b, and c be a Whole Number, $b > c$. Then

$$b = (b - c) + c,$$

$$a(b) = a[(b - c) + c],$$

$$a(b) = a(b - c) + a(c).$$

Since $b > c$, $b - c$ is a Whole Number and the product $a(b - c)$ is a Whole Number. From the definition of subtraction in terms of addition:

$$a(b) - a(c) = a(b - c).$$

The reader should justify each step within the proof.

S5: *The Equal Additions Property*: If $b < a$ and $c = d$, then $a - b = (a + c) - (b + d)$. The Equal Additions Property is a direct result of S3 above. Let each of a, b, c, and d be a Whole Number such that $a > b$ and $c = d$. Then

$$c - d = 0,$$

$$(a - b) + (c - d) = (a - b),$$

and from S3,

$$(a - b) + (c - d) = (a + c) - (b + d).$$

In conclusion,

$$(a - b) = (a + c) - (b + d).$$

S6: If $a = b$ and $c < a$, then $a - c = b - c$. To show S6 to be true, let each of a, b, and c be a Whole Number, $a = b$ and $c < a$. Then

$$a = b,$$

$$a = (a - c) + c,$$

$$a - b = 0,$$

$$[(a - c) + c] - b = 0,$$

$$(a - c) + c = b,$$

$$a - c = b - c.$$

This is an important property, for it is frequently used in "solving" equations. The reader should justify each step above, and also should prove S7 through S9 below:

S7: For all Whole Numbers a, b, and c, if $a - c = b - c$, then $a = b$.

S8: For all Whole Numbers a, b, and c, if $a < b$ and $a > c$, then

$$a - c < b - c.$$

S9: For all Whole Numbers a, b, and c, if $a - c < b - c$, then $a < b$.

The reader should note that many of the properties involving subtraction parallel those properties for addition. The reader should justify each step within these proofs and illustrate each property by replacing letters a, b, c, and d with Whole Numbers and then performing the various calculations.

4.3   THE INTEGERS

When the Universal set was defined as $\{0, 1, 2, 3, \ldots\}$, we found this set to be closed under subtraction in certain particular instances:

(a) If $5 - 3 = x$, then $x = 2$ because $5 = 3 + 2$;
(b) If $7 - 2 = n$, then $n = 5$ because $7 = 2 + 5$.

However, there is no Whole Number, n, for which the following is true:

(c) If $6 - 8 = n$, then n does not exist within $\{0, 1, 2, 3, \ldots\}$;
(d) If $7 - 10 = n$, then n does not exist within $\{0, 1, 2, 3, \ldots\}$.

Hence in (c) and (d) above, there is no *Whole Number* n that satisfies the given conditions. We can conclude that the set of Whole Numbers is *not* closed under subtraction, because for all $a, b \in W$, $a - b \notin W$.

The above indicates a need for defining a new set of numbers so that this new set will be closed under subtraction as well as addition and multiplication conditions. In order to accomplish this, the definition for "an opposite," or "an additive inverse" is given.

Definition 4.4   For every Whole Number n, there is a unique number, $-n$, so that $n + (-n) = 0$. The number $-n$ is the Additive Inverse of the number n; the number n is the Additive Inverse of the number $-n$.

The set of all Whole Numbers together with the Additive Inverse of each Whole Number is called the set of INTEGERS. This particular set of numbers is denoted by the symbol "I."

Definition 4.4 established a one-to-one pairing of numbers. For the Integer   1, there is an Additive Inverse, -1; for the Integer -1, there is an Additive Inverse,   1. This one-to-one correspondence is illustrated below:

$$
\begin{array}{ccccccccc}
0 & 1 & 2 & 3 & 4 & 5 & 6 & 7 & \ldots \\
\updownarrow & \updownarrow & \updownarrow & \updownarrow & \updownarrow & \updownarrow & \updownarrow & \updownarrow & \\
0 & -1 & -2 & -3 & -4 & -5 & -6 & -7 & \ldots
\end{array}
$$

The reader should note that the number   0   is paired with   0, (zero is its own Additive Inverse), since $0 + 0 = 0$.

From the above, we find that the Additive Inverse of -6 is $-(-6) = 6$; the Additive Inverse of $-n$ is $-(-n) = n$, n a Whole Number. Frequently, this set of Integers is pictured on the number line in the following manner:

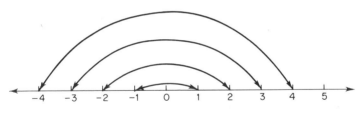

Figure 4.1

NUMBER LINE REPRESENTATION OF INTEGERS

From Definition 4.4 and from the representation of this set on the picture of the number line, we define three distinct subsets of I:

(a) $\{n \mid \quad n > 0\} = \{1, 2, 3, 4, \ldots\}$;
(b) $\{n \mid \quad n < 0\} = \{\ldots, -3, -2, -1\}$;
(c) $\{n \mid \quad n = 0\} = \{0\}$.

The set of Integers greater than zero is generally defined to be the set of Positive Integers. Hence   "3"   is read as "positive 3" and denoted "$+3$:"   "4"   is read "positive 4" and denoted   "$+4$." For work in this text, the   "$+$"   sign is dropped and define $+4 = 4$; $+n = n$; etc.

The set $\quad\{\ldots, -3, -2, -1\}\quad$ is referred to as the set of Negative Integers— $\quad$ "-3" $\quad$ is read "negative 3," $\quad$ "-10" $\quad$ is "negative 10," etc.

The reader should particularly note that if $\quad n \quad$ is an Integer, the symbol $\quad$ "$-n$" does not necessarily mean that $\quad -n \in \{\ldots, -3, -2, -1\}$. For example:

(a) If $\quad n \in \{\ldots, -3, -2, -1\}$, then $\quad -n \in \{1, 2, 3, \ldots\}$. Let $\quad n = -5$. Then $\quad -n = -(-5) = 5$. If $\quad n = -22$, $\quad$ then $\quad -n = -(-22) = 22$.

(b) If $\quad n \in \{1, 2, 3, \ldots\}$, then $\quad -n \in \{\ldots, -3, -2, -1\}$. Let $\quad n = 22$. Then $\quad -n = -22$, etc.

We now proceed to illustrate how $\quad I \quad$ is closed under subtraction:

EXAMPLE 1

If $\quad 7 - 4 = x$, then $\quad 7 = 4 + x$. Therefore $\quad x = 3$ because $\quad 7 = 4 + 3$.

EXAMPLE 2

If $\quad 6 - 9 = x$, then $\quad 6 = 9 + x$. Using Definition 4.4 and (by assuming) various properties of equality:

$$6 = 9 + x,$$

$$6 = (6 + 3) + x,$$

$$6 = 6 + (3 + x).$$

From this, we must conclude that $\quad 3 + x = 0$. Therefore, $\quad x = -3$ because $\quad 3 + (-3) = 0$. In conclusion:

$$6 - 9 = -3.$$

EXAMPLE 3

If $\quad 7 - 12 = x$, then $\quad 7 = 12 + x$.

$$7 = 12 + x,$$

$$7 = (7 + 5) + x,$$

$$7 = 7 + (5 + x).$$

$$x = -5 \quad \text{and} \quad 7 - 12 = -5.$$

EXAMPLE 4

If $\quad (-7) - 12 = x$, then $\quad -7 = 12 + x$.

$$-7 = 12 + x,$$
$$-7 = 12 + (-12) + (-7),$$
$$-7 = (12 + -12) + (-7),$$
$$-7 = 0 + -7.$$
$$x = -19 \quad \text{and} \quad (-7) - 12 = -19.$$

The set of Integers will be defined to preserve *all properties of order, equality, addition, and multiplication* studied within the set of Whole Numbers. Properties relating to the four operations addition, multiplication, subtraction, and division of Integers will be defined in Chapter 10.

PROBLEM SET 4.2

1. Is subtraction commutative? Is subtraction associative? Give two examples to justify your answer.

2. Illustrate the distributive pattern:

$$A \times (B \longrightarrow C) = (A \times B) \longrightarrow (A \times C)$$

if $\quad A = \{1, 2\}, \quad B = \{a, b, c, d\}, \text{ and } \quad C = \{c, d\}.$

3. If each of $\quad a, \quad b, \text{ and } \quad c \quad$ is a Whole Number, prove

(a) $8c - 6c = 2c.$
(b) $(10 + 4)c - (6 + 1)c = 7c.$
(c) $6ab - 4ab = 2ab.$
(d) If $\quad a(a) = a^2,$ prove $\quad 17a^2 - 14a^2 = 3a^2.$
(e) $2(a + b) - (a + b) = a + b.$
(f) $20(b + c) - 15(b + c) = 5(b + c).$
(g) If $\quad a < b,$ prove $\quad 6(b^2 - a^2) - (b^2 - a^2) = 5(b^2 - a^2).$

4. Using S3, show that

(a) $(300 + 40) - (200 + 20) = 100 + 20 = 120.$
(b) $(400 + 50 + 7) - (100 + 40 + 5) = 300 + 10 + 2 = 312.$
(c) $(40 + 7a) - (30 + 2a) = 10 + 5a.$
(d) $(4a^2 + 5b + 3) + (2a^2 + 2b + 1) = 2a^2 + 3b + 2.$
(e) $(4b^3 + 4b^2 + 3b) - (b^3 + 3b^2 + 3b) = 3b^3 + b^2.$

5.

(a) If, $\quad n = -10,$ find $\quad -n.$
(b) If $\quad n < 0,$ find $\quad -n.$
(c) If $\quad x + y > 0,$ find the opposite of $\quad x + y.$

6. Find n, using Definition 4.4, if

(a) $17 - 5 = n$. (b) $13 - 20 = n$.
(c) $12 - 20 = n$. (d) $0 - 14 = n$.
(e) $a - 36 = n$. (f) $-2 - 5 = n$.
(g) $-6 - 23 = n$. (h) $-1 - 7 = n$.
(i) $-5 - 10 = n$. (j) $-a - 12 = n$.

CHAPTER 5

Interesting Whole Numbers

5.1 INTRODUCTION

Some Whole Numbers have certain properties that distinguish them from other Whole Numbers. In sections of the previous chapters, we have studied properties that pertained to all Whole Numbers. It is appropriate that we reinvestigate these Whole Numbers for properties that pertain to only subsets of the Whole Numbers.

5.2 A UNIT AND THE UNITY ELEMENT

Recall from previous study that any Whole Number, no matter how large, could be made by starting with 1 and adding 1's until the desired number was reached. This principle is used extensively for ordering the Whole Numbers and in counting.

To illustrate this property of 1, the number 5 is exhibited as the result of the following sums:

$$1 = 1,$$

$$1 + 1 = 2,$$

$$2 + 1 = 3,$$
$$3 + 1 = 4,$$
$$4 + 1 = 5.$$

For this reason, and other reasons, the number   1   was referred to as the Unity Element from which the ideas of "one more than" and "one less than" are developed. As shown in prior discussion, no other Whole Number possessed all the number properties of   1.

The student should note there is a distinction between a "Unit" and the "Unity Element." For all measures, such as weight, distance, and time, numbers other than   1   are used to define a Unit. For example,

$$16 \text{ ounces} = 1 \text{ pound,}$$
$$12 \text{ inches} = 1 \text{ foot,}$$
$$5280 \text{ feet} = 1 \text{ mile,}$$
$$12 \text{ eggs} = 1 \text{ dozen eggs,}$$
$$12 \text{ months} = 1 \text{ year.}$$

Thus, the quantities of measure, such as   "16 ounces,"   "12 inches," and   "5280 feet "   establish   1   unit of measure. Hence, by this development, we establish a unit of measure. Measures will be studied in a later chapter.

In order to facilitate later study in mathematics, the Multiplicative Identity,   1, is defined to be a Unity Element, for certain sets of numbers. The study of a Unity Element will be undertaken in later chapters.

5.3   EVEN WHOLE NUMBERS AND ODD WHOLE NUMBERS

Each one is familiar with the concept of an even Whole Number and an odd Whole Number from study in the elementary grades. In this section, we shall make explicit definitions and investigate properties that pertain to these even numbers and odd numbers. The definition for an even Whole Number is given.

Definition 5.1—An Even Whole Number   An even Whole Number, n, is a number that can be expressed as a product of the form $2k$, where k is a Whole Number ($n = 2k$).

To illustrate numbers that can be expressed in the form of the product $2k$, consider the following:

$$0 = 2(0), \qquad k = 0,$$

$$8 = 2(4), \qquad k = 4,$$

$$10 = 2(5), \qquad k = 5,$$

$$1024 = 2(512), \qquad k = 512,$$

$$6x = 2(3x). \qquad k = 3x, \qquad x \in \{0, 1, 2, 3, \ldots\}.$$

In earlier chapters, we agreed that $\{0, 2, 4, 6, \ldots\}$ was closed under addition. In other words, we assumed that the sum of any two even numbers was an even number. By formally defining an Even Number, we are now able to prove $\{0, 2, 4, 6, \ldots\}$ is closed under addition.

$T5.1$: The sum of any two even Whole Numbers is an even Whole Number.

Proof. Let the first even Whole Number be $x = 2k$ and the second even Whole Number be $y = 2n$, where each of k and n is a Whole Number. Then

$x + y = 2k + 2n.$	If $a = b$ and $c = d$, then $a + c = b + d$.
$x + y = 2(k + n).$	Distributivity.

Therefore, we may conclude that the sum $x + y$ is an even Whole Number. This is true because the sum $(k + n)$ is a Whole Number. If $z = (k + n)$, then $x + y = 2z$, an even Whole Number by definition. As a logical consequence of T5.1, we conclude that $\{0, 2, 4, 6, \ldots\}$ is closed under addition.

Similarly, $\{0, 2, 4, 6, \ldots\}$ is closed under multiplication. This is proven in Theorem 5.2.

$T5.2$: The product of any two even Whole Numbers is an even Whole Number.

Proof. Let the first even Whole Number be $x = 2k$ and the second even Whole Number be $y = 2n$, where each of k and n is a Whole Number. Then

$x(y) = (2k)(2n).$	If $a = b$ and $c = d$, then $a(c) = b(d)$.
$x(y) = 2[k(2n)].$	Associativity.

From this, we may conclude that the product $x(y)$ is an even Whole Number, for the product $[k(2n)]$ is a Whole Number by the Closure Property of Multiplication. If $z = [k(2n)]$, then $x(y) = 2z$, an even Whole Number by definition. We can truthfully state that $\{0, 2, 4, 6, \ldots\}$ is closed under multiplication.

The concept of an odd Whole Number may be thought of as "an even number + 1," for by adding   1   to each even number, we generate the set of odd numbers:

$$0 + 1 = 1,$$

$$2 + 1 = 3,$$

$$4 + 1 = 5,$$

$$6 + 1 = 7, \text{ etc.}$$

Therefore, we define the odd Whole Numbers, $\{1, 3, 4, 7, \ldots\}$ by using the even Whole Numbers as a basis for the Definition:

Definition 5.2—An Odd Whole Number   An odd Whole Number, a, is a number that can be expressed in the form $2k + 1$, where k is a Whole Number $(a = 2k + 1)$.

An immediate consequence of Definition 5.2 is to illustrate that $\{1, 3, 5, 7, \ldots\}$ is not closed under addition. This is accomplished by means of a counter-example. By selecting any two odd numbers, say   25   and 31, their sum,   50, can be expressed in the form $2(25)$. Since $50 = 2(25)$,   50   is therefore an even Whole Number. Hence the set of odd Whole Numbers is not closed under addition.

We can easily show the product of any two odd Whole Numbers is an odd Whole Number. From this, we can conclude that $\{1, 3, 5, 7, \ldots\}$ is closed under multiplication. Consider the following:

$T5.3$:   The product of any two odd Whole Numbers is an odd Whole Number.

Proof. Let the first odd Whole Number be $x = 2k + 1$ and the second odd Whole Number $y = 2n + 1$, where each of k and n is a Whole Number. Then

$x(y) = (2k + 1)(2y + 1).$ | If $a = b$ and $c = d$, then $ac = bd$.

By repeatedly applying the Distributive and Commutative properties, the product $(2k + 1)(2n + 1)$ may be stated:

$$x(y) = 2[k(2n) + k + n] + 1.$$

We see that the product $x(y)$ is expressed in the form $2z + 1$, where $z = [k(2n) + k + n]$. Therefore, we conclude the product $x(y)$ is an odd Whole Number and $\{1, 3, 5, 7, \ldots\}$ is closed under multiplication.

The following Theorems are left as an exercise for the reader to prove.

$T5.4$:   The sum of an even Whole Number and an odd Whole Number is an odd Whole Number.

$T5.5$:   The sum of an odd Whole Number and an odd Whole Number is an even Whole Number.

$T5.6$:   The product of an even Whole Number and an odd Whole Number is an even Whole Number.

PROBLEM SET 5.1

1.   Express each of the following in the form $x = 2k$ or $x = 2k + 1$. All letters represent Whole Numbers.

(a) $x = 65$.   (b) $x = 86$.
(c) $x = 3(12)$.   (d) $x = 3(9)$.
(e) $x = 26 + 24$.   (f) $x = 21 + 34$.
(g) $x = 4n + 8m$.   (h) $x = 2n + 4m + 9$.
(i) $x = 8b + 16c + 5$.   (j) $x = 4y + 2c + 7$.

2.   Prove T5.4, T5.5, and T5.6.

3.   Prove that $\{3, 6, 9, 12, \dots\}$ is closed under addition.

4.   Prove that $\{3, 6, 9, 12, \dots\}$ is closed under multiplication.

5.   Prove that $\{0, 5, 10, 15, \dots\}$ is closed under multiplication.

6.   Prove that if x is an even Whole Number, $x(x)$ is an even Whole Number.

7.   Prove that if x is an odd Whole Number, $x(x)$ is an odd Whole Number.

5.4 FACTORS OF WHOLE NUMBERS

Terminology encountered in multiplication is sometimes ambivalent, i.e., two different expressions may be used to describe the same term. For example, when expressing the product $3(4)$, the number   *3*   was defined as the multiplier and the number   *4*   was defined as the multiplicand. In the product $4(3)$,   *4*   is the multiplier and   *3*   is the multiplicand.

Henceforth, when multiplying, we shall not use this terminology, but refer to each of   3   and   4   as factors of   12:

$$3(4) = 12.$$

factors

Therefore, the expression "to factor" means to express a Whole Number as the product of two or more Whole Numbers.

Definition 5.3—Factor   If a and b are Whole Numbers, "a is a factor of b" means there is a Whole Number c such that

$$a(c) = b.$$

For example, 6 is a factor of 12 because $6(2) = 12$; 9 is a factor of 27 because $9(3) = 27$; a is a factor of $3ax + 4ay$ because $a(3x + 4y) = 3ax + 4ay$, $x, y \in \{0, 1, 2, 3, \dots \}$.
It should be noted that the numbers 3 and 4 do not form the entire set of factors of 12:

$$12 = 1(12),$$

$$12 = 2(6),$$

$$12 = 3(4).$$

This illustrates that there may be many ways to factor the same number. By collecting the totality of factors involved in the product $x(y) = 12$, the *entire set of factors* is formed. This is $\{1, 2, 3, 4, 6, 12\}$:

Definition 5.4—Entire Set of Factors   If a is a Whole Number, then "the entire set of factors of n" is

$$\{x \mid \quad x \text{ is a Whole Number and} \quad x \text{ is a factor of} \quad n.\}$$

Frequently, "the entire set of factors of n" is simply referred to as "the set of factors of n." These two expressions mean identically the same.

EXAMPLES

NUMBER	ENTIRE SET OF FACTORS
15	$\{1, 3, 5, 15\}$.
21	$\{1, 3, 7, 21\}$.
36	$\{1, 2, 3, 4, 6, 9, 12, 18, 36\}$.

Note. If n is a Whole Number, then 1 and n are always contained within the entire set of Factors of n. This is true because $1(n) = n$.

PROBLEM SET 5.2

1. Express each number as the product of two factors. Each letter represents a Whole Number.

(a) 72

(b) $2x$.

(c) $ab + ac$.

(d) $7x^2 - 2x^2$.

(e) $8(10^2) + 6(10^2)$.

(f) $(2 + w)x + (2 + 2)y$.

(g) $9(10) - 7(10)$.

(h) $4xy - xy$.

2. Find the entire set of factors for each number.

(a) 27

(b) $2ax + 2bx$.

(c) 13.

(d) 49.

(e) $xy^2 + xz^2$

(f) $(3 + y)x + (3 + y)w$.

5.5   PRIME NUMBERS AND COMPOSITE NUMBERS

Before defining a "Prime Number" and a "Composite Number," it should be recalled that the Whole Numbers may be partitioned into several different sets, such as the odd Whole Numbers and the even Whole Numbers:

$$O = \{1, 3, 5, 7, \ldots\},$$

$$E = \{0, 2, 4, 6, \ldots\}.$$

Other partitionings, are listed below:

$$\{0, 5, 10, 15, \ldots\},$$

$$\{0, 3, 6, 9, \ldots\},$$

$$\{0, 4, 8, 12, \ldots\}.$$

Not only can the set of Whole Numbers be partitioned into subsets as above, the set of Whole Numbers can be partitioned into the two distinct subsets of "Prime Numbers" and "Composite Numbers."

Definition 5.5—A Prime Whole Number   A   Prime   Whole   Number (called a prime) is defined as a Whole Number other than *0*   or   *1* that can be expressed as the product of only two factors.

Definition 5.6—A Composite Whole Number   A   Composite   Whole Number is a Whole Number greater than   *1*   that is not a prime number.

(a) {prime numbers} ∩ {composite numbers} = ∅.

(b) {0} ∪ {1} ∪ {primes} ∪ {composites} = W.

Definitions 5.5. and 5.6 also provide a method to determine if any given number is prime or composite. This is accomplished by investigating the entire set of factors for each number:

NUMBER	SET OF FACTORS	CLASSIFICATION
2	$\{1, 2\}$	Prime
3	$\{1, 3\}$	Prime
4	$\{1, 2, 4\}$	Composite
5	$\{1, 5\}$	Prime
6	$\{1, 2, 3, 6\}$	Composite
7	$\{1, 7\}$	Prime

Since the entire set of factors for each number within $\{2, 3, 5, 7\}$ contains only   *1*   and the specified number, the elements of this set are classified as prime numbers.

Is there a largest prime number? The answer is "no," for mathematicians have proven that there is no largest prime. The reader will have to accept this, for the proof is beyond the scope of this text. However, the ancient Greek mathematician named Eratosthenes devised a simple and convenient method to find all primes less than a specified Whole Number. His device is now called the "Sieve of Eratosthenes."

In order to understand the "Sieve of Eratosthenes," we must investigate "multiples" of given numbers.

Definition 5.7—Multiples   If a is a Counting Number,   "b is a multiple of a"   means

(a) There exists a Whole Number c such that $a(c) = b$, or
(b) a is a factor of b.

EXAMPLE

(a) The multiples of   2   are $\{0, 2, 4, 6, 8, \ldots\}$.
(b) The multiples of   3   are $\{0, 3, 6, 9, 12, \ldots\}$.
(c) The multiples of   4   are $\{0, 4, 8, 12, 16, \ldots\}$.
(d) etc.

We can immediately conclude that any multiple of the Whole Number *n, other than zero and* n *itself*, is a *composite* number.

The multiples of $7 = \{0, 7, 14, 21, \ldots\}$, and the entire set of factors for   14, 21, 28   are:

MULTIPLE	ENTIRE SET OF FACTORS
14	$\{1, 2, 7, 14\}$
21	$\{1, 3, 7, 21\}$
28	$\{1, 2, 4, 7, 14, 28\}$

from which we see that   14, 21, 28   are composite numbers. We will use this principle to illustrate the Sieve of Eratosthenes, in which we will find all prime numbers less than   60.

In the number chart below, we wish to leave all prime numbers by marking through all composite numbers. Since   *1*   is not prime by definition, place a mark through   *1*   in the manner indicated. Then progress to   2. Since   2   is prime, do *not* mark through   2, but mark through every multiple of   2   that follows, since each of these multiples of   *2*   is a composite number:

$$
\begin{array}{cccccccccc}
\not{1} & 2 & 3 & \not{4} & 5 & \not{6} & 7 & \not{8} & 9 & \not{10} \\
11 & \not{12} & 13 & \not{14} & 15 & \not{16} & 17 & \not{18} & 19 & \not{20} \\
21 & \not{22} & 23 & \not{24} & 25 & \not{26} & 27 & \not{28} & 29 & \not{30} \\
31 & \not{32} & 33 & \not{34} & 35 & \not{36} & 37 & \not{38} & 39 & \not{40} \\
41 & \not{42} & 43 & \not{44} & 45 & \not{46} & 47 & \not{48} & 49 & \not{50} \\
51 & \not{52} & 53 & \not{54} & 55 & \not{56} & 57 & \not{58} & 59 & \not{60}
\end{array}
$$

Figure 5.1

NUMBER CHART TO DETERMINE PRIMES 60

Next, progress to   *3*. Since   *3*   is prime, do not mark through it, but place a mark through every multiple of   *3*. After marking through all multiples of   *3*, progress to the next prime,   *5*, and repeat the process. Upon marking through all multiples of   *7*, all composite numbers less than   60   will have a mark placed through them. The numbers that remain without a mark through them are primes less than   60:

$$
\begin{array}{cccccccccc}
\not{1} & 2 & 3 & \not{4} & 5 & \not{6} & 7 & \not{8} & \not{9} & \not{10} \\
11 & \not{12} & 13 & \not{14} & \not{15} & \not{16} & 17 & \not{18} & 19 & \not{20} \\
\not{21} & \not{22} & 23 & \not{24} & \not{25} & \not{26} & \not{27} & \not{28} & 29 & \not{30} \\
31 & \not{32} & \not{33} & \not{34} & \not{35} & \not{36} & 37 & \not{38} & \not{39} & \not{40} \\
41 & \not{42} & 43 & \not{44} & \not{45} & \not{46} & 47 & \not{48} & \not{49} & \not{50} \\
\not{51} & \not{52} & 53 & \not{54} & \not{55} & \not{56} & \not{57} & \not{58} & 59 & \not{60}
\end{array}
$$

Figure 5.2

PROBLEM SET 5.3

1. List the elements of the set of all multiples of:
(a) 1.
(b) 2.

2. (a) Express each number as the product of two factors; (b) Express each number as the product two factors different from those in (a), if possible:

(a) 72.   (b) 41.

(c) 13.   (d) 35.
(e) $2ax + 4bx$.   (f) $35x + 5xy$.

3. Using the Sieve of Eratosthenes, find all primes less than   100. List this set of numbers.

4. Many primes differ by   2, i.e.,   3   and   5,   11 and   13, etc. When two primes differ by   2, they are referred to as "twin primes." List each pair of twin primes less than   100.

5. Do you think that the set of twin primes is an infinite set?

6. If n is a Whole Number, is the formula $n^2 - n + 41$ a suitable formula for finding any prime number? Investigate $n^2 - n + 41$ if $n = 0, 1,$ $2, 3, 4$. Investigate $n^2 - n + 41$ if $n = 41$.

7. The *Goldback Conjecture* states that "Every even number greater than   4   can be expressed as the sum of   2   primes." For example, $18 = 7 + 11$. Express the following as the sum of 2 primes:

(a) 8.   (b) 10.
(c) 12.   (d) 14.
(e) 36.   (f) 40.

8. Let $n = (2 \times 3 \times 5) + 1$. Is n prime? Let $n = (2 \times 3 \times 5 \times 7) + 1$. Is n prime? Let each of $p_1, p_2, p_3, \ldots p_n$ be primes, and $x = (p_1 \times p_2 \times p_3 \times \ldots \times p_n) + 1$. (a) Is x prime? (b) Do you think that this formula can be used to generate infinitely many primes? (c) Investigate $x = (3 \times 5 \times 7)$ $+ 1$. (d) Find two other numbers, (using this formula) that are *not* prime. (e) Prime factor each number found in (c) and (d). Can you make a statement regarding the prime factors of the numbers in (c) and (d)?

5.6   THE FUNDAMENTAL THEOREM OF ARITHMETIC

Prime numbers are sometimes referred to as the "building blocks" of the composite numbers. Thus

$$2(2)(2)(3)(3) = 72,$$

$$5(3)(3) = 45,$$

$$2(7) = 14, \text{ etc.}$$

From the above, we see that each Whole Number greater than   1 can be expressed as the product of prime numbers. To express a number n as the product of prime factors is called Prime Factorization:

Definition 5.8—Prime Factorization   If a is a Whole Number greater than   1, the *Prime Factorization* of a is a factorization of a such that every factor of a is prime.

There are many ways to determine the Prime Factorization of any given number. Perhaps the simplest is the "Factor Tree:"

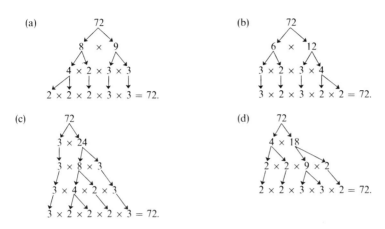

Figure 5.3

FACTOR TREES

Note that, except for the order, there is one and only one way to factor 72 when 72 is expressed as the product of prime factors. Each of the above expresses 72 as the product of prime factors and is called the *Prime Factorization* of 72.

Further investigation will reveal that for every composite number, there is one and only one Prime Factorization for that number. This is a fundamental property for all Whole Numbers greater than one.

The Fundamental Theorem of Arithmetic. Every Whole Number greater than 1 can be expressed as a product of primes in exactly one way, except for the order of the factors.

An intuitive argument is given below to explain this Fundamental Theorem:

Recall that each composite number may be expressed as the product of two factors. Each of these factors may be less than the given composite number, and in certain instances, these factors may be prime numbers. For example,

$$6 = 2(3).$$

If this situation occurs, then the composite number is expressed as the product of primes factors.

In other cases, the initial factors may not be prime such as

$$24 = 4(6).$$

But if one (or more) of these factors is a composite number, it can be expressed as a product of two factors, such that each of these factors will be less than the initial factor (e.g. $24 = 4(6),$ $4 = 2(2),$ $6 = 2(3)$).

But this process must terminate, since the factors get smaller and smaller. Since this process terminates, within a finite (countable) number of steps, we come to a product that will not permit further factoring. When this occurs, the factors are *prime* factors. Hence, every composite number may be expressed as the product of prime factors. It is beyond the scope of this text to prove that there is one, and only one, set of prime factors for each composite number.

Another method to find the set of prime factors for composite number n is by consecutive division of n by prime numbers until the last quotient is prime:

$$2\overline{)72}$$

$$2\overline{)36} \qquad 72 = 2(36)$$

$$2\overline{)18} \qquad 72 = 2(2)(18)$$

$$3\overline{)9} \qquad 72 = 2(2)(2)(9)$$

$$3 \qquad 72 = 2(2)(2)(3)(3).$$

Then the set of divisors and the last quotient constitute the Prime Factorization of n:

$$72 = 2(2)(2)(3)(3).$$

5.7 GREATEST COMMON FACTOR AND GREATEST COMMON DIVISOR

We introduce the concept of common factors by making the following definition.

Definition 5.9—Common Factor Let each of a and b be a Counting Number. Then   "c is a common factor of a and b"   means that c is a factor of a and c is a factor of b.

We may find the entire set of common factors by listing the entire set of factors for each number in question. The Intersection of these sets is then defined as the set of common factors:

NUMBER	ENTIRE SET OF FACTORS
12	$A = \{1, 2, 3, 4, 6, 12\}$.
36	$B = \{1, 2, 3, 4, 6, 9, 12, 18, 36\}$.
72	$C = \{1, 2, 3, 4, 6, 9, 12, 18, 36, 72\}$.

Then the set $A \cap B \cap C = \{1, 2, 3, 4, 6, 12\}$ is defined as the set of common factors for   12,   36, and   72, for each element of this set is a factor of   12   and   36   and   72.

Definition 5.10—Greatest Common Factor   The Greatest Common Factor (g.c.f.) of two Counting Numbers a and b, with sets of factors A and B, respectively, is the largest Counting Number in $A \cap B$.

The Greatest Common factor of a and b is frequently abbreviated   g.c.f.(a, b).

Thus, in order to determine the   g.c.f.(a, b), we must investigate the set of common factors of a and b.

E X A M P L E

The set of factors of $12 = \{1, 2, 3, 4, 6, 12\}$.
The set of factors of $36 = \{1, 2, 3, 4, 6, 9, 12, 18, 36\}$.
The set of factors of $72 = \{1, 2, 3, 4, 6, 9, 12, 18, 36, 72\}$.

We previously determined that the set of common factors of   12, 36, and   72   is

$$\{1, 2, 3, 4, 6, 12\}.$$

Since 12 is the largest number within this set, the   g.c.f.$(12, 36, 72) = 12$.

Another method frequently used to find the   g.c.f.(a, b) is to express each number as a product of prime factors:

$$12 = 2 \cdot 2 \cdot 3,$$

$$36 = 2 \cdot 2 \cdot 3 \cdot 3,$$

$$72 = 2 \cdot 2 \cdot 2 \cdot 3 \cdot 3.$$

Since multiplication is commutative and associative, the factors can be regrouped in the following manner:

$$12 = (2 \cdot 2 \cdot 3),$$

$$36 = (2 \cdot 2 \cdot 3) \cdot 3,$$

$$72 = (2 \cdot 2 \cdot 3) \cdot 2 \cdot 3.$$

The number $(2 \cdot 2 \cdot 3)$ is contained in each factorization, and is the largest number contained in each set of factors. Therefore, $(2 \cdot 2 \cdot 3)$ is the   g.c.f. $(12, 36, 72)$.

Frequently, the   g.c.f.(a, b) is defined as the Greatest Common Divisor of a and b [g.c.d.(a, b)]. We may obtain the   g.c.d.(a, b)

by investigating the set of common factors of a and b. Consider the definition below.

Definition 5.11—Common Divisor If a and b are Whole Numbers, then   "a divides b"   means a is a factor of b.

Definition 5.12—Greatest Common Divisor   The statement that   "k is a divisor of a and b"   means k is a divisor of a and k is a divisor of b. Furthermore,   "k is the greatest common divisor of a and b" means k is the greatest common factor of a and b.

For example,   g.c.f.(12, 36, 72) = 12. Therefore,   g.c.d.(12, 36, 72) = 12.

Of great importance in the study of Fractions and Rational numbers is the idea of numbers that are Relatively Prime numbers.

Definition 5.13—Relatively Prime Numbers If a and b are Counting Numbers, then   "a is Relatively Prime to b"   means   g.c.f. $(a, b) = 1$. Thus $(9, 8)$ are Relatively Prime, for   g.c.f.$(9, 8) = 1$. Similarly, each of $(24, 35)$, $(15, 28)$, $(14, 45)$ are Relatively Prime.

PROBLEM SET 5.4

1. By using the "Factor Tree" to express each number as a product of prime factors, find:

(a) g.c.f.(6, 8, 10).   (b) g.c.d.(10, 14, 18).
(c) g.c.f.(7, 12, 13).   (d) g.c.d.(12, 18, 24).

2. Does every set of two or more numbers have a greatest common factor? If so, what is this number?

3. The statement that a fraction is "reduced to lowest terms" means that the numerator and denominator are Relatively Prime. Although we have not studied fractions, reduce each fraction to its lowest terms. All letters represent Counting Numbers.

(a) $\dfrac{24}{36} = \dfrac{(2 \cdot 2 \cdot 3) \cdot 2}{(2 \cdot 2 \cdot 3) \cdot 3} = \dfrac{2}{3}$.

(b) $\dfrac{9}{12}$.   (c) $\dfrac{18}{72}$.

(d) $\dfrac{14}{56}$.   (e) $\dfrac{104}{128}$.

(f) $\dfrac{2a}{a}$.   (g) $\dfrac{2ab + ab}{ab}$.

(h) $\dfrac{8xy - 4xy}{9xy}$.   (i) $\dfrac{(a + b)x + (a + b)y}{(x + y)}$.

4. The Counting Number a divides the Whole Number b is written $a|b$. Give two examples of each to illustrate the following:

(a) If c is a counting number and a and b are Whole Numbers so that $c|a$ and $c|b$, then $c|(a + b)$.

(b) If c is a counting number and a and b are Whole Numbers so that $c|(a + b)$ and $c|a$, then $c|b$.

(c) (Transitivity) If c and b are Counting Numbers and a is a Whole Number so that $c|b$ and $b|a$, then $c|a$.

5. If $c|(a + b)$, can you conclude $c|a$ and $c|b$? Justify your answer by giving two examples.

5.8   THE LEAST COMMON MULTIPLE

The set of multiples of any Counting Number, x, may be formed by finding the products of x and any whole number, k. For example, each of the multiples of   2   may be expressed in the form:

$$2k, k \in \{0, 1, 2, 3, \dots\}.$$

From this, the set of the multiples of   2   is:

$$\{0, 2, 4, 6, 8, \dots\},$$

and is an infinite set. Note that   0   and   2   are within this set. In general, if n is any Counting Number, then   0   and n will always be within the set of multiples of n.

EXAMPLES

(a) The set of multiples of $12 = \{0, 12, 24, 36, \dots\}$.
(b) The set of multiples of $18 = \{0, 18, 36, 54, \dots\}$.
(c) The set of multiples of $20 = \{0, 20, 40, 60, \dots\}$.

By investigating the set of multiples of   2   and   3, we see that certain numbers are multiples of   2   and   3. This is illustrated on the picture of the number line:

(a) Set of multiples of $2 = \{0, 2, 4, 6, 8, \dots\}$.
(b) Set of multiples of $3 = \{0, 3, 6, 9, 12, \dots\}$.

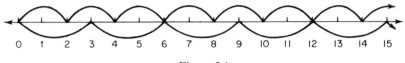

Figure 5.4

COMMON MULTIPLES OF 2 AND 3 = {0, 6, 12, 18, . . .}

The picture of the number line illustrates that certain numbers are common to both sets of multiples. These common numbers are called *common multiples*, and any two (or more) numbers will have a set of common multiples.

Definition 5.14—Common Multiple If a and b are Counting Numbers, then   "c is a common multiple of a and b"   means c is a multiple of a and ⋅ c is a multiple of b.

The set of common multiples of a and b is easily determined by the intersection of the sets of multiples.

EXAMPLE

Consider   2   and   3. Let A and B be their respective sets of multiples:

$$A = \{0, 2, 4, 6, 8, 10, 12, 14, 16, \ldots\},$$

$$B = \{0, 3, 6, 9, 12, 15, 18, 21, 24, \ldots\}.$$

Then the set of common multiples of   2   and   3   is the set

$$A \cap B = \{0, 6, 12, 18, 24, 30, 36, \ldots\}.$$

The smallest Counting Number within a set of common multiples is used extensively to find the sum or difference of fractions. This smallest Counting Number is defined the Least Common Multiple.

Definition 5.15—The Least Common Multiple The Least Common Multiple (L.C.M.) of two Counting Numbers a and b, with sets of multiples A and B, respectively, is the smallest Counting Number in $A \cap B$.

Note that any two numbers have   0   as a common multiple. However,   0   is *not* defined as   L.C.M.(a, b).

PROBLEM SET 5.5

1. Find the set of multiples of   2,   3, and   9. Find their set of common multiples. Find   L.C.M.(2, 3, 9).

2. Find   L.C.M.(a, b) if   (a, b)   equals

(a) (4, 6).   (b) (2, 5).
(c) (6, 8).   (d) (3, 7).

3. Two clocks strike together at 10:00 A.M. One clock strikes every 10 minutes and the other strikes every 20 minutes. List the times they will strike together before 12:00 noon.

4. Two men run a race on an oval track. One man can circle the track in 4 minutes, the other man in 3 minutes. If they start together at 4:00 P.M., list the times they will both be at the starting position before 5:00 P.M.

5. Given the two sets:

$$\{a \quad b \quad a\}.$$

$$\{a \quad b \quad c \quad d\}.$$

Let a transformation be done in the following manner.

$T1$ is:

$$\{\overset{\frown}{a \to b \to c}\} = \{c \quad a \quad b\}.$$

$$\{\overset{\frown}{a \to b \to c \to d}\} = \{d \quad a \quad b \quad c\}.$$

$T2$ is:

$$\{\overset{\frown}{c \to a \to b}\} = \{b \quad c \quad a\}$$

$$\{\overset{\frown}{d \to a \to b \to c}\} = \{c \quad d \quad a \quad b\}.$$

How many transformations will it take so that the sets are rearranged

$$\{a \quad b \quad c\}$$

$$\{a \quad b \quad c \quad d\}?$$

6.

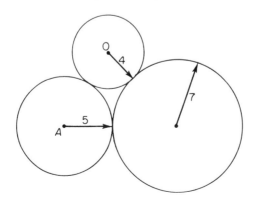

The circumference of the wheel with center (a) at O is 4; (b) at A is 5; and (c) at B is 7. The wheels start spinning at 11:00 A.M. The wheel with center at O completes 1 revolution every 2 minutes. List the times that all three wheels will be at their starting positions before 7:00 P.M.

Systems of Numeration

PART TWO

CHAPTER 6

Primitive Systems
of Numeration

6.1 INTRODUCTION

As noted in earlier chapters, the concept of number probably stems from
man's ability to make the comparisons "more than" and "less than"
when objects were added to or removed from a group of objects. This
comparison was probably accomplished through a one-to-one matching of
elements of two different sets of objects and is assumed to be the first method
designed to keep a count, or for keeping a tally for objects. Thus for each
sheep, a mark in the dirt could be made, or one rock moved from one pile
to another. If objects and tally marks could not be placed in a complete
one-to-one matching, then the observer could see that there were "more
elements in set A" or "fewer elements in set B."

It is assumed that certain vocal sounds were then developed for the
keeping of a tally—one particular sound would be associated with one
object, another particular sound associated with two objects, etc. Still
later, with the development of writing, different symbols (now called numerals) were developed in order to describe "how many" objects were contained
within a particular set of objects.

Many systems have been developed through the centuries to aid in the process of counting. Today, a standard set of names for numbers is used. When counting, a person may associate the name *one* with a single object, the name *two* with two objects and so on. We also have the symbols, 1, 2, 3, . . . , which we use to name numbers.

However, sophisticated number systems, such as our present one, were not always in use. A system such as ours evolved after many centuries of "trial and error" systems. The next few sections present an informal study of a few of these primitive systems.

6.2 NUMBER BASES

It is assumed that the job of accurately describing "how many" objects were contained in a set became more and more complicated as civilization advanced. Thus, the aborigine who counts "one, two, two and one, two-twos, many" is not able to accurately describe the number of objects in a set that has more than four objects for "many" could describe any number greater than four.

The primitive aborigine learned to group by "twos." Similarly, other civilizations learned to group by 5's, 10's, 20's, and in one case by 60's. Grouping by 60 is still in evidence in our civilization as evidenced by 60 seconds to the minute and 60 minutes to the hour. It is not surprising that we presently use a grouping of tens when considered in the light of 10 fingers and 10 toes.

Consider the civilization that had learned to group by 5's. Then the people could count "one, two, three, four, hand, hand and one, hand and two, hand and three, hand and four, two hands, etc." Even our grouping by 10's parallels this, for "eleven" is derived from *ein lifen* (German), which means "one over ten," "twelve" from *twe lif*, which means "two over ten," etc. "Twenty" is derived from *twe-tig*, which means "two tens."

When a number has been selected to denote the groupings, it is then defined as a base b, for counting. Names were then designated for the numbers 1, 2, 3, . . . , b, and as illustrated above, numbers larger than b were denoted by some combination of b and other names selected.

6.3 GROUPING SYSTEMS OF NUMERATION

A system of numeration (a numeration system is a system for naming numbers) as we know it today is a very sophisticated system. Prior to the develop-

---

[1] Refer to "*An Introduction to the History of Mathematics*," by Howard P. Eves, Rinehart & Co., New York, 1956, for detailed reference on this topic.

ment of our system, many others were in existence. One of the earliest systems devised was that of a simple grouping system. In a simple grouping system, symbols were devised to name the numbers $1, b, b^2, b^3, b^4, \ldots$. A very early example of a grouping system was the one devised by the Egyptians in approximately 3400 B.C. Tablets showing the use of this system have been found dating back to 2000 B.C. Grouping systems are additive in nature, (as is ours) and any counting number can be named by repeating the symbols the desired number of times.

The Egyptians selected 10 as the base of their system. The numerals for $1, 10, 10^2, \ldots$, are listed below:

EGYPTIAN NUMERALS	BASE TEN NUMERALS
|	1
∩	10
⌒	100
𝑓	1,000
⫝	10,000
⫝̸	100,000
ⵋ	1,000,000

Figure 6.1

As stated before, a grouping system is additive in nature. To denote the number 3086, the Egyptians would repeat the symbols the desired number of times:

Figure 6.2

The reader should note that the relative position of a symbol within the numeral is immaterial. The Egyptians could have denoted the number 3086 in a reverse manner:

Figure 6.3

Ancient Babylonians also used a grouping system with slight modifications—they introduced a subtraction symbol. The Babylonians used a grouping system to write numbers less than 60: if the number 60 was to be expressed, then the position of the numeral affected the value of the numeral (as in our system). Babylonian numerals for 1 and 10 and the symbol for subtraction are given below:

Figure 6.4

The Babylonians would then express numbers less than 60 in the additive manner:

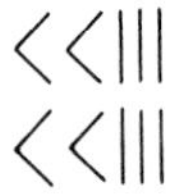

$$\langle\langle|||$$
$$\langle\langle|||$$

To indicate subtraction, instead of addition, the number 47 could be denoted:

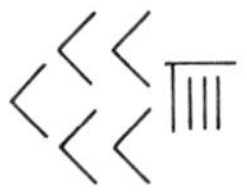

$$\langle\begin{smallmatrix}\langle\langle\\\langle\langle\end{smallmatrix}\overline{||||}$$

The grouping system most familiar to us is that of the Romans. The Roman numerals for 1, 10, 100, and 1000 are listed below:

1	I
10	X
100	C
1000	M

Figure 6.5

In addition, the Romans used other symbols. These symbols were for 5, 50, and 500:

5	V
50	L
500	D

Figure 6.6

The Romans were very ingenious by combining the additive and subtractive process:

(a) If the numeral for a smaller unit occurs *before* the symbol for a larger unit, *subtract* the smaller from the larger.

(b) If the numeral for a smaller unit occurs *after* the symbol for a larger unit, *add* the two.

These symbols could be used only in certain patterns: I before V or X, X before C or L, C before M. Thus,

$$IX = 10 - 1 = 9,$$

$$CX = 100 + 10 = 110,$$

$$XM = 100 - 10 = 90,$$

$$LM = 1000 - 50 = 950,$$

$$LV = 50 + 5 = 55, \text{ etc.}$$

To denote a number such as 1968 using Roman numerals the additive and subtractive processes are used alternately.

$$MCMLXVIII = 1000 + (1000 - 100) + 50 + 10 + 5 + 1 + 1 + 1$$
$$\qquad\quad M \qquad\quad CM \qquad\quad L \quad X \quad V \quad I \quad I \quad I$$

$$1969 = MCMLXIX.$$

PROBLEM SET 6.1

1. Express the following in Egyptian and Roman numerals:

(a) 286. (b) 3264.
(c) 236,202. (d) 4001.
(e) 8050. (f) 2168.

2. Express the following in decimal numerals:

(a)   (b)

(c)  (d) $\quad$ ⅄ ⅄ ♈ ♈ ?

3. Express the following in Babylonian numerals, using the subtractive process:

(a) 47. (b) 58.
(c) 49. (d) 55.

4. Express the following in decimal numerals:

(a) $\langle\langle|||$ (b) $\langle\langle\overline{|||}$

(c) $\begin{array}{l}\langle\langle\\\langle\langle\end{array}\langle\overline{|||||}$ (d) $\begin{array}{l}\langle\langle\\\langle\langle\end{array}\langle\overline{||}$

(e) *MDCCLXXVI*   (f) *MCCCCXCII*
(g) *MCMXLI*   (h) *MDCCCLXIV*

5. The following is a set of numerals used within a base 5 grouping system of numeration. Call this the FIVES system:

$$\Phi = 1$$
$$\triangle = 5$$
$$\odot = 25$$
$$\square = 125$$
$$\boxtimes = 625$$

Express the following in their corresponding decimal numerals:

(a) $\boxtimes\boxtimes\triangle\triangle\triangle\Phi\Phi\Phi$ (b) $\boxtimes\square\odot\odot\Phi\Phi\Phi$
(c) $\square\odot\odot\odot\triangle\triangle\triangle$ (d) $\boxtimes\boxtimes\Phi\Phi$

6. Express the following in numerals of the FIVES system:

(a) 129.   (b) 1800.
(c) 932.   (d) 2499.

7. Devise a set of numerals for a base 8 (EIGHTS) *grouping system,* i.e., a numeral for 1, 8, 64, 512, and 4096. Write 8, 162, 974, and 328 in their corresponding EIGHTS numerals.

8. Devise a set of numerals for a NINES *grouping system.* Include numerals for 1, b, b^2, b^3, and b^4. Write 8000, 926, and 126 in their corresponding NINES numerals.

9. The following symbols are used to denote the indicated powers of a base, b:

$$\odot = b^3$$
$$\square = b^2$$
$$\boxtimes = b$$
$$\phi = 1$$

Write: $\odot\odot\square\boxtimes\boxtimes\boxtimes\phi$ in its corresponding base 10 numeral if $b = 4$; if $b = 7$; if $b = 12$; if $b = 2$.

CHAPTER 7

Positional Numeration Systems: Base Ten, Base *X*

7.1 INTRODUCTION

In systems of numeration such as the simple grouping system, we found only two essential characteristics necessary for naming any number. These were:

(a) a set of symbols, called numerals
(b) a number b, called the base.

The numerals selected named 1, b, b^2, b^3,.... To name a number using a simple grouping system, the numerals were repeated the required number of times. However, for each power of b, there must be a new numeral, and each new numeral must be different from every other numeral. For example, to express a number as large as $b^{1000000}$ would require 1,000,000 distinct numerals.

At some later date, some unknown mathematician hit upon the idea of combining the operations multiplication and addition in a *multiplicative grouping system*. In this system, *two sets of numerals* were used along with certain multiplicative and additive properties (these fundamental ideas of multiplication and addition are still retained in our present system of numeration). In the multiplicative numeration system, a number b is defined to be the base. Then a set of numerals is invented to name the numbers:

$$1, 2, 3, 4, \ldots, (b - 1),$$

and a second set of numerals denotes the numbers:

$$b, \quad b^2, \quad b^3, \ldots.$$

The two sets are then employed in a certain multiplicative and additive manner. For example, let the base be ten with the usual symbols (digits) $1, 2, 3, 4, \ldots, 9$. In order to denote b, b^2, b^3, and b^4, let

$$x = 10$$
$$y = 10^2$$
$$z = 10^3$$
$$w = 10^4.$$

Then the number fifty-six thousand seven hundred twenty-two would be denoted:

$$5w6z7y2x2.$$

$$5(w) + 6(z) + 7(y) + 2(x) + 2 =$$
$$5(10^4) + 6(10^3) + 7(10^2) + 2(10) + 2.$$

From this, we see the beginning of the idea of place value, but the ancient peoples could not be totally committed to the idea of place value as we know it today. This is so because they had no symbol to indicate missing powers of the base. This problem was not solved until approximately 300 B.C.

7.2 POSITIONAL NUMERATION SYSTEMS

With the concept of a symbol to indicate missing powers of the base, we see that a *positional numeration system* logically follows. A positional numeration system does away with the necessity of having a second set of symbols to denote the numbers 1, b, b^2, b^3, b^4, ... The numbers 1, b, b^2, ..., are denoted simply by the relative position of each digit. The symbol zero denotes missing powers of b. We find we can name any number in the following manner.

Definition 7.1 Any number N may be named by expressing N in the form

$$a_n(b^n) + a_{n-1}(b^{n-1}) + a_{n-2}(b^{n-2}) + \ldots + a_1(b) + a_0,$$

$$0 < a_i \leq (b - 1), \quad i \in \{1, 2, 3, \ldots\}.$$

When a number is denoted in the form:

$$a_n b^n + a_{n-1} b^{n-1} + \ldots + a_1 b + a_0,$$

we are still denoting the number in the *multiplicative grouping* form. We may also use the zero symbol to indicate missing powers of the base:

$$N = 5(10^4) + 0(10^3) + 7(10^2) + 8(10^1) + 6.$$

A number expressed in this form is defined as being expressed in *expanded notation* or *expanded form*. This form is still indicative of the multiplicative grouping system, for instead of using letters to denote b, b^2, $b^3, \ldots$, we use 10, 10^2, $10^3, \ldots$.

With the invention of the zero symbol, a total commitment could be made to the idea of place value. In a positional numeration system we do not need to express the number in expanded form, for the value of each digit is determined by its relative position to the other digits. In a base b positional numeration system, the value of each digit is determined according to the following schema:

$$\ldots \;\bigg|\; b^4 \;\bigg|\; b^3 \;\bigg|\; b^2 \;\bigg|\; b \;\bigg|\; 1$$

Figure 7.1

PLACE VALUE SCHEMA

If b is selected to be ten, then the *value* of the digits $0, 1, 2, 3,$ $\ldots, 9$ is determined by the schema:

$$\ldots \;\bigg|\; 10^4 \;\bigg|\; 10^3 \;\bigg|\; 10^2 \;\bigg|\; 10 \;\bigg|\; 1$$

Figure 7.2

PLACE VALUE SCHEMA FOR BASE TEN

To express the number five thousand six hundred and four,

...	10^4	10^3	10^2	10^1	1
		5	6	0	4

Figure 7.3

DECIMAL REPRESENTATION OF 5604

we define   5604   to mean $5(10^3) + 6(10^2) + 0(10^1) + 4(1)$. This leads to the formal definition.

Definition 7.2—Positional Numeration   Any number, N, expressed in the form

$$a_n a_{n-1} a_{n-2} \ldots a_1 a_0,$$

means

$$a_n(b^n) + a_{n-1}(b^{n-1}) + a_{n-2}(b^{n-2}) + \ldots + a_1(b) + a_0,$$

where

$$0 \le a_i \le (b-1), \qquad a_i \in \{0, 1, 2, 3, \ldots\}.$$

If b is   10, $50{,}720_{\text{base ten}}$ means

$$5(10^4) + 0(10^3) + 7(10^2) + 2(10) + 0.$$

If the base b is   five, then $43{,}424_{\text{base five}}$ means

$$4(5^4) + 3(5^3) + 4(5^2) + 4(5) + 4.$$

In general, if digits are denoted by $a_1,$ $a_2,$ $a_3, \ldots$ then, in a positional numeration system with base b,

$$a_1 a_2 a_3 a_4 \text{ base } b \qquad \text{means} \qquad a_1(b^3) + a_2(b^2) + a_3(b) + a_4,$$

where zero is used as a coefficient so that *each decreasing power appears in a numeral.*

In summary, we see that there are four essential characteristics of a positional numeration system. These are:

(a) A number b, called the base.
(b) A set of symbols (digits) to name the numbers $1, 2, 3, \ldots, (b-1)$.
(c) A zero element (generally 0).
(d) Place, or position.

In order to determine the value of any digit within any numeral, find the product of the digit and some specific power of the base. The power of the base is determined by the position of the digit.

EXAMPLE

(a) In 234_{ten}, the value of the digit 3 is $3(10) = 30$.
(b) In 2304_{ten}, the value of the digit 3 is $3(100) = 300$.
(c) In $23,040_{ten}$, the value of the digit 3 is $3(1000) = 3000$.

PROBLEM SET 7.1

1. The numbers below are indicated in their standard form. Denote these in their expanded form.

(a) 5076_{ten},   (b) 4034_{five},
(c) 8703_{nine},   (d) 2375_{eight},

2. Express:

(a) 376 in powers of 7,   (b) 425 in powers of 8,
(c) 24 in powers of 2,   and   (d) 196 in powers of 12.

3. The value of 6 in 6732_{ten} is represented by:

(a) 6×10^3,   (b) 6 thousands,
(c) 60 hundreds,   (d) 600 tens,
(e) all of these,   (f) none of these.

4. In the numeral "4321_{five}," the value of "4" is:

(a) 4×5^3,   (b) 4 one hundred twenty-fives,
(c) 500_{ten},   (d) 4000_{ten},

5. If the number five were selected to be the base of a positional numeral system, how many digits (other than zero) would be necessary to name any number? For a base of eight? For a base of twelve? List your own digits for these systems.

6. The following is an example of multiplicative grouping system, base five. If $x = 5$, $y = 5^2$, $z = 5^3$, then $4z3y5x2$ names what number, base ten?

7. The Chinese–Japanese numeral system is a multiplicative grouping system, base 10. The two sets of numerals are listed below, with the example 3472, written vertically:

1	一	10	十
2	二	10^2	百
3	三	10^3	千
4	四	Example: 3472	三 千 四 百 七 十 二
5	五		
6	六		
7	七		
8	八		
9	九		

Figure 7.4

JAPANESE–CHINESE DIGITS

Using the vertical form, express in Chinese–Japanese numerals:

(a) 4689.   (b) 2156.

7.3 CONVERSION FROM BASE TEN TO BASE X

Many elementary school pupils now study systems of numeration other than a base ten system. One segment of this study involves a renaming process, i.e., converting numerals from one base to their corresponding numerals in another base. In each case, the numerals must name the same number. In this sense, we must develop a method that will enable us to convert a numeral expressed in base ten to a numeral that indicates the same number in base x, and vice versa.

The reader should recall the two basic forms for denoting a number in a positional numeration system:

$$5478_{\text{ten}} = 5(10^3) + 4(10^2) + 7(10) + 8.$$

This may be extended to the general form:

$$a_3 a_2 a_1 a_{0 \text{base } b} = a_3(b^3) + a_2(b^2) + a_1(b) + a_0.$$

EXAMPLES

(a) If $b = 5$, then the corresponding decimal numeral is:

$$4324_{five} \Rightarrow 4(b^3) + 3(b^2) + 3(b) + 4,$$
$$\Rightarrow 4(5^3) + 3(5^2) + 3(5) + 4,$$
$$\Rightarrow 4(125) + 3(25) + 3(5) + 4,$$
$$\Rightarrow 500 + 75 + 15 + 4,$$
$$\Rightarrow 594_{ten}.$$

(b) If $b = 8$, then

$$727_{eight} \Rightarrow 7(8^2) + 2(8) + 7,$$
$$\Rightarrow 7(64) + 2(8) + 7,$$
$$\Rightarrow 448 + 16 + 7,$$
$$\Rightarrow 471_{ten}.$$

Thus we see that in (a) and (b) above,

$$4324_{five} \Rightarrow 594_{ten},$$
$$727_{eight} \Rightarrow 471_{ten}.$$

Hence by expressing the given numerical in expanded form, using the decimal representation for powers of the base, we express a numeral to its corresponding decimal (base ten) numeral.

Thus, the process of renaming a number in its corresponding decimal numeral becomes:

(a) $486_{nine} = 4(9^2) + 8(9) + 6 = 402_{ten},$
(b) $987_{eleven} = 9(11^2) + 8(11) + 7 = 1184_{ten},$
(c) $4533_{seven} = 4(7^3) + 5(7^2) + 3(7) + 3,$
$$= 4(243) + 5(49) + 3(7) + 3,$$
$$= 972 + 245 + 21 + 3,$$
$$= 1241_{ten}.$$

The above illustrates a method to convert any numeral, base x, to a corresponding decimal numeral. However, to convert a decimal numeral to its corresponding base x numeral involves an entirely different process. The use of semi-concrete objects will help in illustrating this process.

Consider the problem of denoting how many objects are in the following array:

$$x \; x \; x \; x \; x \; x \; x \; x \; x \; x \; x \; x$$

$$x \; x \; x \; x \; x \; x \; x \; x \; x \; x.$$

Recall that in a numeration system that uses place value, the place values are assigned, respectively, 1, b, b^2, b^3,... in the following manner:

$$\ldots \ \left| \ b^3 \ \right| \ b^2 \ \left| \ b \ \right| \ 1$$

Figure 7.5

(a) In base 10, the number of objects in the array is denoted 23 since there are two 10's and three ones:

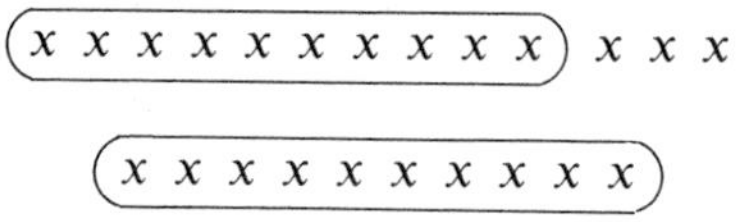

$$(x \ x \ x \ x \ x \ x \ x \ x \ x \ x) \ x \ x \ x$$
$$(x \ x \ x \ x \ x \ x \ x \ x \ x \ x)$$

$\ldots$	10^3	10^2	10	1
			2	3

$= 23_{\text{ten}}.$

Figure 7.6

(b) In base 5, the number of objects is denoted by 43_{five}, since there are four 5's and three ones:

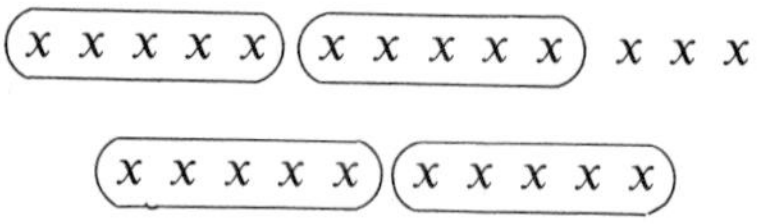

$$(x \ x \ x \ x \ x)(x \ x \ x \ x \ x) \ x \ x \ x$$
$$(x \ x \ x \ x \ x)(x \ x \ x \ x \ x)$$

$\ldots$	5^3	5^2	5	1
			4	3

$= 43_{\text{five}}.$

Figure 7.7

(c) In base 8, the number of objects is denoted by 27_{eight}:

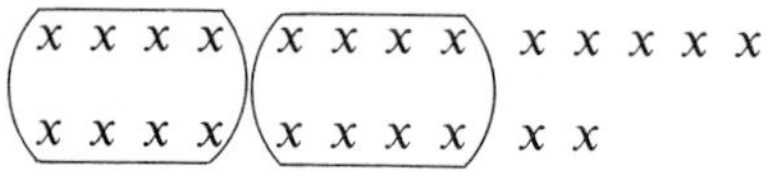

$$\left(\begin{matrix} x \ x \ x \ x \\ x \ x \ x \ x \end{matrix}\right)\!\!\left(\begin{matrix} x \ x \ x \ x \\ x \ x \ x \ x \end{matrix}\right) \begin{matrix} x \ x \ x \ x \ x \\ x \ x \end{matrix}$$

…	8^3	8^2	8	1	
			2	7	$= 27_{\text{eight}}.$

Figure 7.8

(d) In base   3, the number of objects is denoted by 212_{three} :

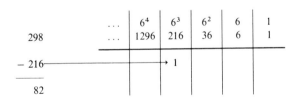

…	3^3	3^2	3	1	
		2	1	2	$= 212_{\text{three}}.$

Figure 7.9

The task of drawing a large number of objects and then regrouping them into groups of   1, b, b^2, b^3, ... may become tedious and exhausting. Therefore, we need to develop a method that will enable us to easily convert a decimal numeral to its corresponding numeral in base x. This may be done by a *Subtractive Process*:

EXAMPLE

Express 298_{ten} in its corresponding base 6 numeral. Since the base is 6, we wish to investigate the powers of 6: $1, 6, 6^2, 6^3, 6^4, \ldots$. These may be written as $1, 6, 36, 216, 1296, \ldots$. We see that the largest power of   6 contained in   278   is   216:

		…	6^4	6^3	6^2	6	1
	298	…	1296	216	36	6	1
	-216			→ 1			
	82						

Figure 7.10

By investigating the remainder,   82, we see that the next largest power contained in   278   is 6^2, which is contained   2   times:

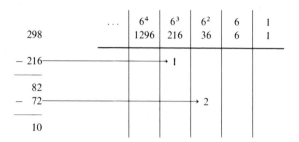

Figure 7.11

The next largest power contained in   278   is   6, which is contained   1   time. We then investigate the ones, and find there are four. The complete process is illustrated below:

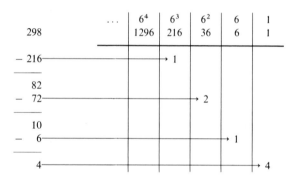

Figure 7.12

In summary, we see that the corresponding numeral base   6, is:

$$298_{ten} \Rightarrow 1(6^3) + 2(6^2) + 1(6) + 4(1)$$
$$\Rightarrow 1214_{six}.$$

In the event the reader wishes to check his work, express 1214_{six} in its corresponding decimal numeral:

$$1214_{six} \Rightarrow 1(6^3) + 2(6^2) + 1(6) + 4(1),$$
$$\Rightarrow 1(216) + 2(36) + 1(6) + 4(1),$$
$$\Rightarrow 216 + 72 + 6 + 4,$$
$$\Rightarrow 298_{ten}.$$

Of particular interest is the Duodecimal System of Numeration. The Duodecimal System is a system that uses twelve as the base. The influence of this system is felt today in our society—consider the groups of twelve in our everyday living: twelve eggs in one dozen, twelve inches in one foot, twelve hours in one-half day, and twelve months in one year, for examples.

In the Duodecimal System, the basic grouping is by $\quad 1, 12, 12^2, 12^3, \ldots$ which follows the same patterns as $\quad 1, \quad b, \quad b^2, \quad b^3, \ldots$ Thus

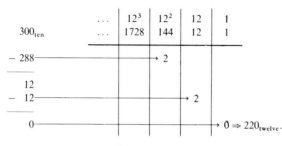

Figure 7.13

However, one particularly interesting facet of dealing with base twelve is that we must make some new numerals. Since the numeral 10_{twelve} indicates one group of $\quad$ twelve $\quad$ and no ones, some new digits for $\quad$ ten and $\quad$ eleven $\quad$ must be developed. Let these new digits be $\quad t \quad$ and e:

$$t_{\text{twelve}} = 10_{\text{ten}},$$

$$e_{\text{twelve}} = 11_{\text{ten}}.$$

We now satisfy the conditions that we have digits $\quad 1, 2, 3, \ldots, (b - 1)$, and these digits are:

$$1, 2, 3, 4, 5, 6, 7, 8, 9, t, e.$$

Thus

$$4t3_{\text{twelve}} \Rightarrow 4(b^2) + t(b) + 3,$$

$$\Rightarrow 4(12^2) + 10(12) + 3,$$

$$\Rightarrow 4(144) + 120 + 3,$$

$$\Rightarrow 576 + 120 + 3,$$

$$\Rightarrow 699_{\text{ten}}.$$

To convert $\quad 3186_{\text{ten}} \quad$ to its corresponding base $\quad$ twelve $\quad$ numeral, we may use a subtractive process:

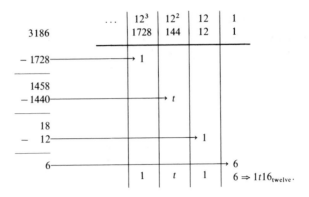

Figure 7.14

Check:

$$1t16 \Rightarrow 1(12^3) + t(12^2) + 1(12) + 6(1),$$

$$\Rightarrow 1(1728) + 10(144) + 1(12) + 5(1),$$

$$\Rightarrow 1728 + 1440 + 12 + 6,$$

$$\Rightarrow 3186_{ten}.$$

With the invention of the high speed digital computer, the Binary (base two), system of numeration became of especial importance.

The base of the binary system is   two   and the powers of this base are $1, 2, 2^2, 2^3, 2^4, 2^5, 2^6, \ldots$. The digits are   0   and   1:

$$101101_{two} \Rightarrow 1(2^5) + 0(2^4) + 1(2^3) + 1(2^2) + 0(2) + 1,$$

$$\Rightarrow 1(32) + 0(16) + 1(8) + 1(4) + 0(2) + 1,$$

$$\Rightarrow 32 + 8 + 4 + 1,$$

$$\Rightarrow 45_{ten}.$$

Similarly, the corresponding binary numeral for 62_{ten} is:

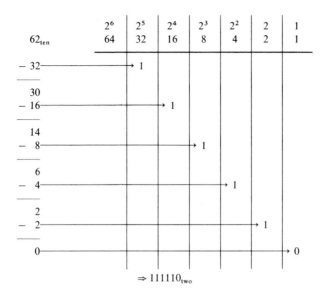

Figure 7.15

PROBLEM SET 7.2

1. Write the expanded form of   33   (a) in powers of   2; (b) in powers of   3; (c) in powers of   4; (d) in powers of   12.

2. Convert each of the following to its base   ten   numeral:

(a) 234_{five},   (b) 1101101_{two},

(c) 2122_{three},   (d) $4e7_{twelve}$,

(e) ete_{twelve}.

3. Convert 42_{ten} (a) to its base   two   numeral; (b) to its base   five   numeral; (c) to its base   seven   numeral; (d) to its base   twelve   numeral.

4. Design a set of digits in order to express base   ten   numerals in their corresponding base   thirteen   numerals. Convert each of (a) 87_{ten}; (b) 143_{ten}; and (c) 2200_{ten} to its corresponding base   thirteen   numeral.

5. Write the first twenty-five decimal (base ten) numerals in their corresponding (a) base   two   numerals: (b) base   seven   numerals: (c) base   twelve   numerals.

7.4 THE MAYAN SYSTEM OF NUMERATION

The Mayan Indians of the Yucatan Peninsula were one of the first of the ancient civilizations to incorporate the zero symbol.

The digits for the Mayan Numeration system are:

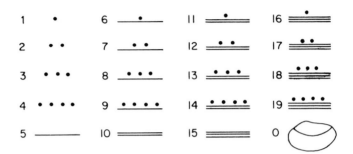

Figure 7.16

MAYAN DIGITS

The Mayans used as their base a modified base   twenty. Instead of $1, 20, 20^2, 20^3, \ldots$ they used $1, 20, 18(20), 18(20^2), \ldots$. In order to express a decimal numeral in its corresponding Mayan numeral, we use the modified base   twenty:

	...	$18(20^3)$	$18(20^2)$	$18(20)$	20	1
$17{,}592_{\text{ten}}$		$144{,}000$	7200	360	20	1
$- 14{,}400$			$\rightarrow 2$			
$3{,}192$						
$- 2{,}880$				$\rightarrow 8$		
312						
$- 300$					$\rightarrow 15$	
12						$\rightarrow 12$

Figure 7.17

The Mayan digits were written in a vertical form, and had their relative place values:

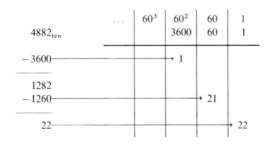

Figure 7.18

The Babylonians developed a system of numeration using   60   as a base, and also used a system of place values. Recall that the digits of this system were $| = 1, \langle = 10$. Then the corresponding Babylonian numeral for 4882_{ten} was:

	...	60^3	60^2	60	1
4882_{ten}			3600	60	1
-3600		→ 1			
1282					
-1260			→ 21		
22				→ 22	

Figure 7.19

To indicate the corresponding Babylonian numeral:

$$4882_{ten} = \left| (60^2) + \left.\begin{matrix}\langle \\ \langle\end{matrix}\right|(60) + \left.\begin{matrix}\langle \\ \langle\end{matrix}\right|\right|,$$

$$= \left|\begin{matrix}\langle & \langle \\ \langle & \langle\end{matrix}\right|\right|.$$

However, the Babylonians had not advanced in their civilization to invent the zero symbol. Consider the problem in writing the corresponding

Babylonian numeral for 7242_{ten}:

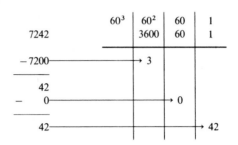

Figure 7.20

Written in the Babylonian numerals,

Figure 7.21

If this is written as $\left\|{}^{\langle\langle}_{\langle\langle}\right\|$, then the false numeral

$$\left\|(60) + {}^{\langle\langle}_{\langle\langle}\right\| = 120 + 42 = 162,$$

is written.

This problem illustrates the importance of a zero element, and particularly the importance of this element to correctly position the digits within a numeral.

PROBLEM SET 7.3

1. Let a simulated Babylonian zero symbol be X. Using Babylonian digits   1 and $\langle$, correctly express 7242_{ten} in this fictitious system.

2. Using the zero symbol X, and the Babylonian digits   1   and $\langle$, (a) express 7224_{ten} in corresponding "Babylonian" numerals; (b) in corresponding Mayan numerals, using vertical form.

3. Invent an entirely new set of digits for a base   fifteen   numeration system. Express (a) 3656_{ten} and (b) 6127_{ten} in their corresponding base   fifteen numerals.

CHAPTER 8

Algorithms: Addition, Subtraction, Multiplication

8.1 INTRODUCTION

An algorithm is a method of calculating using the digits $1, 2, 3, \ldots,$ $(b - 1)$ and the zero symbol, where b is the base of a system of numeration.

In early elementary grades, pupils are taught the "basic number facts," which generally include all combinational sums of the numbers 0–10. The knowledge of these basic addition facts are very important to the pupils in performing the algorithms that involve the four arithmetic operations.

Children are also taught that each number has many names. This is the beginning of "carrying" and "borrowing." The idea that each number has many names is generally introduced through use of concrete or semiconcrete materials. The most familiar of these materials are the "place value charts," the abacus, and the "Counting Men."

In order to illustrate that each number has many names, consider the place value chart which denotes the number 27. This is illustrated in

Figure 8.1. (For brevity we shall let t = tens, h = hundreds, and th = thousands throughout this chapter.)

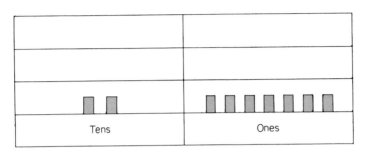

Figure 8.1

PLACE VALUE CHART REPRESENTATION OF 27.
$$27 = 2t + 7 \text{ ONES}$$

Other names for   27   are indicated in Figures 8.2 and 8.3:

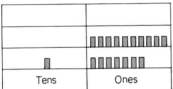   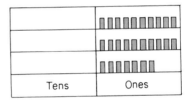

Figure 8.2   Figure 8.3

$27 = 1t + 17$ ONES $27 = 0t + 27$ ONES

Similarly, with the place value chart, we can illustrate particular names for   19   in Figures 8.4 and 8.5:

Figure 8.4   Figure 8.5

$19 = 0t + 19$ ONES $19 = 1t + 9$ ONES

Through illustrations such as the ones above, the reader is introduced to the *grouping* and *decomposition* properties. These are listed below:

$$10 \text{ ones} = 1t,$$

$$1t = 10 \text{ ones.}$$

Similarly,

$$10t = 1h,$$

$$1h = 10t,$$

$$10h = 1th,$$

$$1th = 10h,$$

and so on.

These ideas, along with the Distributive, Commutative, and Associative properties, and with the ability to express numerals in their expanded form are essential to the analysis of the various algorithms.

8.2   ANALYSIS OF THE ADDITION AND SUBTRACTION ALGORITHMS

To analyze the addition algorithm, consider

$$
\begin{array}{r}
237 \\
+ \ 498 \\
\hline
735
\end{array}
$$

When written in expanded form,

$$237 = 2h + 3t + 7,$$

$$498 = 4h + 9t + 8,$$

and the sum: $237 + 498 = (2h + 3t + 7 \text{ ones}) + (4h + 9t + 8 \text{ ones}).$

By separately using the Commutative and Associative properties for addition:

$$237 + 498 = (2h + 4h) + (3t + 9t) + (7 + 8) \text{ ones,}$$

and by using the Distributive Property of Multiplication over addition,

$$237 + 498 = (2 + 4)h + (3 + 9)t + (7 + 8) \text{ ones.}$$

This illustrates the reason for "adding ones to ones," "tens to tens," "hundreds to hundreds," in the vertical form:

2	3	7
+ 4	9	8

Figure 8.6

But it must be remembered that

$$(7 + 8) \text{ ones} = 1t + 5 \text{ ones},$$
$$(9 + 3) \text{ tens} = 1h + 2t.$$

Thus we "rename" (7 + 8) ones and (9 + 3) tens. This is the basis for the "carrying process." We frequently see the term *reassociate* used in place of "*carry*" or "*borrow*" since the associative property is at the heart of the process:

$$\begin{aligned} 237 + 498 &= (2 + 4)h + (3 + 9)t + (7 + 8) \text{ ones}, \\ &= 6h + 12t + 15 \text{ ones}, \\ &= 6h + (1h + 2t) + 1t + 5 \text{ ones}, \\ &= (6h + 1h) + (2t + 1t) + 5 \text{ ones}, \\ &= 7h + 3t + 5 \text{ ones}, \\ &= 735. \end{aligned}$$

The "renaming process" is shortened in the vertical form as the "carrying process:"

	①	
2	3	7
+ 4	9	8
		5

Figure 8.7

RENAMING OF 15 ONES = $1t$ + 5 ONES

The "renaming" process is continued:

$$
\begin{array}{c|c|c}
\textcircled{1} & \textcircled{1} & \\
2 & 3 & 7 \\
+\,4 & 9 & 8 \\
\hline
 & 3 & 5 \\
\end{array}
$$

Figure 8.8

RENAMING OF $13t = 1h + 3t$

and finally, the sum is given

$$
\begin{array}{c|c|c}
\textcircled{1} & \textcircled{1} & \\
2 & 3 & 7 \\
+\,4 & 9 & 8 \\
\hline
7 & 3 & 5 \\
\end{array}
$$

Figure 8.9

Hence we see the *carrying process* is essentially a renaming process.

Similarly, subtraction relies upon the Commutative, Associative, and Distributive properties. Also, the subtraction algorithm uses the fact that numbers have many names along with the particular theorem proven in a prior chapter.

$S3$: If each of a, b, c, and d is a Whole Number, $a > c$ and $b > d$, then

$$(a + b) - (c + d) = (a - c) + (b - d).$$

If we had not proven this theorem, we could not explain the Subtraction Algorithm. This is illustrated in the problem below which analyzes the subtraction process:

$$
\begin{array}{r}
917 \\
-\,439 \\
\hline
478 \\
\end{array}
$$

When written in expanded form:

$$917 = 9h + 1t + 7 \text{ ones,}$$

$$439 = 4h + 3t + 9 \text{ ones,}$$

and their difference can be expressed by S3 above:

$$917 - 439 = (9h + 1t + 7 \text{ ones}) - (4h + 3t + 9 \text{ ones}),$$
$$= (9h - 4h) + (1t - 3t) + (7 \text{ ones} - 9 \text{ ones}),$$
$$= 5h + (1t - 3t) + (7 \text{ ones} - 9 \text{ ones}).$$

We see immediately that we cannot subtract the   9 ones from the 7 ones and have a remainder that is a Whole Number. Similarly, $3t$ cannot be subtracted from $1t$ and have a remainder that is a Whole Number. However, we can alleviate this by renaming:

$$917 = 9h + 0t + 17 \text{ ones}$$
$$= 8h + 10t + 17 \text{ ones}.$$

When   917   is named as $8h + 10t + 17$ ones, we now can state the problem:

$$917 - 439 = (8h + 10t + 17 \text{ ones}) - (4h + 3t + 9 \text{ ones}),$$
$$= (8h - 4h) + (10t - 3t) + (17 \text{ ones} - 9 \text{ ones}),$$
$$= 4h + 7t + 8 \text{ ones},$$
$$= 478.$$

The renaming of the minuend is a 2-step process when the subtraction is performed in the vertical form. This is illustrated in Figures 8.10 and 8.11 below:

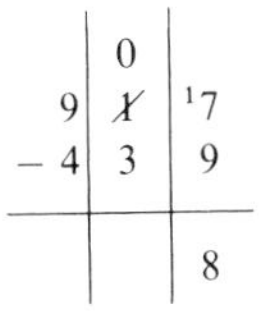

Figure 8.10

RENAMING OF 917 AS $9h + 0t + 17$ ONES

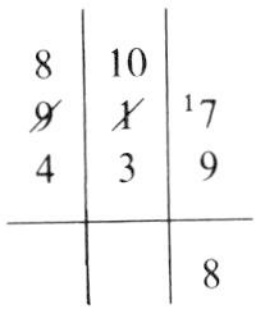

Figure 8.11

RENAMING OF $9h + 0t + 17$ AS $8h + 10t + 17$

Since the renaming process satisfies the conditions established by *Theorem* S3, we can now determine the remainder,   478.

8.3 ANALYSIS OF THE MULTIPLICATION ALGORITHM

As in the cases of the addition and subtraction algorithms, the multiplication algorithm relies upon the renaming process and the commutative, associative, and distributive properties.

In order to find the product 23×44,

$$23 \times 44 = (20 + 3)(40 + 4),$$
$$= (20 + 3)40 + (20 + 3)4,$$
$$= (20)(40) + 3(40) + (20)4 + 3(4),$$
$$= 800 + 120 + 80 + 12,$$
$$= (12 + 120) + (80 + 800).$$

Multiplication is essentially reduced to knowing the basic multiplication facts and the algorithms for addition:

$$
\begin{array}{r}
44 \\
\times\ 23 \\
\hline
12 \\
120 \\
80 \\
800 \\
\hline
1012 \\
\end{array}
$$

$(3 \times 4 = 12)$
$(3 \times 40 = 120)$
$(20 \times 4 = 80)$
$(20 \times 40 = 800)$

Figure 8.12

THE PRODUCT 23×44 EXPRESSED AS SUMS

The renaming of the sums $120 + 12$ and $80 + 800$ is generally accomplished in a separate step and uses the principles of renaming as in addition:

$$(40 + 4)3 = 12t + 12 \text{ ones} = (1h + 2t) + 1t + 2 \text{ ones}),$$
$$= 1h + 3t + 2 \text{ ones},$$
$$= 132,$$

$$(40 + 4)(20) = 80t + 80 \text{ ones} = 8h + 8t + 0 \text{ ones,}$$
$$= 880.$$

PROBLEM SET 8.1

1. Give reasons to justify each step in the following: (It should be noted that $t^2 = h$).

(a) $25 \times 36 = (2t + 5)(3t + 6)$,
$= (2t + 5)3t + (2t + 5)6$,
$= 6t^2 + 5(3t) + (2t)6 + 5(6)$,
$= 6h + 15t + 12t + 30$,
$= 6h + 15t + 12t + 3t$,
$= 6h + (15 + 12 + 3)t$,
$= 6h + 30t$,
$= 6h + 3h$,
$= (6 + 3)h$,
$= 9h$,
$= 900$.

(b) $72 + 46 = (7t + 2) + (4t + 6)$,
$= 7t + [2 + (4t + 6)]$,
$= 7t + [(2 + 4t) + 6]$,
$= 7t + [(4t + 2) + 6]$,
$= (7t + 4t) + (2 + 6)$,
$= (7 + 4)t + (2 + 6)$,
$= 11t + (2 + 6)$,
$= 1h + 1t + 8$,
$= 118$.

(c) $903 - 728 = (9h + 0t + 3) - (7h + 2t + 8)$,
$= (8h + 10t + 3) - (7h + 2t + 8)$,
$= (8h + 9t + 13) - (7h + 2t + 8)$,
$= (8h - 7h) + (9t - 2t) + (13 - 8)$,
$= (8 - 7)h + (9 - 2)t + (13 - 8)$,
$= 1h + 7t + 5$,
$= 175$.

8.4 ADDITION, SUBTRACTION, AND MULTIPLICATION IN NON-DECIMAL BASES

In order to perform calculations in nondecimal bases, it will be helpful if the reader is familiar with counting processes and the *grouping* and *decomposition* properties in a non-decimal base. We shall consider a positional numeration system of base   five   and investigate the addition, subtraction, and multiplication algorithms.

Recall that in a positional numeration system, the place values are 1, b, b^2, b^3, ... In such a system with base five the place value schema is:

$$\cdots \left| \; 625 \; \right| \; 125 \; \left| \; 25 \; \right| \; 5 \; \left| \; 1 \right.$$

Figure 8.13

PLACE VALUE SCHEMA FOR BASE FIVE

Similarly, the digits in a place value system, base five will be 1, 2, 3, 4 and the zero element, 0. This is according to the definition that the digits be assigned to name the numbers $1, 2, 3, \ldots, (b - 1)$; and an element to denote missing powers of the base.

(For the sake of simplicity, let f mean five, tf mean twenty-five, and htf mean one hundred twenty-five. These abbreviations will be used throughout the discussion.)

Counting, base five parallels that of base ten from 1 through 4:

Base ten	1	2	3	4	5	6	7	8	9	10	...
Base five	1	2	3	4							

Figure 8.14

However, to denote the number of objects in the array

we use the numeral 10_{five}, (read "one-zero, base five"), as illustrated in the place value charts below:

Fives	Ones

Figure 8.15

FIVE ONES $= 0f +$ FIVE ONES

However,   5   ones is equivalent to   1   five:

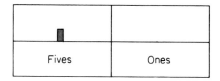

Figure 8.16

FIVE ONES IS ONE GROUP OF FIVE

Thus to indicate one group of five and no ones, we use the numeral 10_{five} as illustrated by the place value chart. We can now extend the counting chart using base   five   numerals and their corresponding base ten   numerals:

Base	ten	1	2	3	4	5	6	7	8	9	10
Base	five	1	2	3	4	10	11	12	13	14	20

11	12	13	14	15	16	17	18	19	20	21	22	23	24	25
21	22	23	24	30	31	32	33	34	40	41	42	43	44	100

Figure 8.17

The reader can easily verify that these base   five   numerals are correct by converting each to its corresponding decimal numeral. For example:

(a) $100_{five} = 1(25) + 0(5) + 0(1) = 25_{ten}$;
(b) $32_{five} = 3(5) + 2(1) = 15 + 2 = 17_{ten}$;
(c) $22_{five} = 2(5) + 2(1) = 10 + 2 = 12_{ten}$.

The reader should note particularly that:

$$1_{five} = 1_{ten},$$
$$10_{five} = 5_{ten},$$
$$100_{five} = 25_{ten},$$
$$1000_{five} = 125_{ten},$$
$$10,000_{five} = 625_{ten} \text{ etc.}$$

These numerals are most important for use in the various algorithms. These new numerals, along with their respective place values, are illustrated in the place value schema below.

		125	25	5	1
BASE TEN NUMERAL	...	125	25	5	1
BASE FIVE NUMERAL	...	1000	100	10	1
BASE FIVE NUMERAL	...	10^3	10^2	10^1	1

Figure 8.18

We express in expanded notation *in base   five*:

(a) $234_{five} = 2(10^2) + 3(10) + 4]_{five}$,
(b) $1242_{five} = 1(10^3) + 2(10^2) + 4(10) + 1]_{five}$,
(c) $304_{five} = 3(10^2) + 0(10) + 4]_{five}$,

and then express each to its *corresponding base ten numerals*:

(a) $234_{five} = 2(10^2) + 3(10) + 4]_{five}$,
      $= 2(25) + 3(5) + 4 = 69_{ten}$,
(b) $1242_{five} = 1(10^3) + 2(10^2) + 4(10) + 2]_{five}$,
      $= 1(125) + 2(25) + 4(5) + 2 = 197_{ten}$,
(c) $304_{five} = 3(10^2) + 0(10) + 4]_{five}$,
      $= 3(25) + 0(5) + 4 = 79_{ten}$.

The numerals $1, 10, 10^2, 10^3, \ldots$ occur in base   ten   as well as any base other than   ten   and are used in each instance to represent $1, \quad b, \quad b^2, \quad b^3, \ldots$.

The algorithms of addition, subtraction, and multiplication, base   five, parallel those algorithms for base   ten. In order to perform these algorithms, it is beneficial if the reader has at his disposal a chart of the basic addition and multiplication "facts." Complete these charts:

+	0	1	2	3	4
0	0				
1		2			
2			4		
3				11	
4					13

×	0	1	2	3	4
0	0				
1		1			
2			4		
3				14	
4					31

Figure 8.19

ADDITION AND MULTIPLICATION CHARTS, BASE FIVE

Recall that to add or subtract base   ten,   we used the fact that numbers had many names. This is also true for base   five:

(a) $24_{\text{five}} = 2f + 4$ ones,
$= 1f + 14$ ones,
$= 0f + 24$ ones,
(b) $32_{\text{five}} = 3f + 2$ ones,
$= 2f + 12$ ones,
$= 1f + 22$ ones,
$= 0f + 32$ ones.

This renaming process is the basis for "carrying" and "borrowing" in the algorithms of addition and subtraction. Also, the Commutative, Associative, and Distributive Properties for addition play their usual roles:

EXAMPLE

Find the sum $14_{\text{five}} + 13_{\text{five}}$.

$$14_{\text{five}} + 13_{\text{five}} = (1f + 4) + (1f + 3),$$
$$= (1f + 1f) + (4 + 3),$$
$$= (1 + 1)f + 12,$$
$$= 2f + (1f + 2),$$
$$= (2f + 1f) + 2,$$
$$= (2 + 1)f + 2,$$
$$= 3f + 2 = 32_{\text{five}}.$$

Therefore, we see that we rename   12   ones as   1   five + 2 ones. This is done in the usual vertical manner by "carrying:"

$$\begin{array}{r} \textcircled{1} \\ 14_{\text{five}} \\ + 13_{\text{five}} \\ \hline 2 \end{array}$$

from which we determine the sum

$$\begin{array}{r} \textcircled{1} \\ 14_{\text{five}} \\ + 13_{\text{five}} \\ \hline 32_{\text{five}}. \end{array}$$

Similarly, the "borrowing" process is a renaming process:

EXAMPLE

Find the difference $41_{five} - 23_{five}$.

$$41_{five} - 23_{five} = (4f + 1) - (2f + 3),$$
$$= (3f + 11) - (2f + 3),$$
$$= (3f - 2f) + (11 - 3),$$
$$= 1f + 3 = 13_{five}.$$

In the vertical form, the renaming is done as needed. The number 41_{five} is renamed in the first step as $3f + 11$ and is called "borrowing:"

$$\begin{array}{r} 3 \\ \cancel{4}^{1}1_{five} \\ -\ 2\ 3_{five} \\ \hline 1\ 3_{five} \end{array}$$

then the difference of the two numbers is found in the usual manner:

$$\begin{array}{r} 3 \\ \cancel{4}^{1}1_{five} \\ -\ 2\ 3_{five} \\ \hline 1\ 3_{five}. \end{array}$$

In multiplication, the Distributive Property of Multiplication over Addition plays its usual important role.

EXAMPLE

Find the product $32_{five} \times 24_{five}$. (In order to better illustrate the renaming, the numerals   5,   25,   125 are used.)

$$32_{five} \times 24_{five} = (3(5) + 2) \times (2(5) + 4),$$
$$= 3(5)[2(5) + 4] + 2[2(5) + 4],$$
$$= 11(5^2) + 22(5) + 4(5) + 13,$$
$$= [1(125) + 1(5^2) + 2(5^2) + 2(5)] + [4(5) + 1(5) + 3],$$
$$= 1(125) + (1 + 2)5^2 + (2 + 4 + 1)5 + 3,$$
$$= 1(125) + 3(5^2) + 12(5) + 3,$$

$$= 1(125) + 3(5^2) + 1(5^2) + 2(5) + 5,$$

$$= 1(125) + (3 + 1)5^2 + 2(5) + 3,$$

$$= 1423_{\text{five}}.$$

We see there is generally a great deal of renaming in the multiplication algorithm. This is accomplished in the short form:

②
24_{five}
$\times\ 32_{\text{five}}$

$$103 \rightarrow 2(2f + 4) = 4f + 13 = 10f + 3,$$
$$= 1tf + 0f + 3 = 103$$
$$1320 \rightarrow 3f(2f + 4) = 11tf + 22f$$
$$= 11tf + 1tf + 2tf + 2f$$
$$= 1htf + 3tf + 2f$$
$$= 1320$$

$1423_{\text{five}}.$

Hence addition, multiplication, and subtraction, base five, parallel those algorithms established for base ten. The processes of renaming play a very important role in each of these.

PROBLEM SET 8.2

1. Express each numeral in its expanded form. Then, by using the Commutative, Associative, and Distributive Properties of Multiplication over Addition or Subtraction, find the sums, products, or differences as noted. The base is ten. Therefore, you may use t, h, th for tens, hundreds, and thousands wherever necessary.

(a) $280 + 42 = (2h + 8t + 0) + (4t + 2),$
$$= 2h + (8t + 4t) + (0 + 2),$$
$$=$$
$$=$$

(b) $47 + 58 =$ (c) $64 + 82 =$
(d) $194 + 6 =$ (e) $3076 + 24 =$
(f) $96 - 49 =$ (g) $101 - 87 =$
(h) $200 - 46 =$ (i) $103 - 65 =$
(j) $700 - 90 =$ (k) $23 \times 8 =$
(l) $107 \times 3 =$ (m) $21 \times 5 =$
(n) $22 \times 16 =$ (o) $45 \times 24 =$

2. List the number of fives, twenty-fives, one hundred twenty-fives, etc. that is denoted in each numeral:

(a) 14_{five} = _____ fives + _____.

(b) 33_{five} = _____ fives + _____.

(c) 423_{five} = _____ twenty-fives + _____ fives + _____.

(d) 2033_{five} =

(e) 3142_{five} =

3. Write the base   five   numeral that tells how many objects are in each set.

(a) *xxxxx   xxxxx*   (b) *xxxxx*   (c) *xxxxx   xxxxx*
    xxxxx   xxxxx   *xxxxx*   *xxxxx   xxxxx*
    xxxxx   xxxxx   *xxxxx*   *xxxxx   xxxxx*
    xxxxx   xxxxx   *xxxxx*   *xxxxx   xxx*
    xxxxx   xxxxx

4. Express each numeral in its expanded form, base five. Then, as in Problem 1, find the sums, products, or differences. If you wish you may use f for 5, tf for 25, htf for 125. All numerals are denoted in base five.

(a) $32 + 4 = (3f + 2) + 4 = 3f + 11,$
$$= 3f + (1f + 1),$$
$$= (3f + 1f) + 1,$$
$$= (3 + 1)f + 1,$$
$$= 4f + 1 = 41_{\text{five}}.$$

(b) $104 + 23 =$ (c) $130 + 40 =$

(d) $400 + 324 =$ (e) $23 + 44 =$

(f) $21 - 4 =$ (g) $100 - 3 =$

(h) $42 - 24 =$ (i) $1000 - 200 =$

(j) $1010 - 44 =$ (k) $12 \times 4 =$

(l) $22 \times 4 =$ (m) $202 \times 3 =$

(n) $20 \times 30 =$ (o) $21 \times 42 =$

CHAPTER 9

Division of Whole Numbers: Analysis of Division Algorithms

9.1 INTRODUCTION

From prior study of arithmetic, the student is probably familiar with the terms divisor, dividend, and quotient. In the statement

$$36 \div 12 = 3,$$

the divisor is   12, the dividend is   36, and the quotient is   3. Division is also indicated by the sentences:

(a) $\dfrac{12\overline{)36}}{3}$ and   (b) $\dfrac{36}{12} = 3.$

Each sentence is read "thirty-six divided by twelve equals (is) three."
Elementary curricula emphasize "checking the answer" for problems involving division. To "check an answer," the division problem is stated as

a problem in terms of multiplication:

(a) $12\overline{)36}$ over 3 check: $12(3) = 36$.

(b) $9\overline{)45}$ over 5 check: $9(5) = 45$.

The method of "checking an answer" in division by using multiplication shows that division is the inverse operation for multiplication. This forms the basis for defining division.

Definition 9.1—Division If each of a and c is a Whole Number, b a Counting Number, then

$$a/b = c, \text{ if and only if }\quad a = b(c).$$

In Definition 9.1, the reader should note particularly that

(a) the divisor, b must be a Counting Number, (this will be explored in a following section), and
(b) the statements $a/b = c$ and $a = b(c)$ are identically the same statements.

From (b) above, the association between multiplication and division is illustrated:

(a) If $\dfrac{75}{25} = x$, then $x = 3$ because $75 = 25(3)$.

If $75 = 25(3)$ then $\dfrac{75}{25} = 3$ and $\dfrac{75}{3} = 25$.

(b) If $\dfrac{72}{x} = 8$, then $x = 9$ because $72 = 9(8)$.

If $72 = 9(x)$, then $\dfrac{72}{9} = x$ and $\dfrac{72}{x} = 8$.

(c) If $\dfrac{30 + x}{17} = 3$, then $30 + x = 51$ and $x = 21$ because

$30 + 21 = 17(3)$.

If $30 + x = 17(3)$ then $\dfrac{30 + x}{17} = 3$ and $\dfrac{30 + x}{3}$

$= 17$.

Hence, division is defined as the inverse operation of multiplication, and that by definition, each sentence involving division is resolved by resorting to multiplication.

9.2 CLOSURE, COMMUTATIVE, AND ASSOCIATIVE PROPERTIES

The set of Whole Numbers is not closed under division. This is easily demonstrated by an illustration. If $a = 21$ and $b = 5$, then there is no Whole Number, c, such that

$$21 = 5(c).$$

Since the set of Whole Numbers is not closed under division, a new set of numbers, called the *Rational Numbers*, will be defined in the following chapters. The question of closure under division is not resolved until a study of this set of numbers is undertaken.

Similarly, division is not commutative nor is division associative. This is illustrated below:

(a) DIVISION IS NOT COMMUTATIVE:
  1. $25 \div 5 \neq 5 \div 25$.
  2. $49 \div 7 \neq 7 \div 49$.

(b) DIVISION IS NOT ASSOCIATIVE:
  1. $(20 \div 10) \div 2 = 2 \div 2 = 1.$ $(1 \neq 4)$
    $20 \div (10 \div 2) = 20 \div 5 = 4.$
  2. $(100 \div 50) \div 2 = 2 \div 2 = 1.$ $(1 \neq 4)$
    $100 \div (50 \div 2) = 100 \div 25 = 4.$

In summary, we find (a) the set of Whole Numbers is not closed under division, (b) division is not commutative, and (c) division is not associative.

PROBLEM SET 9.1

1. Find Whole Numbers which will illustrate in some cases, that $a \div b = b \div a$ and $(a \div b) \div c = a \div (b \div c)$.

2. Justify each of the following by Definition 9.1, if in every instance a is a Counting Number:

(a) If $\dfrac{72}{a} = 12$ then $a = $ _____ because _____.

(b) If $\dfrac{30a}{15} = 120$ then $30a = $ _____. $a = $ _____ because _____.

(c) If $\dfrac{72}{a + 2} = 8$ then $72 = $ _____ , $a + 2 = $ _____ , and $a = $ _____ .

(d) If $\dfrac{30 + a}{19} = 3$ then $30 + a = $ _____   and $a = $ _____ .

2. Using Definition 9.1 and the addition, multiplication, and cancellation properties studied previously, find the value of n in each instance. Justify each sentence.

(a) If $\dfrac{n}{5} = 20$, then $n = $ _____   because _____ .

(b) If $\dfrac{5n}{6} = 25$, then $n = $ _____   because _____ .

(c) If $\dfrac{n}{5} + 10 = 20$, find the value of n.

(d) If $\dfrac{n - 8}{2} + 8 = 6$, find the value of n.

(e) If $\dfrac{n + 4}{2} - 10 = 2$, find the value of n.

9.3   SPECIAL PROPERTIES CONCERNING DIVISION

In this section, we wish to investigate, by using Definition 9.1, some special properties pertaining to division. These are presented as Properties D1–D7. These properties are most important, for some of them are used within the system of Rational Numbers and others are used to find a solution to equations of the type "Find n if $20 + 30n = 40$." Both topics are important to elementary teachers for many curricula contain problems using these concepts.

D1: $n \div n = 1$, $n \neq 0$. This is used when working with Rational Numbers, a study to be made in later chapters. This is also used for "reducing a fraction to lowest terms" in addition and subtraction of fractions. Using Definition 9.1, the proof is very simple and is left as an exercise for the student.

D2: $0 \div 0$ *is NOT DEFINED.* From Definition 9.1, if $0/0 = c$, then $0 = 0(c)$.

Recall that the product of any number, c and 0 is 0.

$$0 = 0(0),$$

$$0 = 0(1),$$

$$0 = 0(2),$$

$$0 = 0(3),$$

$$\vdots$$

$$0 = 0(c), \; c \in \{0, 1, 2, 3, \ldots\}$$

Since the number c is any Whole Number, $0/0$ is not a unique number. The reader should note that an operation is always *well defined*, i.e., the result is always unique. Consequently, $0 \div 0$ is *not defined*.

D3: $c \div 0$ *IS UNDEFINED.* The last special property of division is to find the value of any Counting Number, c when divided by 0.

$$\text{If} \quad \frac{c}{0} = x, \text{then} \quad c = 0(x).$$

But $0(x) = 0$ for every number c. Therefore, we conclude in all cases there is no Whole Number x such that $c = 0(x)$. We can then state that if $c = 0$, $c/0$ is *undefined*.

The following theorems, D4–D6 deal with special topics generally encountered in solving equations. These theorems will terminate by proving the multiplicative cancellation property:

D4: If each of a, b, and c is a Whole Number, $c \neq 0$, then

$$\frac{a(c)}{c} = a.$$

D4 is particularly useful for finding the solution to equations of the type:

(a) If $\dfrac{2x}{2} = 4$, then $x = 4$.

(b) If $\dfrac{3(x + 2)}{3} = 10$, then $x + 2 = 10$ from which we can conclude $x = 8$.

The proof of this is very simple. Let each of a, b, and c be Whole numbers, $c \neq 0$. Then

$a(c) = a(c).$	Reflexivity.
$a(c) = c(a).$	Commutative Property for Multiplication.
$\therefore \dfrac{a(c)}{c} = a.$	By Definition 9.1.

D5: If each of a, b, c, and d is a Whole Number, $a = b$, $c \neq 0$, and if a/c exists, then b/c exists, and

$$\frac{a}{c} = \frac{b}{c}.$$

To illustrate D5, consider finding the number x if

(a) $2x = 10$. If $2x = 10$, then, if D5 is true,

$$\frac{2x}{2} = \frac{10}{2},$$

and by D4,

$$x = 5.$$

(b) $3x + 12 = 15$,

$3(x + 4) = 15$,

$$\frac{3(x + 4)}{3} = \frac{15}{3},$$

$x + 4 = 5$,

$x = 1$.

Proof. Let each of a, b, c, and d be a Whole Number, $a = b$, $c \neq 0$ and a/c exists. If a/c exists, there is a Whole Number, d, such that

$$a = c(d),   \text{by Definition 9.1.}$$

If $a = b$, then by substitution,

$$b = c(d).$$

Therefore, by Definition 9.1, b/c exists and

$$\frac{b}{c} = d.$$

Therefore, $\dfrac{a}{c} = \dfrac{b}{c}$, by substitution.

Theorem D4 allows us to prove a theorem that deals with the multiplicative cancellation property:

D6: If each of a, b, and c be a Whole Number, $c \neq 0$, $a(c) = b(c)$, then

$$a = b$$

Proof. Let each of a, b, and c be a Whole Number $c \neq 0$, $a(c) = b(c)$. If $a(c) = b(c)$, then by D4,

$$\frac{a(c)}{c} = \frac{b(c)}{c},$$

from which we conclude, by D4, that

$$a = b.$$

The last theorem illustrates that there is a Distributive Property of Division over Addition in *some cases*. For example,

(a) $\dfrac{8}{2} = \dfrac{6 + 2}{2} = \dfrac{6}{2} + \dfrac{2}{2} = 3 + 1 = 4$, but

(b) $\dfrac{8}{2} = \dfrac{5 + 3}{2} = \dfrac{5}{2} + \dfrac{3}{2}$. There is no Whole Number x such that $\dfrac{5}{2} = x$ and there is no whole number y such that $\dfrac{3}{2} = y$.

Hence the sentence $(a + b) \div c = \dfrac{a}{c} + \dfrac{b}{c}$ is true for only *particular* Whole Numbers a, b, and c. Such a law does exist for Rational Numbers and for Real Numbers.

D7: If each of a, b, and c is a Whole Number, $c \neq 0$, and if $\dfrac{a}{c}$ exists and $\dfrac{b}{c}$ exists, then

$$\frac{a + b}{c} = \frac{a}{b} + \frac{b}{c}.$$

Proof. Let $\dfrac{a}{c} = x$ and $\dfrac{b}{c} = y$. Then

$a = c(x)$ and $b = c(y)$,

$a + b = c(x) + c(y)$,   If $a = b$ and $c = d$, then
                               $a + c = b + d$.

$a + b = c(x + y)$,   Distributive Property.

$\dfrac{a + b}{c} = x + y$,   Definition 9.1.

$\dfrac{a + b}{c} = \dfrac{a}{c} + \dfrac{b}{c}$.   Substitution.

Theorem D7 is defined a "right-hand distributive property." For division, there is no "left-hand distributive property:"

$$a \div (b + c) \neq \frac{a}{c} + \frac{a}{c}.$$

EXAMPLES

(a) $(4 + 8) \div 2 = \dfrac{4}{2} + \dfrac{8}{2} = 2 + 4 = 6.$

(b) $(3 + 5) \div 2 \neq \dfrac{3}{2} + \dfrac{5}{2}.$ This is true since $\dfrac{3}{2}$ and $\dfrac{5}{2}$ are not *Whole* Numbers.*

(c) $18 \div (3 + 6) \neq \dfrac{18}{3} + \dfrac{18}{6} = 6 + 3 = 9.$

The following problems illustrate how Theorems D1–D6 and properties and definitions previously studied are used to find the Whole Number solution for equations in one variable. Assume all subtraction and division exists. Justification for each sentence is listed to the right of the page.

EXAMPLE

Find the number n if $20 + 2n = 40.$

Solution. If $20 + 2n = 40$, then

$(20 - 20) + 2n = (40 - 20),$	If $a = b$ then $a - c = b - c,$ $a > c.$
$0 + 2n = 20,$	Renaming.
$2n = 20,$	$0 + x = x.$
$\dfrac{2n}{2} = \dfrac{20}{2},$	Theorem D6.
$n = 10.$	Theorem D4.

EXAMPLE

Find the number n if $\dfrac{n}{7} - 20 = 0.$

* This is an illustration which shows that the right-hand distributive property is true for Rational Numbers.

Solution. If $\dfrac{n}{7} - 20 = 0$, then

$20 + \left(\dfrac{n}{7} - 20\right) = 0 + 20,$	If $a = b$ then $a - c = b - c.$
$(20 - 20) + \dfrac{n}{7} = 0 + 20,$	Renaming. Repeated use of Associative Properties for Addition.
$0 + \dfrac{n}{7} = 20,$	$x - x = 0.$
$\dfrac{n}{7} = 20,$	$0 + n = n.$
$7\left(\dfrac{n}{7}\right) = 7(20),$	If $a = b$ then $c(a) = c(b).$
$n = 140.$	Renaming. Theorem D4.

The above illustrates particular uses of the Theorems that pertain to division. Some of the problems below will be similar to these examples above.

PROBLEM SET 9.2

1. Prove Theorem D1.

2. The following is a proof that $2 = 1$. Find the error.

$0 = 0,$	Reflexivity.
$0(1 + 1) = 0(1),$	$0(n) = 0.$
$(1 - 1)(1 + 1) = (1 - 1)(1),$	Substitution. $1 - 1 = 0.$
$\dfrac{(1 - 1)(1 + 1)}{(1 - 1)} = \dfrac{(1 - 1)(1)}{(1 - 1)},$	If $ab = ac,$ $\dfrac{ab}{a} = \dfrac{ac}{a}.$
$(1 + 1) = 1.$	
$2 = 1.$	Renaming.

3. Find the number n as indicated below. Justify each step by stating a definition or property. Assume all subtraction and division exists.

(a) $\dfrac{n}{5} = 20.$ (b) $4n = 24.$

(c) $4n + 24 = 40.$ (d) $\dfrac{n}{5} + 10 = 12.$

(e) $2n - 20 = 40$.

(f) $\dfrac{n}{3} - 4 = 6$.

(g) $\dfrac{5n}{6} = 25$.

(h) $\dfrac{2n}{3} - 4 = 6$.

(i) $\dfrac{n + 1}{4} = 2$.

(j) $\dfrac{n - 8}{2} + 6 = 8$.

(k) $\dfrac{4}{n} = 2$.

(l) $\dfrac{4}{n} + 8 = 12$.

(m) $\dfrac{3(n - 1)}{4} = 6$.

(n) $\dfrac{n + 4}{2} - 10 = 2$.

(o) $\dfrac{2(n + 2)}{3} + 4 = 6$.

(p) $\dfrac{2(n - 3)}{5} - 4 = 2$.

4. There are certain numbers a, b, and c such that $a \div (b + c) = \dfrac{a}{b} + \dfrac{a}{c}$. Find three Whole Numbers so that this sentence is true.

5. State whether each of the following is "Defined," or "Undefined." All letters represent Whole Numbers. If Defined, find the value of the statement.

(a) $(6 \times 0) \div (8 - 8)$.

(b) $(16 - 16) \div 2$.

(c) $(n + 0) \times 0$.

(d) $(n \times 0) \div 0$.

(e) $(2n - n) \div (3n - 2n)$.

(f) $36 \div (18 - 18)$.

6. Illustrate that $(200 \div 100) \div 2 \neq 200 \div (100 \div 2)$.

7. Using D7, find the value of n in each sentence: Each letter represents a Whole Number $\neq 0$.

(a) $\dfrac{(20 + 25)}{5} = n$.

(b) $\dfrac{10 + 18}{2} = n$.

(c) $\dfrac{6n + 12n}{6} = n$.

(d) $\dfrac{4n + 8n}{n} = n$.

(e) $\dfrac{4(x + y) + (x + y)}{(x + y)} = n$.

(f) $\dfrac{4(r + s) + 6(r + s)}{2(r + s)} = n$. $2(r + s)$

9.4 SUBTRACTIVE, PARTITIVE, AND MEASUREMENT DIVISION

In mathematics, many operations are defined to be the *inverse operation* of another operation. For example:

(a) Subtraction is the *inverse* of addition.

(b) Division is the *inverse* of multiplication.

Similarly, many operations are defined as a repeated operation of another operation. This is true for multiplication:

$$4(3) = 3 + 3 + 3 + 3 \qquad \text{(4 summands).}$$

As multiplication may be defined as repeated addition, division may be defined in terms of repeated subtraction. The inverse operation of multiplication, division, may be defined in terms of the inverse operation of addition, subtraction. In the problem $\frac{10}{2} = x$, subtractive division answers the question, "how many 2's are contained within 10?" This is illustrated:

$$
\begin{array}{r}
10 \\
-2 \\
\hline
8 \\
-2 \\
\hline
6 \\
-2 \\
\hline
4 \\
-2 \\
\hline
2 \\
-2 \\
\hline
0
\end{array}
\qquad
\begin{array}{l}
10 = 1(2) + 8, \\
\\
10 = 2(2) + 6, \\
\\
10 = 3(2) + 4, \\
\\
10 = 4(2) + 2, \\
\\
10 = 5(2) + 0.
\end{array}
$$

Parallel to Subtractive Division is *Measurement Division*. In the problem $\frac{10}{2} = x$, the question is resolved: "How many disjoint sets of two are contained within a set of ten objects?" This is illustrated in Figure 9.1:

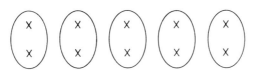

Figure 9.1

ILLUSTRATION OF MEASUREMENT DIVISION $\frac{10}{2} = 5$

From Figure 9.1, we see that there are five disjoint sets of two within a set of ten objects, or

$$\frac{10}{2} = 5.$$

In the above, we are principally concerned with "how many equal groups of two objects are contained within   10   objects." However, we can restate the above as: "If   10   objects are separated into two groups, how many objects are in each group?" This is termed *Partitive Division*, and the sentence $\frac{10}{2} = 5$ is illustrated:

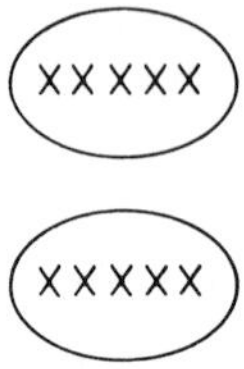

Figure 9.2

ILLUSTRATION OF PARTITIVE DIVISION $\frac{10}{2} = 5$

In the first case, we were interested in "how many groups (Measurement Division)" and in the second case we were interested in "how many were in each group (Partitive Division)."

Further illustration of Measurement Division and Partitive Division are given.

Measurement. David had   30   pieces of candy. He gave each class-mate   5   pieces until it was gone. How many classmates got some candy?

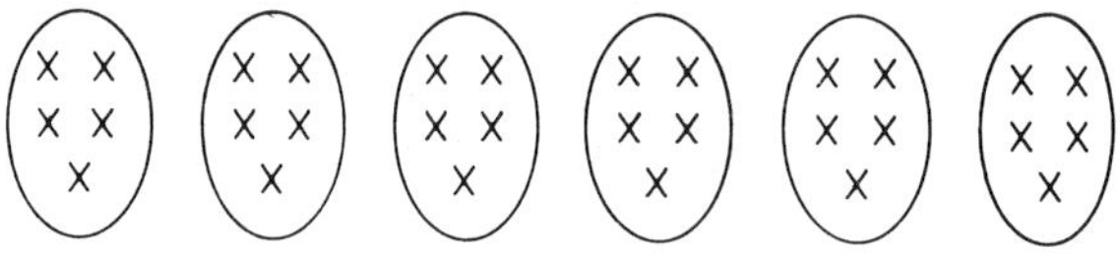

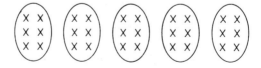

Figure 9.3

6 classmates each received   5   pieces: $\frac{30}{5} = 6$.

How many groups?

Partitive. David had   30   pieces of candy. He divided the candy equally among   5   classmates. How many pieces of candy did each classmate receive?

Figure 9.4

Each classmate received   6   pieces: $\frac{30}{5} = 6$.

How many objects in each group?

Only in certain instances can a set of n objects be partitioned into b disjoint sets of c objects. Consider the problem of partitioning 18   objects into disjoint sets, each set containing   5   objects:

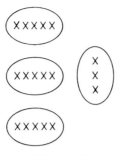

Figure 9.5

We see that the related division sentence $\frac{18}{5} = n$ has no meaning in the set of Whole Numbers, for there is no Whole Number n such that $18 = 5n$. However, we see that 18 can be expressed as

$$18 = 5(3) + 3,$$

or that 18 objects can be partitioned into 3 disjoint sets of 5 objects and have a "remainder" of 3 objects.

Hence the concept of a "remainder" is introduced. In general, any Whole Number, n can be expressed in the form

$$n = b(q) + r,$$

where $b < n,$ $0 \le r < b.$ In the above, n is called the *dividend*, b is called the *divisor*, q is the *quotient*, and r is the *remainder*:

dividend = (divisor × quotient) + remainder

It can also be proven that the quotient q and the remainder r are unique. This means that when any Whole Number n is divided by any Whole Number $b,$ $b \ne 0$ and $b \le n,$ there is *one and only one* quotient and *one* and only one remainder such that $0 \le r < b.$ This is known as the **Division Algorithm for Whole Numbers.** Illustrations of this algorithm are given below:

n	b	q	r	$n = b(q) + 4$
47	6	7	5	$47 = 6(7) + 5$
17	3	5	2	$17 = 3(5) + 2$
120	6	20	0	$120 = 6(20) + 0$
70	2	35	0	$70 = 2(35) + 0.$

Figure 9.6

ILLUSTRATIONS OF $n = b(q) + r$

It should be noted that if only n and r are given, b
and q are not necessarily unique. If $n = 27$ and $r = 7$, then
the possible solutions to $n = bq + r$ are:

n	b	q	r
27	20	1	7
27	10	2	7

Figure 9.7

$$27 = bq + 7; \qquad 0 \le 7 < b$$

PROBLEM SET 9.3

1.   Each of (a)–(f) is an illustration of Partitive Division or Measurement Division.
Classify each and then solve.

(a) Ten children were separated into two equal groups. How many children were in
each group?

(b) Forty pieces of candy were distributed equally among 10 children. How many
pieces of candy did each child receive?

(c) Seven houses were built with a total cost of $91,000. What was the average cost
per house?

(d) A groceryman bought bread at 20¢ per loaf. If his total bread bill was $15.00, how
many loaves did he purchase?

(e) A certain mailman delivers daily an average of 10,000 letters. If there are 1000
persons on his route, how many letters does each person receive, on the average, per day?

(f) A service station grossed $400, $700, and $600 on Friday, Saturday, and Sunday,
respectively. What was the average gross intake for the 3 days?

2.   Illustrate, using the Subtractive process that

(a) $\dfrac{45}{9} = 5,$ (b) $\dfrac{100}{25} = 4.$

3.   Given a dividend and a divisor. Find the quotient and remainder so that $0 \le$
remainder $<$ divisor:

(a) (97, 5).   (b) (81, 9).
(c) (105, 17).   (d) (221, 14).
(e) (147, 18).   (f) (342, 23).

4.   Given a dividend and a remainder. Find *all* quotients and all *divisors* so that
dividend = (divisor × quotient) + remainder, 0 < remainder < divisor

(a) (31, 1).   (b) (42, 4).
(c) (53, 3).   (d) (64, 4).

9.5 THE EUCLIDEAN ALGORITHM

Euclid, in Book VII of his *"Elements,"* found an algorithm which enables a person to find the greatest common factor for any two Whole Numbers a and b, $a < b$. This algorithm makes extensive use of the Division Algorithm for Whole Numbers. This is explained by the following example:

Given $a = 1320$ and $b = 1890$. Find the hcf(1320, 1890):
(a) Divide 1890 by 1320:

$$\begin{array}{r} 1 \\ 1320\overline{)1890} \\ 1320 \\ \hline 570 \end{array}$$

(b) Divide 1320 by 570:

$$\begin{array}{r} 2 \\ 570\overline{)1320} \\ 1140 \\ \hline 180 \end{array}$$

(c) Divide 570 by 180:

$$\begin{array}{r} 3 \\ 180\overline{)570} \\ 540 \\ \hline 30 \end{array}$$

(d) Divide 180 by 30:

$$\begin{array}{r} 6 \\ 30\overline{)180} \\ 180 \\ \hline 0 \end{array} \leftarrow \boxed{\text{Remainder is zero.}}$$

In general, if $a < b$, divide b by a. Then divide the divisor by the remainder. Continue the process of dividing the divisor by the remainder *until the division is exact* (i.e., until a remainder of 0 is obtained). This final divisor is hcf(a, b). In the above, hcf(1320, 1890) = 30.

EXAMPLE

Find the hcf(112, 168).

$$\begin{array}{r} 1 \\ 112\overline{)168} \\ 112 \\ \hline 56 \end{array} \qquad \begin{array}{r} 2 \\ 56\overline{)112} \\ 112 \\ \hline 0 \end{array}$$

(a)   (b)   (c) Therefore, hcf(112, 168) = 56.

9.6   ANALYSIS OF LONG DIVISION

The long division algorithm has been one of the more complicated algorithms to teach to pupils with understanding. Many textbooks now present the long division as a combination of the Subtractive division and Measurement division processes. We shall investigate these processes before discussing the long division algorithm.

The Subtractive process involves an estimation of the answer and the subtraction of the partial products from the given dividend. The following illustrates two estimated quotients in the problem $495 \div 20 = ?$

$$
\begin{array}{r}
20\overline{)490} \\
\end{array}
$$

First Partial Product $\rightarrow$ 200 $\quad$ 10 $\leftarrow$ Estimated Partial Quotient
First Remainder $\longrightarrow$ 290

The first estimated quotient is satisfactory as long as the product of the divisor and the estimated quotient is not greater than the dividend. Similarly, succeeding products of the estimated quotient times the divisor must not exceed the remainder:

(a) $20\overline{)490}$ $\quad$ (b) $20\overline{)490}$
$\qquad$ 200 | 10 $\qquad$ 400 | 20
$\qquad$ 290 $\qquad\qquad$ 90
$\qquad$ 200 | 10 $\qquad$ 140 | 7 $\leftarrow$ Estimate not valid
$\qquad$ 90

In (b) above, we see that the estimated quotient is not valid, for $7 \times 20 = 140 > 90$. Two correct solutions for finding the quotient are given below:

(a) $20\overline{)490}$ $\qquad\qquad\qquad$ (b) $20\overline{)490}$
$\qquad$ 200 | 10 $\qquad\qquad\qquad\qquad$ 400 | 20
$\qquad$ 290 $\qquad\qquad\qquad\qquad\qquad$ 90
$\qquad$ 200 | 10 $\qquad\qquad\qquad\qquad$ 80 | 4
$\qquad$ 90 $\qquad\qquad$ Remainder $= 10$ | 24 $=$ Quotient
$\qquad$ 60 | 3
$\qquad$ 30
$\qquad$ 20 | 1
Remainder $= 10$ | 24 $=$ Quotient

We see that the underlying thought is "how many 20's are contained within 490?" We see that

(a) $490 = (20 \times 10) + (20 \times 10) + (20 \times 3) + (20 \times 1) + 10,$

$\qquad = 20(10 + 10 + 3 + 1) + 10,$

$\qquad = 20(24) + 10.$

(b) $490 = (20 \times 20) + (20 \times 4) + 10,$

$\qquad = 20(20 + 4) + 10,$

$\qquad = 20(24) + 10.$

This is in keeping with $\quad n = bq + r, \quad 0 \le r < b,$ the Division Algorithm.

In the conventional method, greater emphasis is placed on the estimated quotients:

$$
\begin{array}{r}
5 \\
40
\end{array} \Big\} \; 45
$$

$$
\begin{array}{r}
86\overline{)3942} \\
3440 \\
\hline
502 \\
430 \\
\hline
72
\end{array}
\quad
\begin{array}{l}
\\
86 \times 40 \\
\\
86 \times 5 \\
\text{Remainder}
\end{array}
$$

$$3942 = 86(45) + 72.$$

Again, we see that $\quad n = b(q) + r, \quad 0 \le r < b.$ The traditional method is generally contracted

$$
\begin{array}{r}
45 \\
86\overline{)3942} \\
344 \\
\hline
502 \\
430 \\
\hline
72
\end{array}
\quad
\begin{array}{l}
\\
\leftarrow 86 \times 40. \\
\\
\leftarrow 86 \times 5. \\
\leftarrow \text{Remainder.}
\end{array}
$$

PROBLEM SET 9.4

1. Using the Euclidean Algorithm, find $\quad$ hcf$(a, b)\quad$ if $\quad (a, b)$ is

(a) (6, 17).   (b) (22, 48).   (c) (21, 36).

(d) (14, 120).   (e) (72, 216).   (f) (54, 78).

2. Using the Subtractive Process, find the quotient and remainder, if the divisor and dividend is

(a) (9, 37).   (b) (15, 48).   (c) (136, 428).

(d) (13, 97).   (e) (472, 1416).   (f) (283, 967).

3. Find the quotient and remainder of (a)–(f) in Problem 2, above, using the Conventional Method.

4. In the exact division problem $a/b = 150$, how is the quotient affected if:

(a) The dividend is doubled?
(b) The divisor is doubled?
(c) The dividend is halved?
(d) The divisor is halved?

The Integers

PART THREE

CHAPTER 10

The Set of Integers: Addition, Multiplication, Subtraction, Division

10.1 INTRODUCTION

In Chapter 4, an introduction was given to the set of INTEGERS. In particular, we defined a set that would be closed under subtraction, but we wished also to define a system that

1. Retained all number properties of W.
2. Retained all number operations of W so that these would still be true when considering the Integers.
3. Contained a new kind of number.

As shown in the following paragraphs, the new system of numbers defined below will allow us to satisfy the conditions outlined in 1–3, above.

Definition 10.1 For every Whole Number n, there is a unique number $-n$, such that $n + (-n) = 0$. The number $-n$ is the Additive

Inverse of n; the number n is the Additive Inverse of $-n$. This set of numbers is defined as the set of INTEGERS, denoted by the symbol "I."

As in the case of Whole Numbers, the set of Integers may be pictorially represented on the number line. The reader should note that the construction of the number line is similar to that for Whole Numbers, except that each of the Integers of $\{-1, -2, -3, \ldots\}$ is associated with a point that is $1, 2, 3, \ldots$ units *to the left of zero*, respectively. Hence, we retain the ideas of distance and direction established for the set of Whole Numbers. The number line representation for the set I is pictured as:

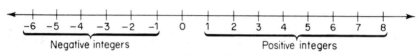

Figure 10.1

REPRESENTATION OF INTEGERS ON NUMBER LINE

As stated above, we wish to define a set I of numbers so that the properties of I will parallel the properties of W. This is so because the set of non-negative Integers, defined $\{0, 1, 2, 3, \ldots\}$, very closely resembles the set of Whole Numbers when considering addition, subtraction, multiplication, and division, and the properties of equality and inequality. Particularly, the properties associated with Integers are listed below.

For every Integer a, for every Integer b, and for every Integer c (except as denoted below):

$P1$:   *Closure*: $a + b \in I$; $a(b) \in I$.

$P2$:   *Commutativity*: $a + b = b + a$; $a(b) = b(a)$.

$P3$:   *Associativity*: $a + (b + c) = (a + b) + c$; $a(bc) = (ab)c$.

$P4$:   *Additive Identity*: There is a unique Integer 0 such that $a + 0 = 0 + a = a$.

$P5$:   *Additive Inverses*: For every Integer a, there is a unique number $-a$ such that $a + (-a) = 0$.

$P6$:   *Multiplicative Identity*: There is a unique Integer 1 such that $a(1) = 1(a) = a$.

$P7$:   *Distributivity*: $a(b + c) = ab + ac$.

The six properties for Equality are:

$P8$:   *Dichotomy*: $a = b$ or $a \neq b$.

$P9$:   *Reflexivity*: $a = a$.

$P10$:   *Symmetry*:   If $a = b$, $b = a$.

$P11$:   *Transitivity*:   If $a = b$ and $b = c$, then $a = c$.

$P12$:   *Addition*:   If $a = b$, $c + a = c + b$.

$P13$:   *Cancellation for Addition*:   If $a + c = b + c$, then $a = b$.

$P14$:   *Multiplication*:   If $a = b$, $ca = cb$.

$P15$:   *Cancellation for Multiplication*:   If $ac = bc$, $c \neq 0$, $a = b$.

For the set of Integers, the order relation is defined below.

Definition 10.2   The Integer a is less than the Integer b if and only if there is an Integer $c > 0$ such that $a + c = b$.

The six order properties are retained. Proofs of these properties are based on properties of equality and certain other properties.

$I1$:   *Trichotomy*: $a = b$ or $a < b$ or $a > b$.

$I2$:   *Transitivity*:   If $a < b$ and $b < c$, then $a < c$.

$I3$:   *Addition*:   If $a < b$, then $a + c < b + c$.

$I4$:   *Multiplication*:   If $a < b$ and $c > 0$, then $ac < bc$.

$I5$:   *Cancellation Property for Addition*:   If $a + c < b + c$,   then $a < b$.

$I6$:   *Cancellation Property for Multiplication*:   If $ac < bc$, $c > 0$, then $a < b$. If $ac < bc$ and $c < 0$, then $a > b$.

PROBLEM SET 10.1

1. Answer the following true or false. Give an illustration or write a short sentence to justify your answer.

(a) Is there a smallest non-negative Integer?
(b) Is there an Integer that is neither positive nor negative?
(c) Is there a largest Negative Integer?
(d) Is there a largest Positive Integer?
(e) Is there a smallest Negative Integer?
(f) Does every Negative Integer have an Additive Inverse?

2. List the elements of:

(a) The set of non-negative Integers.

(b) The Integer that is neither positive nor negative.

(c) The Additive Inverses of $\{\ldots, -3, -2, -1\}$.

3. List the elements of the following sets if the Universal Set is I. Illustrate each set on a picture of the number line.

(a) $\{n|$ $n > 7\}$.

(b) $\{n|$ $-5 \leq n \leq 10\}$.

(c) $\{n|$ $n < 0\}$.

(d) $\{n|$ $-10 \leq n \leq 0\}$.

(e) $\{n|$ $-20 \leq n < -5\}$.

4. Let set A be the domain of a Relation R and set B be the Range of R. Graph, on coordinate axes $A \times B$ if the Universal Set is I.

(a) $A = \{n|$ $0 \leq n \leq 5\}$, $B = \{n|$ $0 \leq n \leq 7\}$.

(b) $A = B = \{n|$ $-4 \leq n \leq 5\}$.

(c) $A = \{n|$ $-7 \leq n \leq 8\}$, $B = \{n|$ $0 \leq n \leq 8\}$.

5. List the elements of the following sets if the Universal Set is I:

(a) $\{n|$ $4 + n \leq 12\}$.

(b) $\{n|$ $-10 + n < 0\}$.

(c) $\{n|$ $n + 10 \geq 4\}$.

(d) $\{n|$ $n + 10 < 20$ and $n > -4\}$.

(e) $\{n|$ $n \leq -20$ or $n > 0\}$.

6. On the picture of the Number line, graph the sets described in (a)–(e) of Problem 5.

10.2   ADDITION AND SUBTRACTION

The basic concepts of number are generally taught from the concept of set. Addition and subtraction are then defined as number operations that parallel set operations. Another device useful to teaching the ideas of number and to teaching addition and subtraction is the use of the number line.

Many current texts*, using models to teach addition of Integers on the number line, find that important concepts must be developed.

Each Integer denotes:

1. A change in position by a certain number of units, and
2. A change in position that involves one of two opposite directions.

The number line provides an excellent model to develop the two ideas above, for we can consider a change in position (from the beginning point) *to the left* as being opposite to a change in position *to the right* of the same

* See "Unit 1—Arithmetic of Real Numbers," published by the University of Illinois Committee on School Mathematics, Max Beberman, Director, for one of the very best methods for teaching the four basic operations involving the Integers.

beginning point. Arrows pointing to the left or right on the number line are used to denote both (a) distance and (b) direction. Hence, a change in position of   4   units to the right (represented by the Integer 4) from the point associated with   − 2   is illustrated by the arrow below:

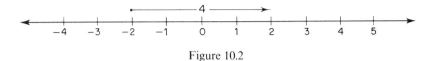

Figure 10.2

NUMBER LINE REPRESENTATION OF THE INTEGER   4

A change in position of   4   units *to the left* (represented by the Integer − 4) from the point associated with   5   is illustrated by the arrow below:

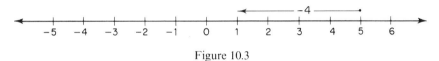

Figure 10.3

NUMBER LINE REPRESENTATION OF THE INTEGER   − 4

The beginning point of the arrow representing   4   is   − 2 and the terminal point is   2; the beginning point of the arrow representing − 4   is   5   and the terminal point is   1. Elementary textbooks arbitrarily decide that if $n > 0$, then the terminal point of the arrow representing n lies to the *right* of the beginning point; if $n < 0$, the terminal point of n lies to the *left* of the beginning point.

Other representations of   4   and   − 4   are illustrated below:

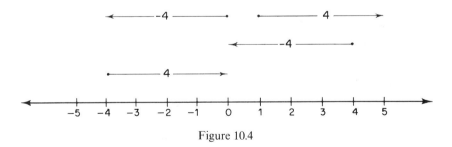

Figure 10.4

Addition on the picture of the number line is thought of as an "attaching on" operation. To represent the sum $a + b$ the *beginning* point of the arrow representing a is *always*   *0*. The *terminal* point of the arrow representing a is then assigned as the *beginning* point of the arrow

representing   *b*. The sum,   *a + b*   is then associated with a number
c, such that the arrow representing   *c*   describes the distance and direction from   *0*   to the terminal point of the vector representing   *b*:

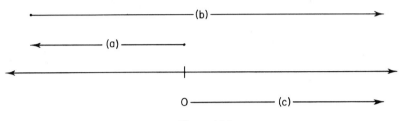

Figure 10.5

NUMBER LINE REPRESENTATION OF $a + b = c$

Various sums are illustrated below:

(a) $2 + 3 = 5$:

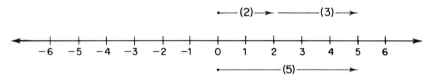

Figure 10.6

(b) $(-4) + (-2) = -6$:

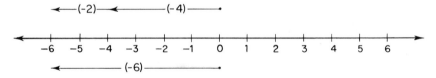

Figure 10.7

(c) $5 + (-7) = -2$:

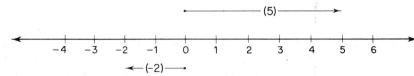

Figure 10.8

(d) $-2 + 7 = 5$:

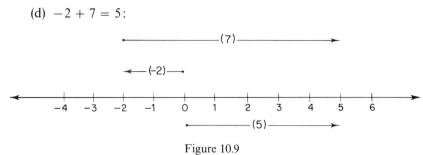

Figure 10.9

The intuitive illustration exhibited in (a) above, reveals that for each summand a and b, $a, b > 0$, addition of Integers parallels that of addition for Whole Numbers. However, (b), (c), and (d) each represent addition that is not parallel to that for Whole Numbers. In (b) above, we need to show that the sum of the Additive Inverse of a and the Additive Inverse of b equals the Additive Inverse of the sum of a and b. In order to accomplish this, we must show that the following is true.

Theorem 10.1 For all Integers x and y, if $x = y$, then the sum of x and the Additive Inverse of y equals 0:

Proof: Let each of x and y be integers, $x = y$.

If $x = y$,

$x + (-y) = y + (-y)$, | If $a = b$, $a + c = b + c$,

$x + (-y) = 0$. | $a + (-a) = 0$.

Similarly, if $x + (-y) = 0$, then $x = y$:

$$x + (-y) = 0,$$

$$x + [y + (-y)] = y + 0,$$

$$x + [y + (-y)] = y,$$

$$x + 0 = y,$$

$$x = y.$$

We can now proceed to the problem above.

Theorem 10.2 If each of a and b is an Integer,

$$(-a) + (-b) = -(a + b).$$

In order to prove this, recall that $-(a + b)$ is the Additive Inverse of the sum $a + b$. Then the Additive Inverse of $-(a + b)$ is $-[-(a + b)] = (a + b)$. From Theorem 4.1 above, if the sum $(-a) + (-b) +$ [the Additive Inverse of $-(a + b)$] $= 0$, then $(a + b)$ is the Additive Inverse of $(-a) + (-b)$ and hence $(-a) + (-b) = -(a + b)$:

$(-a) + (-b) + (a + b) =$	
$[(-a) + (a)] + [(-b) + b],$	Repeated application of commutative and associative properties for addition.
$= 0 + 0,$	$n + (-n) = 0.$
$= 0.$	$0 + 0 = 0.$

Hence we can conclude for (b) above that $-4 + (-2) = -(4 + 2) = -6$; $-7 + (-8) = -(7 + 8) = -15$, etc. Problems illustrated by (a) and (b) above show methods by which we form the sum of Integers, (a) each of which is greater than zero, or (b) each of which is less than zero.

But if $a < 0$ and $b > 0$, or $a > 0$ and $b < 0$, as in cases (c) and (d) above, the sum $a + b$ must be calculated in a different manner. In order to do this, a definition for the subtraction of Integers must be given.

Definition 10.3—Subtraction for Integers   If each of $a,$ $b,$ and c is an Integer, $a - b = c$ if and only if $a = b + c$.

For example, if $7 - 5 = x$, then $x = 2$ because $7 = 5 + 2$; if $(-10) - (-4) = x$, then $-10 = -4 + x$. We conclude that $x = -6$,   because $-10 = -4 + (-6) = -(4 + 6) = -10$. However, these are only specific examples of subtraction in terms of addition, and as illustrated below, addition will be defined in terms of subtraction.

We are now in a position to define addition of two Integers in terms of subtraction so that we may solve problems as in cases (c) and (d) above.

Theorem 10.3   For every Integer a, for every Integer b,

$$a + (-b) = -(b - a).$$

This is a very important Theorem, because it also states that addition may be expressed in terms of subtraction, and that all situations involving subtraction may be resolved in terms of addition.

Thus we can now say that $17 + (-69) = -(69 - 17) = -52$; $23 + (-47) = -(47 - 23) = -24$, etc.

The preceding sections revealed somewhat complicated methods to find the sum of two Integers. In order to simplify this addition, the ABSOLUTE VALUE (sometimes called the Whole Number value) of an Integer is defined. To indicate the absolute value of any Integer n, the symbol "$|n|$" is used:

(a) If $n > 0$, $|n| = n$.
(b) If $n = 0$, $|n| = n$.
(c) If $n < 0$, $|n| = -n$.

Hence the absolute value of 9, $|9| = 9$. The absolute value of 0, $|0| = 0$, and the absolute value of -9, $|-9| = -(-9) = 9$.

The reader should note that $|10| = |-10|$; $|3| = |-3|$; $|n| = |-n|$. This reveals that each Integer and the Additive Inverse of the Integer have the same Absolute Value.

In order to utilize Absolute Values for addition of Integers, the relative size of the Absolute Values of the Integers is considered:

EXAMPLE

(a) $|10| = 10$ and $|3| = 3$. $|10| > |3|$.
(b) $|-3| = 3$ and $|-10| = 10$. $|-3| < |-10|$.
(c) $|10| = 10$ and $|-20| = 20$. $|10| < |-20|$.

Use of Inequalities in Absolute Value is easily introduced into the addition of Integers. In order to show how it is used, consider the specific problems:

(a) $17 + (-3) = 17 - 3 = 14$.
(b) $24 + (-8) = 24 - 8 = 16$.

Each sum is the sum of an Integer less than zero and an Integer greater than zero, and in this instance *their sum is greater than zero*. It should be noted in every case that the absolute value of the Integer greater than zero is greater than the Absolute Value of the Integer less than zero:

$$|17| > |-3|.$$

$$|24| > |-8|.$$

Similarly, if the sum $a + b$ is less than zero,

(a) $-17 + 8 = [-9 + (-8)] + 8 = -9 + (-8 + 8) = -9$.
(b) $-10 + 4 = [-6 + (-4)] + 4 = -6 + (-4 + 4) = -6$.

An investigation of the sum shows that *each sum is less than zero*. Similarly, the absolute value of the Integer less than zero is greater than the absolute value of the Integer greater than zero:

$$|-17| > |8|,$$
$$|-10| > |4|.$$

This is summarized below:

1. If $a > 0$ and $b < 0$ and $|a| > |b|$ then
   $a + b > 0$:
   Example: $29 + (-18) = 29 - 18 = 11$.
2. If $a < 0$ and $b > 0$ and $|a| > |b|$ then
   $a + b < 0$:
   Example: $-27 + 3 = -(27 - 3) = -24$.

Using the concept of Absolute Value, we may develop a set of *rules* which in some cases will considerably shorten the work of adding Integers.

Compare the following pairs of statements:

(a) $19 + (-10) = (19 - 10) = 9$ by T2.
(b) $19 + (-10) = (|19|) - |-10|) = (19 - 10) = 9$.

(a) $-27 + 10 = -(27 - 10) = -17$ by T2.
(b) $-27 + 10 = -(|27| - |10|) = -(27 - 10) = -17$.

(a) $10 + (-36) = 10 + [-10 + (-26)] = [10 + (-10)] + (-26) = -26$.
(b) $10 + (-36) = -(|-36| - |10|) = -(36 - 10) = -26$.

(a) $(+7) + (+10) = +(7 + 10) = +17$.
(b) $(+7) + (+10) = +(|+7| + |+10|) = +(7 + 10) = +17$.

(a) $(-12) + (-26) = -(12 + 26) = -38$.
(b) $(-12) + (-26) = -(|-12| + |-26|) = -(12 + 26) = -38$.

These illustrations indicate that four distinct cases arise when considering addition of Integers, and that we may define addition in terms of Absolute Value. These are summarized below:

Observation: For every Integer a and for every Integer b,
   $O1$: If $a > 0$ and $b > 0$, then $a + b = (|a| + |b|)$.
   $O2$: If $a < 0$ and $b < 0$, then $a + b = -(|a| + |b|)$.
   $O3$: If $a > 0$ and $b < 0$ and $|a| > |b|$,   then $a + b = (|a| - |b|)$.
   $O4$: If $a < 0$ and $b > 0$ and $|a| > |b|$,   then $a + b = -(|a| - |b|)$.

Thus we have rephrased Theorems 10.1, 10.2, and 10.3 in the form of *Rules* which may be applied to fit any situation. In summary:

(a) *to add two numbers of like sign, add their absolute values and prefix this sum with the common sign of the summands.*

(b) *to add two numbers of unlike sign, find the difference of their Absolute Values, then prefix the sign of the larger in Absolute Value to this difference.*

PROBLEM SET 10.2

1. If the distance between each point below represents 1 unit of measure, what Integer could be used to describe the distance and direction from the beginning point of the first arrow to the terminal point of the second arrow? (*Hint*: Consider an arrow that points to the right as representing a Positive Integer.) State the related addition fact for each model.

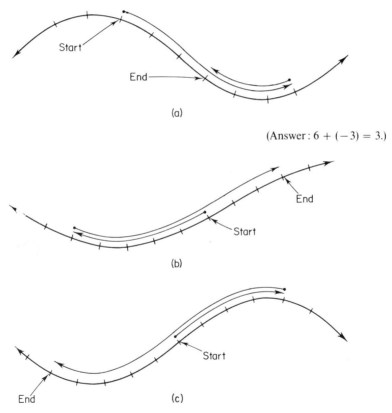

(a)

(Answer: $6 + (-3) = 3$.)

(b)

(c)

(d) If each arrow that points to the right represents a Negative Integer and if each arrow that points to the left represents a Positive Integer, state the related addition fact for each of (a), (b), and (c) above.

2. Is the set of Integers closed under addition? Commutative? Associative? What number is the Additive Identity?

3. Illustrate on the picture of the number line the following sums:

(a) $6 + 9$.   (b) $(-6) + (-2)$.
(c) $(-8) + 10$.   (d) $10 + (-8)$.
(e) $(-25) + 20$.   (f) $(-7) + (18)$.
(g) $(9) + (-3)$.   (h) $(-10) + 14$.
(i) If $-4 + n = -0$, then $n = $ _____.
(j) If $n + (-6) = -11$, then $n = $ _____.
(k) If $n + (-6) = 11$, then $n = $ _____.
(l) If $4 + n = -9$, then $n = $ _____.

4. Find the Absolute Value of:

(a) 9.   (b) 31.   (c) 19.
(d) -8.   (e) -6.   (f) -11.
(g) -32.   (h) 22.   (i) -25.

5.

(a) $|-9| = $ _____.   (b) $|32| = $ _____.   (c) $|-13| = $ _____.
(d) $|-21| = $ _____.   (e) $|-5| = $ _____,   (f) $|-51| = $ _____.

6. Find the Absolute Value of each Integer in the given pairs of Integers. Then determine if the Absolute Value of the first Integer is $>$ or $<$ the Absolute Value of the second Integer.

(a) $13, 8$.   (b) $21, 25$.   (c) $13, -8$.
(d) $21, -25$.   (e) $-10, -12$.   (f) $-13, -7$.
(g) $-21, 7$.   (h) $-6, 10$.   (i) $-22, -14$.

7. State whether you add or subtract the Absolute Value of the given Integers to form their sum.

(a) $9 + 8$.   (b) $-12 + (-9)$.   (c) $16 + (-20)$.
(d) $-20 + 12$.   (e) $9 + (-13)$.   (f) $-10 + (-8)$.
(g) $4 + 6$.   (h) $-8 + 17$.   (i) $-12 + 13$.
(j) $-6 + 4$.   (k) $8 + 4$.   (l) $-2 + (-7)$.

8. Using your knowledge of Absolute Value and Definition 10.3, find the sum of the following Integers:

(a) $9 + 8 = $ _____.   (b) $9 + (-13) = $ _____.
(c) $-12 + 13 = $ _____.   (d) $-12 + (-9) = $ _____.
(e) $-10 + (-8) = $ _____.   (h) $4 + 6 = $ _____.
(i) $8 + 5 = $ _____.   (j) $-20 + 12 = $ _____.
(k) $-8 + 17 = $ _____.   (l) $-2 + (-7) = $ _____.

Many mathematical situations may be stated in terms of Integers, although we probably do not recognize the situations as such—problems that deal with elevation, temperature, direction, time, etc. This is true because each situation involves a gain or loss when compared to some referent point. The following illustrates this concept.

9. On December 20, the temperature of Nome, Alaska was $-40°F$. On December 21, the temperature dropped an additional $16°F$. What was the temperature on December 21?

10. The freezing point of water is   0°C. If a cube of ice at −64°C   is melted to water at   90°C, what is the total temperature change?

11. Water, at   120°F   is converted to ice at   32°F   and then the temperature is dropped to   −94°F. What is the total temperature change?

12. A certain traveler from Mudville goes   80   miles East to the nearest city (consider this direction positive). He then reverses his direction and travels   172 miles West (consider this direction negative). Express the distance from Mudville *to the end of his last trip*, as either positive or negative.

13. Addition is sometimes performed within the Absolute Value symbols. The following illustrates some of these operations:

$$|9 + 8| = |17| = 17.$$

$$|-9 + 8| = |-1| = 1.$$

$$|-9 + (-8)| = |-17| = 17.$$

Find the value of the following as indicated above:

(a) $|8 + 6| = $ _____ .

(b) $|5 + (-2)| = $ _____ .

(c) $|2 + (-13)| = $ _____ .

(d) $|-9 + (-3)| = $ _____ .

(e) $|-10 + (-8)| = $ _____ .

(f) $|-8 + 17| = $ _____ .

(g) $|-17 + 9| = $ _____ .

(h) $|-9 + (-3)| = $ _____ .

(i) $|16 + (-20)| = $ _____ .

(j) $|9 + (-13)| = $ _____ .

14. Which is the smaller number? Using Definition 10.2, explain your choice. Assume $n > 0$.

(a) $14, -2$.

(b) $0, -7$.

(c) $18, 9$.

(d) $-18, -9$.

(e) $-n, -(n + 1)$.

(f) $-n, -(n - 1)$.

15. Prove for every Integer a, for every Integer b, and for every Integer c, if $a + b = a + c$, then $a = b$.

16. Prove that for every Integer a, there is exactly one additive inverse. (*Hint*: Assume the Integer a has two additive inverses, $-a$ and $a*$).

17. State whether each of the following is true or false. Justify your answer by citing one of P1–P15 or I1–I5.

(a) If $7n = 49$, then $n = 7$.

(b) If $n = 6$, then $-7n = -42$.

(c) If $n < 4$, then $-6n < -24$.

(d) $4 < n$, $-6 + 4 < -6 + 4n$.

(e) If $n < -5$, $7n < -35$.

18. State whether each of the following is true or false. If true, list the set to which n could belong.

(a) If $-n < -5$, then $n > 0$.

(b) If $-n > 4$, then $n < 0$.

(c) If $n < 4$, then $4 < -n$.

(d) If $-n < 0$, then $n > 0$.

19. The table below presents all possible addition "facts" within a finite number system. Determine (a) the additive identity element; (b) the additive inverse of each element within this system. The totality of elements is $\{0, 1, 2, \ldots, 6\}$.

+	0	1	2	3	4	5	6
0	0	1	2	3	4	5	6
1	1	2	3	4	5	6	0
2	2	3	4	5	6	0	1
3	3	4	5	6	0	1	2
4	4	5	6	0	1	2	3
5	5	6	0	1	2	3	4
6	6	0	1	2	3	4	5

20.   Find and graph, on the picture of the number line, the solution set to each problem. The universal Set is the set of Integers.

(a) $\{n \mid \quad |n| < 5\}$.
(b) $\{n \mid \quad |n| < 7\}$.
(c) $\{n \mid \quad |n| > 4\}$.
(d) $\{n \mid \quad |n| > 4$ and $\quad |n| < 11\}$.
(e) $\{n \mid \quad |n| < 3$ or $\quad |n| > 10\}$.
(f) $\{n \mid \quad |n| < 2\} \cup \{n \mid \quad |n| > 4\}$.
(g) $\{n \mid \quad |n| > 5\} \cap \{n \mid \quad |n| < 5\}$.
(h) $\{n \mid \quad |n + 10| = 2\}$.
(i) $\{n \mid \quad |-4 + n| = 5\}$.
(j) $\{n \mid \quad |n - 2| < 5\}$.
(k) $\{n \mid \quad |n - 4| > 8\}$.
(l) $\{n \mid \quad |n + (-3)| < 7\}$.

10.3   SUBTRACTION

Recall that Subtraction was defined in terms of addition within the previous section. This is repeated.

Definition 10.4—Subtraction of Integers   If each of a, b, and c is an Integer, $a - b = c$ if and only if $a = b + c$.

Using Definition 10.3, we were able to prove two theorems relating to subtraction. These are also restated.

$T2$:   For every Integer a, for every Integer b,

$$a - b = a + (-b).$$

$T3$:   For every Integer a, for every Integer b,

$$-(b - a) = a + (-b).$$

Theorems T2 and T3 are particularly useful for expressing all differences as sums. A typical example of the use of T2 is the following:

EXAMPLE 1

$n = 8 - 9 + 7 - 6 - 4$. Find n.

$$\begin{aligned}
n = 8 - 9 + 7 - 6 - 4 &= 8 + (-9) + 7 + (-6) + (-4) \\
&= -1 + 7 + (-6) + (-4) \\
&= 6 + (-6) + (-4) \\
&= 0 + (-4) \\
&= -4.
\end{aligned}$$

Similarly, the use of Theorem T2 is illustrated in example 2.

EXAMPLE 2

$$\begin{aligned}
n &= (-8) - (-7) + 9 - 6 \\
&= (-8) + [-(-7)] + 9 + (-6) \\
&= (-8) + 7 + 9 + (-6) \\
&= (-1) + 9 + (-6) \\
&= 8 + (-6) \\
&= 2.
\end{aligned}$$

We see that all subtraction situations may be expressed in terms of addition. However, there is one more case worth proving as Theorem T4, for it is used quite frequently. Suppose we wish to know the value n when $2 - (-3) = n$.

Using the Definition of Subtraction in terms of addition, we restate and illustrate on the picture of the number line:

(a) If $2 - (-3) = n$, then $2 = n + (-3)$.

(b) When stated in terms of addition, $2 = n + (-3)$ is pictured:

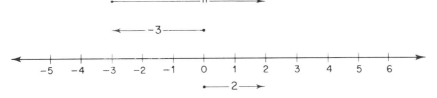

Figure 10.10

REPRESENTATION OF THE DIFFERENCE

$2 - (-3) = n$ IN TERMS OF ADDITION

When stated in terms of addition, then $n = 5$ because $2 = 5 + (-3)$. We are asked "what number must I add to (-3) so that their sum will be 2?" The answer of course is 5, or $2 - (-3) = 5$. But $2 + 3$ also is 5, hence we may conclude that $2 - (-3) = 2 + 3$. This is proven as Theorem T4.

$T4$:   For every Integer a, for every Integer b,

$$a - (-b) = a + b.$$

Proof: If we can prove that $-b + (a + b) = a$, then from Definition 4.6, we can conclude that $a + b = a - (-b)$:

$-b + (a + b) = -b + (b + a)$	Commutativity
$= (-b + b) + a$	Associativity
$= 0 + a$	$-n + n = 0$
$= a.$	Zero property.

From this, and Definition 4.6,

$$a - (-b) = a + b.$$

Theorems T2, T3, and T4 suggest that subtraction is accomplished by "changing the sign of the subtrahend and then adding." This is illustrated below.

(a) $7 - 5 = 7 + (-5) = 2$,   (by T2).
(b) $8 - 10 = 8 + (-10) = -2$,   (by T2).
(c) $(-4) - 5 = -4 + 5 = 1$,   (by T2).
(d) $4 - (-6) = 4 + 6 = 10$,   (by T2 or T4).
(e) $(-4) - (-7) = (-4) + 7 = 3$,   (by T2 or T4).

PROBLEM SET 10.3

1. Simplify by first expressing each as the sum of two Integers as in the immediately preceding examples:

(a) $16 - (-9)$.   (b) $22 - (-7)$.
(c) $(-10) - 12$.   (d) $(-12) - (-7)$.
(e) $(-2) - (-12)$.   (f) $(3) - (-14)$.
(g) $7 - 9$.   (h) $22 - 18$.
(i) $(-7) - 9$.   (j) $(-21) - 9$.

2. Express each difference as a sum to find the value for n:

(a) $n = 9 - 7 + 6 - 10$.
(b) $n = (-9) - 10 + 3 - 8$.

(c) $n = x + 10 - x - 10 - 5$.
(d) $n = 5 - x - 6 + x$.

3. Illustrate, on the picture of the number line, by first stating each problem as an addition problem.

(a) $18 - 6 = c$.   (b) $(-19) - 6 = c$.
(c) $(-9) - 8 = c$.   (d) $0 - 8 = c$.
(e) $0 - (-9) = c$.   (f) $9 - (-9) = c$.
(g) $8 - (-9) = c$.   (h) $0 - (-9) = c$.
(i) $(-2) - 14 = c$.   (j) $0 - 14 = c$.

4. Assume the Sea Lab II is   520   feet under the surface of the ocean. A certain diver descends   70   feet from Sea Lab II. (Consider descent as negative.) He then ascends   200   feet. (Consider ascent as positive.) What is the elevation, expressed as either positive or negative, from Sea Lab II? What is the elevation of the diver from the surface of the ocean?

5. On December 20, Nome, Alaska recorded a temperature of $-8°F$. On December 21, the temperature dropped an additional $12°F$. What was the temperature on December 21?

10.4 MULTIPLICATION AND DIVISION

Multiplication for Positive Integers is sometimes defined to parallel that for Counting Numbers, i.e, it is defined as repeated addition:

(a) $4(5) = \underbrace{5 + 5 + 5 + 5}_{} = 20$.

4 summands

(b) $6(4) = \underbrace{4 + 4 + 4 + 4 + 4 + 4}_{} = 24$.

6 summands

Similarly, the product $4(1)$ may be defined in terms of repeated addition, but $(-1)(4)$ will have no meaning:

$$4(-1) = (-1) + (-1) + (-1) + (-1) = -4;$$

$$(-1)(4)   \text{ has no meaning.}$$

For this reason, we must prove as special cases the products $(-a)b$, $b(-a)$, and $(-a)(-b)$. We will use previously proven Theorems and Definitions in order to accomplish this.

$T5$: For every Integer a, for every Integer b,

$$(-a)(b) = -(ab).$$

We know that $ab + (-ab) = 0$ from Definition 10.1. So if we can prove that $ab + (-a)b = 0$, we can conclude that $-ab = (-a)b$:

$ab + (-a)b = [a + (-a)]b$	Distributivity
$= 0(b)$	$n + (-n) = 0$
$= 0.$	Multiplication property for zero.

Therefore, since $ab + (-ab) = ab + (-a)b$, we conclude that

$$-ab = (-a)b.$$

By a similar proof, $-ab = b(-a)$. This is left as an exercise for the reader.

T6:   For every Integer a, for every Integer b,

$$(-a)(-b) = ab.$$

In order to prove this, we know that $ab + (-ab) = 0$, and by T5 that $-ab = (-a)b$. If we can show that $(-a)(-b) + (-ab) = 0$, we can then conclude that $(-a)(-b) = ab$:

$(-a)(-b) + (-ab) = (-a)(-b) + (-a)b$	by T5
$= -a[(-b) + b]$	Distributivity
$= -a(0)$	$-n + n = 0$
$= 0.$	Multiplication property of zero.

In summary, since $ab + (-ab) = 0$,   and $(-a)(-b) + (-ab) = 0$,

$$ab + (-ab) = (-a)(-b) + (-ab),$$

$$ab = (-a)(-b)$$

Observation: The above Theorems lead to the following conclusions:

(a) *the product of two numbers with like signs is a positive number.*
(b) *the product of two numbers with unlike signs is a negative number.*

EXAMPLES

(a) $4(-3) = -12.$ (b) $(-8)4 = -32.$
(c) $(-9)(-4) = 36.$ (d) $(-a)(-n) = an.$

Division is defined in terms of multiplication as subtraction was defined in terms of addition:

Definition 10.5—Division of Integers   If each of a, b, and c
is an Integer, $a/b = c$ if and only if $a = b(c)$.

By definition 10.5, all division problems may be stated as problems in
terms of multiplication:

(a) If $a > 0$ and $b > 0$, $a/b > 0$.

EXAMPLE

If $\frac{24}{6} = x$, then $x = 4$ because $24 = 6(4)$.

(b) If $a < 0$ and $b > 0$, $a/b < 0$.

EXAMPLE

If $\frac{-4}{2} = x$, then $x = -2$ because $-4 = 2(-2)$.

(c) If $a > 0$ and $b < 0$, $a/b < 0$.

EXAMPLES

If $\frac{8}{-4} = x$, then $x = -2$ because $8 = (-2)(-4)$.

(d) If $a < 0$, and $b < 0$, then $a/b > 0$.

EXAMPLE

If $\frac{-16}{-8} = x$, then $x = 2$ because $-16 = (-8)2$.

From Definition 10.5, and from illustration of the division of Integers as
indicated above, we find certain parallels between the two operations of
multiplication and division, because every division problem is stated in
terms of multiplication.

PROBLEM SET 10.4

1.   All letters in the following represent INTEGERS such that no denominator is zero.
Find n if:

(a) $\dfrac{-8}{4} = n$.

(b) $\dfrac{10}{5} = n$.

(c) $\dfrac{-6}{n + 2} = 3$.

(d) $\dfrac{10}{n - 7} = -4$.

(e) $4 = \dfrac{-n}{n + 10}$.

(f) $-n = \dfrac{-4}{2}$.

2. Using Definition 10.5, show that:

(a) $\dfrac{-8}{4} = \dfrac{8}{-4}$.

(b) $\dfrac{-8}{-4} = \dfrac{8}{4}$.

(c) $\dfrac{32}{-16} = \dfrac{-32}{16}$.

(d) $\dfrac{10}{5} = \dfrac{-10}{-5}$.

Fractions and
the Rational Numbers

PART FOUR

CHAPTER 11

Fractions and
The Rational Numbers:
Basic Definitions

11.1 INTRODUCTION

Study within previous chapters introduced the concepts and properties associated with Counting Numbers, Whole Numbers, and Integers. One of the reasons for the definition of Integers was that a solution exists to mathematical sentences of the type "If $7-23 = x$, then $x = -16$ because $7 = 23 + (-16)$," and "If $-3 - 21 = n$, then $n = -24$ because $-3 = 21 + (-24)$." However, there is no number n within the Counting Numbers, Whole Numbers, or Integers so that

$$\frac{20}{6} = n \quad \text{or that} \quad \frac{-40}{7} = n.$$

This is so, because there is no Integer n such that

(a) $20 = 6(n)$.
(b) $-40 = 7(n)$.

The purpose of this chapter is to define a set of numbers so that sentences of the type illustrated in (a) and (b) above will have a solution. This new set of numbers will be defined as the set of *Rational Numbers*.

From studies in elementary school, each one is probably familiar with the mathematical concept of fraction and is also familiar with physical situations that may be described by a fraction. We shall quickly review some of these situations, and from them, define a fraction.

11.2 PHYSICAL SITUATIONS DESCRIBED BY THE FRACTION CONCEPT

The need for fractions arises from the physical, as well as the mathematical world, for many physical situations cannot be described using Integers. This is illustrated by the following example.

EXAMPLE

John, Tom, and Jerry .cut a piece of wood into three congruent segments. John received one of these segments. Describe, *mathematically*, the amount of wood John received, relative to the total amount of wood. The physical situation is pictured below:

Figure 11.1

ONE OF THREE CONGRUENT SECTIONS

First, the wood was cut into three congruent parts. These three parts may be described mathematically by the Integer   3. Secondly, John received one of these parts. This is described mathematically by the Integer 1. From this, we have a pair of Integers,   1   and   3. To indicate the amount of wood John received, *relative to the total amount of wood*, the Integers are arranged in the form $\frac{1}{3}$, read "one-third." Hence, we illustrate a **new number**—a number composed of two Integers *but which is itself an entity*. Numbers of this type are generally defined as Fractional Numbers or Fractions, and the arrangement $\frac{1}{3}$, is arbitrarily chosen.

When fractions are used to describe physical situations such as the above, they are used in the Partitive sense, i.e.,   *a*   of   *b*   congruent parts. In Figure 11.2, we see that the shaded area within the rectangle represents   5   of   8   congruent parts, when considering their area. Thus we define the two numbers $a = 5,$ $b = 8$ and the relative number of shaded portions as $\frac{5}{8}$:

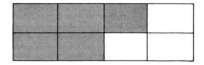

Figure 11.2

$\frac{5}{8}$ OF THE CONGRUENT PORTIONS ARE SHADED

To state in words any Fractional Number such as the above is a–n'th, where n is the total number of congruent parts:

(a) 3/13   is read "three-thirteenths."
(b) 1/12   is read "one-twelfth."
(c) 5/32   is read "five thirty-seconds."

From physical situations which can be described mathematically by two Integers, we define a fraction.

Definition 11.1—Fraction   A fraction is a number pair, (a, b), in which a is an Integer, b is an Integer, and b is never 0.

The number described by a is the numerator and the one described by b is the denominator. Since one is familiar with the arrangement:

$$\frac{a}{b}, \quad a/b, \text{ or } \quad (a, b),$$

this notation will be used. The reader should note that b is never zero. He should further note that since   2   does not necessarily mean "2 miles," "2 yards," or "2 days," neither does   1/3   mean "1/3 of the cake," "1/3 of an hour," or "1/3 of the distance." These are physical situations which can be described mathematically.

Fractions are generally referred to as either *proper fractions* or as *improper fractions*. Fraction $\frac{a}{b}$,   an improper fraction, means $a \geq b$. The fractions $\frac{5}{5}, \frac{7}{3},$ and $\frac{4n}{n}$, are all improper fractions, because the numerator in each instance is greater than or equal to the denominator.

Fraction $\dfrac{a}{b}$, a *proper fraction*, means $a < b$. Fractions $\dfrac{2}{3}$, $\dfrac{4}{5}$,

and $\dfrac{7}{8}$ is each a proper fraction.

Other Interpretations for Fractions.   The fact that the number depicted by b   may never be zero is a consequence of the use of fractions to indicate *division.* One should recall that $n/0$ was not defined when $n = 0$.
   If $6/0 = x$, then $6 = 0(x)$. There is no number represented by   x such that $6 = 0(x)$. For this reason, $6/0$ is nondefined.
   Fractions are used in division to answer the question "the number of elements in set   A   is *how many times as great as* the number of elements in set   B?" For example, assume David earns \$1000 per week and Bill earns \$250 per week. To make the "how many times" comparison, we resort to division and are able to state "David earns   4   *times the number of dollars* that Bill earns."
   However, the "how many times" comparison is limited, if we are restricted to Counting Numbers. For instance, if David has   5¢ and Bill has 3¢, then we *cannot* state that "David has   n   times as much money as Bill,   n   being a Counting Number." In this case, we resort to making "ratio" or "proportional" statements. We state "the number of pennies that David has is to the number of pennies that Bill has as   5 is to 3."
   Again, we see that we have an ordered pair of numbers,   a   and b, $b \neq 0$. This is another use of Fractional Numbers.

Definition 11.2—Ratio   The ratio of number   a   to number   b is the fractional number $\dfrac{a}{b}$.

When fractions are used to denote comparisons of the number of objects in one set to those in another set, the fractions are read as "a   to   b." If $n(A) = a$, $n(B) = b$, and if the number of objects in set   A   and those in set   B   is denoted by (a, b) then

   (a) $(7, 5)$ is read "7 to 5" and their ratio is denoted by the fraction $\dfrac{7}{5}$.
   (b) $(6, 1)$ is read "6 to 1" and their ratio is denoted by the fraction $\dfrac{6}{1}$.
   (c) $(2, 7)$ is read "2 to 7" and their ratio is denoted by the fraction $\dfrac{2}{7}$.

We encounter the concept of ratio in typical situations such as "two pencils for five cents," "sixteen miles per gallon of gasoline," "eight dollars per hour," or "the stock split is three for one."
   Some ratios are referred to as *rates.* The term rate is used if each "unit" of set   A   is different from each "unit" in set   B. In the statement

"two *pencils* for five *cents*," we may state that "the number of *pencils* is to the number of *cents* as   2 is to 5."

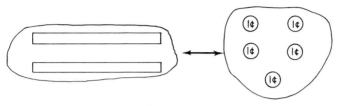

Figure 11.3

Thus we establish a   2 for 5   correspondence and the fraction 2/5   is used to denote this correspondence.

A statement of equality between two ratios is defined as a proportion. For example, assume that a stick is cut into two pieces and the ratio of the lengths of the two pieces is as   1 is to 2.

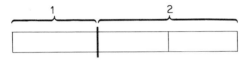

Figure 11.4

If the shorter portion of the stick is   3   inches, we may determine the length of the longer portion using correspondence:

$$1 \Leftrightarrow 2$$
$$1 \Leftrightarrow 2$$
$$\frac{1}{3} \Leftrightarrow \frac{2}{6}$$

We see that "1 is to 2   as   3 is to 6."

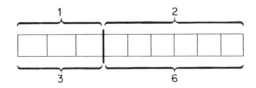

Figure 11.5

Using the notation of proportionality, the above would be written as:

$$\frac{1}{2} = \frac{3}{6}.$$

Similarly,

$$\frac{1}{2} = \frac{2}{4}$$

$$\frac{1}{2} = \frac{4}{8}$$

$$\frac{1}{2} = \frac{5}{10}$$

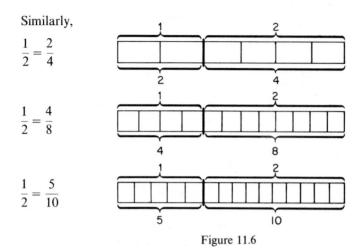

Figure 11.6

In general, we may state that we have found a set of fractions so that each fraction within this set is proportional to $\frac{1}{2}$. This is denoted by:

$$\frac{1}{2} = \left\{ \frac{1}{2}, \frac{2}{4}, \frac{3}{6}, \frac{5}{10}, \cdots \right\}.$$

By observation, we see that the n'th term is $\dfrac{1n}{2n}$, $n \in \{1, 2, 3, \dots\}$. If:

(a) $n = 1$, then $\quad \dfrac{1n}{2n} = \dfrac{1(1)}{2(1)} = \dfrac{1}{2}.$

(b) $n = 2$, then $\quad \dfrac{1n}{2n} = \dfrac{1(2)}{2(2)} = \dfrac{2}{4}.$

(c) $n = 3$, then $\quad \dfrac{1n}{2n} = \dfrac{1(3)}{2(3)} = \dfrac{3}{6}.$

(d) $n = 4$, then $\quad \dfrac{1n}{2n} = \dfrac{1(4)}{2(4)} = \dfrac{4}{8}.$

(e) $n = 5$, then $\quad \dfrac{1n}{2n} = \dfrac{1(5)}{2(5)} = \dfrac{5}{10};$ etc.

This provides a convenient algorithm for finding a set of fractions proportional to a given fraction. For example, the set which contains all fractions proportional to $\dfrac{3}{4}$ may be found by successive replacements of n in $\dfrac{3n}{4n}, n \in \{1, 2, 3, 4, \dots\}.$

(a) $\dfrac{3(1)}{4(1)} = \dfrac{3}{4}$.

(b) $\dfrac{3(2)}{4(2)} = \dfrac{6}{8}$.

(c) $\dfrac{3(3)}{4(3)} = \dfrac{9}{12}$.

(d) $\dfrac{3(4)}{4(4)} = \dfrac{12}{16}$.

(e) $\dfrac{3(5)}{4(5)} = \dfrac{15}{20}$; etc.

In general, $\frac{3}{4} = \{\frac{3}{4}, \frac{6}{8}, \frac{9}{12}, \frac{12}{16}, \frac{15}{20}, \ldots\}$.

Not only is every ratio within $\{\frac{3}{4}, \frac{6}{8}, \frac{9}{12}, \ldots\}$ proportional to $\frac{3}{4}$, but each fraction within this set is proportional to every other fraction within the set. For example, "3 is to 4   as   6 is to 8" may be illustrated by:

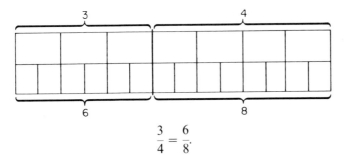

$$\frac{3}{4} = \frac{6}{8}.$$

Figure 11.7

Also, "6 is to 8   as   9 is to 12" is illustrated by:

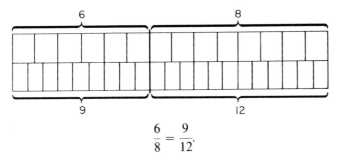

$$\frac{6}{8} = \frac{9}{12}.$$

Figure 11.8

Using the fractions   3/4,   6/8, and   9/12, let us make the following observations:

(a) $\dfrac{3}{4} = \dfrac{6}{8}$ and $3(8) = 4(6)$; $(24 = 24)$.

(b) $\dfrac{3}{4} = \dfrac{9}{12}$ and $3(12) = 4(9)$; $(36 = 36)$.

(c) $\dfrac{6}{8} = \dfrac{9}{12}$ and $6(12) = 8(9)$; $(72 = 72)$.

In general, we see that if "a is to b as c is to d," then $a(d) = b(c)$. In

$$\left\{ \frac{3}{4}, \frac{6}{8}, \frac{9}{12}, \frac{12}{16}, \frac{15}{20}, \cdots \right\},$$

we see that

(a) $\dfrac{9}{12} = \dfrac{15}{20}$ and $9(20) = 12(15)$; $(180 = 180)$.

(b) $\dfrac{18}{24} = \dfrac{21}{28}$ and $18(28) = 24(21)$; $(504 = 504)$.

(c) $\dfrac{3}{4} = \dfrac{3n}{4n}$ and $3(4n) = 4(3n)$; $(12n = 12n)$.

We observe that each fraction within

$$\left\{ \frac{3}{4}, \frac{6}{8}, \frac{9}{12}, \frac{15}{20}, \cdots \right\}$$

is proportional to every other fraction within this set, and the algorithm of the "cross products" provides an easy method to determine if two fractions are proportional.

Proportion is used when finding a solution to problems of the type: "If a man walks 5 miles in 3 hours, how far can he walk in 24 hours, provided he continues walking at the same rate?" This is restated as "5 is to 3   as x is to 24," and the man is essentially trying to find x in the proportion

$$\frac{x}{24} = \frac{5}{3}.$$

By using the "cross product algorithm" we find:

$$\frac{x}{24} = \frac{5}{3}.$$

$$x(3) = 24(5),$$

$$3x = 120,$$

$$x = 40.$$

The man may conclude that since "5 is to 3   as   40 is to 24," he can walk 40 miles, provided he continues to walk at the same rate.

PROBLEM SET 11.1

1. Given the following ratios a/b and c/d. By using the "cross product algorithm," find if the ratios are in the same proportion. All letters represent Counting Numbers.

(a) $1/2, 5n/10n$.   (b) $17/14, 51/42$.

(c) $7/8, 8/9$.   (d) $17/14, 68/56$.

(e) $\dfrac{7}{8}, \dfrac{7-1}{8-1}$ (f) $7/8, (7+1)/(8+1)$.

2. Find three other ratios that belong to the sets:

(a) $\dfrac{4}{7} = \left\{\dfrac{4}{7}, \dfrac{8}{14}, \text{——}, \text{——}, \text{——}, \cdots, \dfrac{4n}{7n}\right\}$.

(b) $\dfrac{5}{9} = \left\{\dfrac{5}{9}, \dfrac{10}{18}, \text{——}, \text{——}, \text{——}, \cdots, \dfrac{5n}{9n}\right\}$.

(c) $\dfrac{3}{2} = \left\{\dfrac{3}{2}, \dfrac{6}{4}, \text{——}, \text{——}, \cdots, \dfrac{3n}{2n}\right\}$.

(d) $\dfrac{5}{1} = \left\{\dfrac{5}{1}, \dfrac{10}{2}, \text{——}, \text{——}, \cdots, \dfrac{5n}{1n}\right\}$.

(e) $\dfrac{3}{13} = \left\{\dfrac{3}{13}, \dfrac{6}{26}, \text{——}, \text{——}, \cdots, \dfrac{3n}{13n}\right\}$.

(f) $\dfrac{0}{5} = \left\{\dfrac{0}{5}, \dfrac{0}{10}, \text{——}, \text{——}, \cdots, \dfrac{0}{n}\right\}$.

(g) $\dfrac{1}{1} = \left\{\dfrac{1}{1}, \dfrac{2}{2}, \text{——}, \text{——}, \cdots, \dfrac{n}{n}\right\}$.

3. Which of the following are proportional?

$$\frac{3}{18}, \frac{21}{125}, \frac{216}{1296}, \text{ and } \frac{27}{162}.$$

4. There were 30 pupils in an arithmetic class. However, the class had only 10 arithmetic books. This was a rate of how many books for every 6 pupils?

5. Nine cans of pineapple sell for $1.35. At this rate, how much money would 3 cans of pineapple cost?

6. Jim spent $72 in 6 weeks. If he spent at the same rate during this time, how much money had he spent at the end of 2 weeks?

7. A recipe in a cake called for 15 eggs and 9 cups of milk. If the recipe is reduced to a smaller quantity, how many eggs would be necessary if only 3 cups of milk were used?

8. On a motorcycle trip, David rode 54 miles in 6 hours. At this rate, how many miles did he ride in 2 hours?

9. Nickie saved 10 cents a day, and Kay saved 16 cents a day. How much money will Nickie save if Kay saves $1.60?

10. A map states that the scale is 50,000 miles to 1 inch. If the distance between two points on the map is 3 inches, how many miles are represented between the two points?

11. Mr. Jones has a wall that is 10 feet high and 15 feet long. If a scale model of the wall is 5 inches high, how long is the scale model?

12. David rode 18 miles on his bicycle during the same time that Jim rode 15 miles. How far did Jim ride during the time that David rode 6 miles?

13. A wheel in a machine shop turns 160 revolutions in 1 minute. Another wheel turns 120 revolutions in 1 minute. When the first wheel had made 40 revolutions, how many revolutions had the second wheel made?

11.3 EQUIVALENCE CLASSES OF FRACTIONS

As illustrated in the preceding section, different fractions are used to represent the same ratio, and a statement of equality of two ratios is said to be a proportion. Let us investigate, on the picture of the Number Line:

$$\frac{3}{5} = \left\{ \frac{3}{5}, \frac{6}{10}, \frac{9}{15}, \frac{12}{20}, \cdots \right\}.$$

By investigating the set above and its relation to the Number Line, we are dealing with still another physical interpretation that may be described mathematically in terms of fractions. To illustrate this, establish a unit segment and then partition this segment into five congruent segments in the following manner as shown in Figure 11.9.

Figure 11.9

Next, designate the first of the 5 congruent portions by starting at zero and progressing to the right.

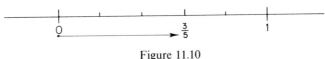

Figure 11.10

We shall designate the length of this segment as "three of five congruent parts," and associate the terminal point of this segment with the fraction 3/5. Note that   3/5   denotes two things—the *length* of a segment on the diagram of the number line and an association with a particular *point* on the drawing of the number line.

Similarly, fractions   6/10,   and   12/20   may be used to denote the same segment and the same point on the picture of the number line as shown in Figure 11.11.

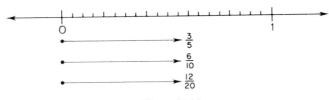

Figure 11.11

The above diagram illustrates that each member of $\{\frac{3}{5}, \frac{6}{10}, \frac{12}{20}, \frac{15}{25}, \ldots\}$ may be used to indicate the same length on the diagram of the number line and that each member denotes the same point on this line. By using the idea of the number line, we can extend this line to the left of   0 (as in the case for Integers) to show negative fractions:

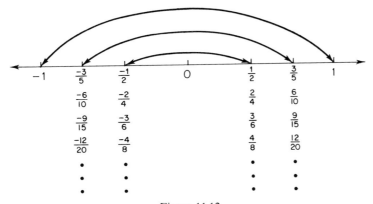

Figure 11.12

From this, we can state that each member of the set:

(a) $\{\frac{-3}{5}, \frac{-6}{10}, \frac{-9}{15}, \frac{-12}{20}, \ldots\}$ denotes the same point on the number line;

(b) $\{\frac{-1}{2}, \frac{-2}{4}, \frac{-3}{6}, \frac{-4}{8}, \ldots\}$ denotes the same point on the number line;

(c) $\{\frac{1}{2}, \frac{2}{4}, \frac{3}{6}, \frac{4}{8}, \ldots\}$ denotes the same point on the number line;

(d) $\{\frac{3}{5}, \frac{6}{10}, \frac{9}{15}, \frac{12}{20}, \ldots\}$ denotes the same point on the number line.

When considered in this manner we establish a common property among the elements of $\{\frac{-1}{2}, \frac{-2}{4}, \frac{-9}{15}, \frac{-12}{20}, \ldots\}$, among the elements of $\{\frac{1}{2}, \frac{2}{4}, \frac{3}{6}, \frac{4}{8}, \ldots\}$, among the elements of $\{\frac{3}{5}, \frac{6}{10}, \frac{9}{15}, \frac{12}{20}, \ldots\}$, etc. We define this common property as to be that of Equivalence.

Definition 11.3—The Equivalence Relation   For every fraction a/b and for every fraction c/d, a/b,   and c/d are equivalent and we write

$$\frac{a}{b} \sim \frac{c}{d} \quad \text{if and only if} \quad a(d) = b(c).$$

For example, we can say:

(a) $\dfrac{3}{5} \sim \dfrac{3}{5}$ because $3(5) = 5(3);$ $(15 = 15).$

(b) $\dfrac{-3}{5} \sim \dfrac{-12}{20}$ because $-3(20) = 5(-12);$ $(-60 = -60).$

(c) $\dfrac{9}{15} \sim \dfrac{12}{20}$ because $9(20) = 15(12);$ $(180 = 180).$

(d) $\dfrac{-2}{4} \sim \dfrac{-16}{32}$ because $-2(32) = 4(-16);$ $(-64 = -64).$

As a direct consequence of this definition, we can conclude that for every fraction a/b

(e) $\dfrac{-a}{b} \sim \dfrac{a}{-b}$ because $-a(b) = b(-a);$ $(-ab = -ab).$

(f) $\dfrac{-a}{-b} \sim \dfrac{a}{b}$ because $-a(b) = -b(a);$ $(-ab = -ab).$

Parts (e) and (f) above provide essentially a method whereby every fraction can be expressed *with a Positive Integer as denominator*. To express a fraction with a Positive Integer as denominator is to express the fraction in Standard Form. The following fractions are expressed in Standard

Form:

Fraction	Standard Form of Fraction
$\dfrac{3}{-5}$	$\dfrac{-3}{5}$
$\dfrac{-3}{-5}$	$\dfrac{3}{5}$
$\dfrac{-a}{-b}$	$\dfrac{a}{b}$
$\dfrac{a}{-b}$	$\dfrac{-a}{b}$

The reader should note that Definition 11.3 does not mean that fractions 3/5 and 6/10 are equal fractions, for the ordered pair (3, 5) is not the same as (6, 10). Equal fractions may be defined below.

Definition 11.4—Equal Fractions   For every fraction a/b and for every fraction c/d, a/b and c/d are equal and we write

$$\frac{a}{b} = \frac{c}{d} \quad \text{if and only if} \quad a = c \quad \text{and} \quad b = d.$$

Hence, for two fractions to be equal, the numerator of one fraction must be the same number as the numerator of the second fraction. Similarly the denominator of the first fraction must be the same as the denominator of the second. For example, we may state the following:

(a) $\dfrac{2}{4} = \dfrac{2(1)}{2(2)}$ because $2 = 2(1)$ and $4 = 2(2)$.

(b) $\dfrac{81}{27} = \dfrac{3(27)}{3(9)}$ because $81 = 3(27)$ and $27 = 3(9)$.

(c) $\dfrac{-6}{6} = \dfrac{-2(3)}{2(3)}$ because $-6 = -2(3)$ and $6 = 2(3)$.

(d) $\dfrac{-4}{9} = \dfrac{-2(2)}{3(3)}$ because $-4 = -2(2)$ and $9 = 3(3)$.

11.4 PROPERTIES OF THE EQUIVALENCE RELATION ~

We shall consider the properties of reflexivity, symmetry, and transitivity, for each of these are important and will be used extensively in the following sections.

The Equivalence Relation ~ is Reflexive. For the Equivalence Relation to be Reflexive, it must be shown that $\frac{a}{b} \sim \frac{a}{b}$. This is proven as a direct result of Definition 11.3 and is left as an exercise for the reader.

The Equivalence Relation ~ is Symmetric. In order to prove symmetry, we must show that if $\frac{a}{b} \sim \frac{c}{d}$ then $\frac{c}{d} \sim \frac{a}{b}$. This is accomplished by Definition 11.3 and from the properties of Integers. It is presented in a formal manner for clarity:

1. If $\frac{a}{b} \sim \frac{c}{d}$, then $ad = bc$ by Definition 11.3.

2. If $ad = bc$, then $bc = ad$, since the relation $=$ is symmetric for Integers.

3. If $bc = ad$ then $cb = da$ by the Commutative Property for Multiplication of Integers.

4. If $cb = da$, then $\frac{c}{d} \sim \frac{a}{b}$ by Definition 11.3. Symmetry is proven.

The Equivalence Relation ~ is Transitive. To prove transitivity, we must show that for all fractions $\frac{a}{b}$, $\frac{c}{d}$ and $\frac{e}{f}$, if $\frac{a}{b} \sim \frac{c}{d}$ and $\frac{c}{d} \sim \frac{e}{f}$, then $\frac{a}{b} \sim \frac{e}{f}$:

1. If $\frac{a}{b} \sim \frac{c}{d}$ then $a(d) = b(c)$.

2. If $\frac{c}{d} \sim \frac{e}{f}$ then $c(f) = d(e)$.

In order to show $\frac{a}{b} \sim \frac{e}{f}$, we must show $af = be$. In order to do this, multiply 1. $ad = bc$ by f, and in 2. $cf = de$ by b:

3. If $ad = bc$ then $fad = fbc$,   and   if $cf = de$ then $bcf = bde$.

4. If $fad = fbc$ and if $bcf = bde$, we conclude that $fad = bde$, since the relation $=$ is transitive for Integers.

5. If $fad = bde$,   we   conclude   that $af = be$ and $\dfrac{a}{b} \sim \dfrac{e}{f}$

by the Cancellation Property of Multiplication and by Definition 11.3.

In a prior section, we noted that numbers have many different names. For example, we saw that each of

$$\left\{ \cdots, \frac{-9}{-15}, \frac{-6}{-10}, \frac{-3}{-5}, \frac{3}{5}, \frac{6}{10}, \frac{9}{15}, \frac{12}{20}, \cdots \right\}$$

named the same point on the number line, and also that each fraction was equivalent to every other fraction. By proving the following Theorem, we will have a process for finding any number of fractions that are each equivalent to a given fraction.

*T*11.1.   For every fraction $\dfrac{a}{b}$ and for every Integer $n \neq 0$,

$$\frac{a}{b} \sim \frac{na}{nb}.$$

Assume a is an Integer and each of b and n is an Integer, $a, b, n \neq 0$. Then

$a[nb] = a[nb]$, since the relation $=$ is reflexive.
$a[nb] = b[na]$, by repeated use of the Commutative and Associative Properties for Multiplication.

Therefore, $\dfrac{a}{b} \sim \dfrac{na}{nb}$ by Definition 11.3.

Theorem T11.1 is used extensively for (a) reducing fractions to "lowest terms" and (b) finding common denominators in problems that involve addition or subtraction of fractions. Each is a process of "finding a fraction that is equivalent to a given fraction." To express a fraction in "lowest terms" means to express the fraction in an equivalent form so that the numerator and denominator are relatively prime.

EXAMPLES

(a) $\dfrac{12}{36} = \dfrac{2(6)}{2(18)} \sim \dfrac{6}{18} = \dfrac{2(3)}{2(9)} \sim \dfrac{3}{9} = \dfrac{3(1)}{3(3)} \sim \dfrac{1}{3}$; therefore $\dfrac{12}{36} \sim \dfrac{6}{18} \sim \dfrac{3}{9} \sim \dfrac{1}{3}$.

since the relation $\sim$ is transitive.

(b) $\dfrac{14}{28} = \dfrac{2(7)}{2(14)} \sim \dfrac{7}{14} = \dfrac{7(1)}{7(2)} \sim \dfrac{1}{2}$, and $\quad \dfrac{14}{28} \sim \dfrac{7}{14} \sim \dfrac{1}{2}.$

Similarly,

(c) $\dfrac{1}{3} \sim \dfrac{2(1)}{2(3)} = \dfrac{2}{6}.$

$\dfrac{1}{3} \sim \dfrac{3(1)}{3(3)} = \dfrac{3}{9}.$

$\dfrac{1}{3} \sim \dfrac{4(1)}{4(3)} = \dfrac{4}{12}.$

$\dfrac{1}{3} \sim \dfrac{5(1)}{5(3)} = \dfrac{5}{15},$ or

$\dfrac{1}{3} \sim \dfrac{2}{6} \sim \dfrac{3}{9} \sim \dfrac{4}{12} \sim \dfrac{5}{15}.$

Using the method described in Theorem T11.1, we can partition the set of all fractions into separate classes of fractions. Some of these classes are listed below. The letter n represents an Integer, $n \neq 0$:

$$\left\{ \dots, \frac{-3}{-6}, \frac{-2}{-4}, \frac{-1}{-2}, \frac{1}{2}, \frac{2}{4}, \frac{3}{6}, \dots, \frac{n}{2n} \right\}.$$

$$\left\{ \frac{-1}{3}, \frac{-2}{6}, \frac{-3}{9}, \dots, \frac{-n}{3n} \right\}.$$

$$\left\{ \frac{-3}{-21}, \frac{-2}{-14}, \frac{-1}{-7}, \frac{1}{7}, \frac{2}{14}, \frac{3}{21}, \dots, \frac{-n}{-7n} \right\}.$$

$$\left\{ \frac{-2}{5}, \frac{-4}{10}, \frac{-6}{15}, \dots, \frac{-2n}{5n} \right\}.$$

We see that every fraction within a specific class of fractions is equivalent to every other fraction within a particular class. For this reason, these classes of fractions are defined as Equivalence Classes of Fractions.

Definition 11.5—An Equivalence Class of Fractions   For every fraction a/b and for every fraction c/d, a/b and c/d belong to the same class of fractions, if and only if they are equivalent fractions. The class of fractions to which a/b and c/d belong is called an Equivalence Class of Fractions.

The Equivalence class to which $\dfrac{3}{5}$ belongs is:

$$\left\{ \dots, \dfrac{-9}{15}, \dfrac{-6}{-10}, \dfrac{-3}{-5}, \dfrac{3}{5}, \dfrac{6}{10}, \dfrac{9}{15}, \dfrac{12}{20}, \dfrac{15}{25}, \dots \right\}.$$

We denote this particular Equivalence Class by $[\frac{3}{5}]$, or $[\frac{6}{10}]$, or $[\frac{9}{15}]$, or by using any other member of this class. Hence $[\frac{9}{15}]$ denotes the same Equivalence Class as $[\frac{-18}{-30}]$ and each of these denotes the same class as $[\frac{3}{5}]$.

The reader should note the difference between $[\frac{1}{3}]$ and $\frac{1}{3}$—$[\frac{1}{3}]$ which denotes the class for which $\frac{1}{3}$ is a member; $\frac{1}{3}$ is a representative of the class $[\frac{1}{3}]$. Similarly, $[\frac{4}{5}]$ denotes

$$\left\{ \dots, \dfrac{-20}{-25}, \dfrac{-16}{-20}, \dfrac{-8}{-10}, \dfrac{-4}{-5}, \dfrac{4}{5}, \dfrac{8}{10}, \dfrac{16}{20}, \dfrac{20}{25}, \dots \right\},$$

$\frac{4}{5}$ is a member of this class and $\frac{4}{5}$ is a representative of the class $[\frac{4}{5}]$.

PROBLEM SET 11.2

1. Find six members of the designated Equivalence Class of fractions. You may use Theorem T11.1 if necessary

(a) $\begin{bmatrix} 2 \\ 3 \end{bmatrix}$ and $\begin{bmatrix} -2 \\ 3 \end{bmatrix}$.　(b) $\begin{bmatrix} 1 \\ 1 \end{bmatrix}$ and $\begin{bmatrix} -1 \\ 1 \end{bmatrix}$.

(c) $\begin{bmatrix} 0 \\ 1 \end{bmatrix}$.　(d) $\begin{bmatrix} 3 \\ 8 \end{bmatrix}$ and $\begin{bmatrix} -3 \\ 8 \end{bmatrix}$.

(e) $\begin{bmatrix} 4 \\ 3 \end{bmatrix}$ and $\begin{bmatrix} -4 \\ 3 \end{bmatrix}$.　(f) $\begin{bmatrix} 5 \\ 2 \end{bmatrix}$ and $\begin{bmatrix} -5 \\ 2 \end{bmatrix}$.

2. Reduce to "lowest terms," i.e., state each fraction so that the numerator and denominator are relatively prime.

(a) 21/248.　(b) 38/20.　(c) 12/50.
(d) 18/12.　(e) 39/36.　(f) 18/14.

3. Prove that the Equivalence Relation $\sim$ is Reflexive.

4. Show that each of the following pairs of fractions belong to the same Equivalence Class. All letters represent Counting Numbers.

(a) $\dfrac{a}{b}$ and $\dfrac{-4a}{-4b}$.　(b) $\dfrac{-7}{8}$ and $\dfrac{-5(7)}{5(8)}$.

(c) $\dfrac{-2a}{-8a}$.

(d) $\dfrac{-5ab}{7}$ and $\dfrac{-10ab}{14}$.

5. Illustrate that the relation $\sim$ is transitive using the fractions below.

(a) $\dfrac{1}{7}$, $\dfrac{3}{21}$, and $\dfrac{2}{15}$.

(b) $\dfrac{3}{5}$, $\dfrac{12}{20}$, and $\dfrac{6}{10}$.

(c) $\dfrac{a}{b}$, $\dfrac{3a}{3b}$, and $\dfrac{7a}{7b}$, $a,b \neq 0$.

6. Denote the Equivalence Class to which each of the following belongs. All letters represent Counting Numbers. Find the simplest name for these classes, i.e., the names where the numerator and denominator are Relatively Prime:

(a) $\dfrac{-4a}{7a}$.

(b) $\dfrac{8x + 4y}{2x + y}$.

(c) $\dfrac{3x + 9y}{12x + 36y}$.

(d) $\dfrac{8(x + y) + 7(x + y)}{5(x + y)}$.

7. Using Theorem T11.1, find the value for n which makes the following sentences true. All letters represent Counting Numbers.

(a) $\dfrac{-8}{11} \sim \dfrac{-n}{132}$.

(b) $\dfrac{-n}{77} \sim \dfrac{-2}{7}$.

(c) $\dfrac{n}{4} \sim \dfrac{4(x + y)}{8x + 8y}$.

(d) $\dfrac{15}{n} \sim \dfrac{2(x + y) + 3(x + y)}{(x + y)}$.

8. Express the given fraction in terms of an equivalent fraction using Theorem T11.1 as indicated:

(a) Express $\dfrac{-3}{4}$ with denominator $8x + 12$.

(b) Express $\dfrac{5}{8}$ with numerator $10 + 20x$.

(c) Express $\dfrac{2}{x}$ with denominator $10x + xy$.

9. Rename each fraction within the given sets so that each fraction within the set has a common denominator:

(a) $\left\{ \dfrac{-1}{2}, \dfrac{2}{3}, \dfrac{3}{4} \right\}$.

(b) $\left\{ \dfrac{a}{b}, \dfrac{-b}{-a}, \dfrac{2}{3} \right\}$.

(c) $\left\{\dfrac{-b}{b+a},\dfrac{-c}{d},\dfrac{-3}{5}\right\}.$

(d) $\left\{\dfrac{2}{a+b},\dfrac{3}{a-b},\dfrac{5}{7}\right\}.$

11.5 RATIONAL NUMBERS AS EQUIVALENCE CLASSES OF FRACTIONS

When illustrated on the diagram of the number line, each fraction $\dfrac{a}{b}$ within the particular Equivalence class $\left[\dfrac{a}{b}\right]$ could be associated with the same point. Some of these classes are illustrated below:

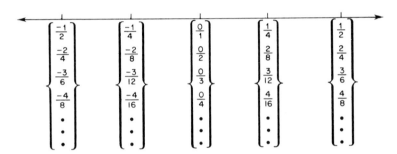

Figure 11.13

The illustration above indicates that for $\left[\frac{0}{1}\right]$, each element is associated with the point called "zero." Another, different class is associated with the points referred to as "1/4," "−1/4," "−1/2." Using the idea that an entire class is associated with a unique point on the number line, the following definition is given for a Rational Number.

Definition 11.6—A Rational Number The Equivalence Class of Fractions $[a/b]$ is defined as a *Rational Number*. This Rational Number may be represented by any element, $\dfrac{a}{b}$, contained within $\left[\dfrac{a}{b}\right].$

By defining an Equivalence Class of fractions to be a Rational Number, all properties pertaining to fractions are retained for study of the Rational Numbers.

We read the symbol $\left[\dfrac{a}{b}\right]$ as "the Rational Number a over b," and we read the symbol $\left[\dfrac{-a}{b}\right]$ as "the Additive Inverse of a over b."

Note that any fraction, $\dfrac{a}{b}$, is a representative of the Rational Number $\left[\dfrac{a}{b}\right]$. Definitions for the four basic operations will be made in terms of the representatives of the classes. Therefore, any symbol naming a particular fraction within a Rational Number names the Rational Number.

Any of These Symbols	Represents	The Entire Equivalence Class
$\cdots, \dfrac{-2}{-8}, \dfrac{-1}{-4}, \dfrac{1}{4}, \dfrac{2}{8}, \dfrac{3}{12}, \cdots$	$\longrightarrow$	$\left[\dfrac{1}{4}\right]$
$\dfrac{-1}{3}, \dfrac{-2}{6}, \dfrac{-3}{9}, \cdots$	$\longrightarrow$	$\left[\dfrac{-1}{3}\right]$
$\cdots, \dfrac{-2}{-4}, \dfrac{-1}{-2}, \dfrac{1}{2}, \dfrac{2}{4}, \dfrac{3}{6}, \cdots$	$\longrightarrow$	$\left[\dfrac{1}{2}\right]$
$\dfrac{-3}{4}, \dfrac{-6}{8}, \dfrac{-9}{12}, \cdots$	$\longrightarrow$	$\left[\dfrac{-3}{4}\right]$

Figure 11.14

As you know, we frequently think of the set of Rational Numbers $\left\{\ldots, \left[\dfrac{-3}{1}\right], \left[\dfrac{-2}{1}\right], \left[\dfrac{-1}{1}\right], \left[\dfrac{0}{1}\right], \left[\dfrac{1}{1}\right], \left[\dfrac{2}{1}\right], \left[\dfrac{3}{1}\right], \ldots\right\}$ as being the same set as $\{\ldots, -3, -2, -1, 0, 1, 2, 3, \ldots\}$. There is a complete one-to-one correspondence between these sets. This is illustrated on the drawing of the number line.

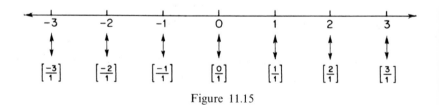

Figure 11.15

In division, we found that for every Whole Number n,

$$\frac{n}{1} = n \quad \text{because} \quad n = 1(n).$$

It seems logical to let the set $\{\ldots, [-3], [-2], [-1], [0], [1], [2], [3], \ldots\}$ also denote the particular Rational Numbers $\{\ldots, [\frac{-3}{1}], [\frac{-2}{1}], [\frac{-1}{1}], [\frac{0}{1}], [\frac{1}{1}], [\frac{2}{1}], [\frac{3}{1}], \ldots\}$. This is defined below:

	Integer Representation of Rational Numbers	
The Numeral		The Entire Equivalence Class
$\vdots$		$\vdots$
$[-2]$	$----$ Represents $----\rightarrow$	$\begin{bmatrix}\dfrac{-2}{1}\end{bmatrix}$
$[-1]$	$----$ Represents $----\rightarrow$	$\begin{bmatrix}\dfrac{-1}{1}\end{bmatrix}$
$[0]$	$----$ Represents $----\rightarrow$	$\begin{bmatrix}\dfrac{0}{1}\end{bmatrix}$
$[1]$	$----$ Represents $----\rightarrow$	$\begin{bmatrix}\dfrac{1}{1}\end{bmatrix}$
$[2]$	$----$ Represents $----\rightarrow$	$\begin{bmatrix}\dfrac{2}{1}\end{bmatrix}$
$\vdots$	$----$ Represents $----\rightarrow$	$\vdots$

This concludes the basic definitions for Rational Numbers and for the symbols used to represent them. In the following chapters, we shall investigate addition, subtraction, multiplication, division, and the properties for equality and for inequality as defined within this new set of numbers.

PROBLEM SET 11.3

1. List five members of $\begin{bmatrix}\dfrac{-3}{11}\end{bmatrix}$.

2. List five members, in Standard Form, of $\begin{bmatrix}\dfrac{-3}{-8}\end{bmatrix}$.

3. List five members, in Standard Form, of $[0]$.

4. List five members, in Standard Form, of $[1]$.

5. List five fractions, in Standard Form, that may be used to represent $\begin{bmatrix}\dfrac{-9}{22}\end{bmatrix}$.

6. Draw a number line and associate the following Rational Numbers with appropriate points on this line:

$$\left[\frac{-1}{-1}\right], \quad \left[\frac{0}{-1}\right], \quad [-2], \quad \left[\frac{-3}{-3}\right], \quad \left[\frac{0}{8}\right], \quad \left[\frac{-6}{3}\right], \quad \left[\frac{3}{-1}\right], \quad \left[\frac{-3}{1}\right], \quad [2].$$

CHAPTER 12

The Rational Numbers: Addition and Subtraction

12.1 INTRODUCTION

One recalls, from the study of Integers, that three criteria were established for defining a new system of numbers. These criteria were:

1. That the new system of numbers retains all properties of previously defined systems.

2. Retention of all number operations of previously defined number systems so that these operations are still true within the new system, and

3. The new system contains a new kind of number.

Since we wish the Rationals to strictly adhere to the above criteria, we declare that all properties for equality, inequality, and properties relating to the four basic operations previously studied are directly transferred to the system of Rationals. However, since we defined a system that contains a new kind of number, there must be some slight modifications to accommodate these new numbers. Also, some new properties and some new algorithms must be studied to accommodate these new numbers.

The statements of the preceding paragraph may be rationalized in the following manner:

1. Integers were so defined as to retain all properties of Whole Numbers.
2. Fractions were defined in terms of Integers, thereby retaining all properties of Integers;
3. Rationals were defined in terms of fractions, thereby retaining all properties of fractions, Integers, and Whole Numbers.

In order to define addition for Rational Numbers and keep this definition meaningful, we shall first investigate the relation $=$ in the light that the equals relation presents a method for providing "names for the same Rational Number." For example, we may find two numbers, such as $\frac{10}{18}$ and $\frac{-15}{-27}$ not to look the same, but they will be related by the relation $=$ in the sense that they "name the same number"—each is a representative of the Equivalence Class $[\frac{5}{9}]$. Therefore, when considered in this manner, the relation $=$ for Rational Numbers presents a situation not totally different from that encountered in the study of Whole Numbers, Integers, and fractions. However, it should be remembered that an Equivalence Class of fractions is defined as a Rational Number, and therefore some differences must exist in order to determine if different symbols do, or do not, represent the same Rational Number.

Definition 12.1—Equality for Rational Numbers If each of a/b and c/d is a fraction that represents a Rational Number, then the Rational Number represented by a/b *equals* the rational number represented by c/d and we write:

$$\frac{a}{b} = \frac{c}{d} \quad \text{if and only if} \quad ad = bc.*$$

Using this definition for equality, we declare that *equivalent fractions designate equal Rational Numbers.* Note that we use the representative of Rational Numbers, although the definition could be stated as:

$$\left[\frac{a}{b}\right] = \left[\frac{c}{d}\right] \quad \text{if and only if} \quad ad = bc.$$

---

* In effect, this compares the numerators of fractions expressed with a common denominator:

$$\frac{a(d)}{b(d)} = \frac{c(b)}{b(d)}.$$

EXAMPLE

The fraction $\frac{1}{3}$ represents a Rational Number and the fraction $\frac{4}{12}$ represents a Rational Number. Using the above definition, we find they both represent the same Rational Number:

  $\frac{1}{3} = \frac{4}{12}$ because $1(12) = 3(4)$. Hence they are both representatives of $[\frac{1}{3}]$.

EXAMPLE

Does $[\frac{4}{12}] = [\frac{15}{45}]$? The answer is yes, because $4(45) = 12(15)$.

Just as the relation $\sim$ was reflexive, symmetric, and transitive, so is the relation = for the set of Rational Numbers. This is left as an exercise for the reader.

Prior to defining the Inequality Relation for the set of Rational Numbers, one recalls that on the drawing of the number line, if Integer a was less than Integer b, then a was represented to the left of b.

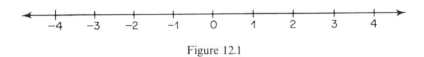

Figure 12.1

Similarly, Rational Numbers can be depicted in the same manner.

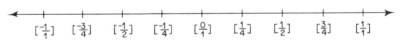

Figure 12.2

From the picture of the number line, we can easily determine that

$$\ldots < \left[\frac{-1}{1}\right] < \left[\frac{-3}{4}\right] < \left[\frac{-1}{2}\right] < \left[\frac{-1}{4}\right] < \left[\frac{0}{1}\right] < \left[\frac{1}{4}\right] < \left[\frac{1}{2}\right]$$

$$< \left[\frac{3}{4}\right] < \left[\frac{1}{1}\right] < \ldots.$$

However, to determine if $[\frac{31}{45}]$ is less than $[\frac{29}{44}]$, a method other than a visual method is needed, since these two Rational Numbers would appear "very close" to each other on the diagram of the number line. For this reason, the following definition is given.

Definition 12.2—Inequality for Rational Numbers   If   each   of $\dfrac{a}{b}$

and $\dfrac{c}{d}$ is a fraction (in Standard Form) that represents a Rational

Number, then the Rational Number represented by $\dfrac{a}{b}$ is less than the

Rational Number represented by $\dfrac{c}{d}$ and we write:

$$\frac{a}{b} < \frac{c}{d} \quad \text{if and only if} \quad ad < bc.$$

The statement that $\dfrac{a}{d} < \dfrac{c}{d}$ also means that $\dfrac{c}{d}$ is greater than

$\dfrac{a}{b}$. Using this definition, we determine that

(a) $\dfrac{29}{44} < \dfrac{31}{45}$ because $29(45) < 44(31)$. $(1305 < 1364)$.

(b) $\dfrac{-5}{7} < \dfrac{4}{5}$ because $-5(5) < 7(4)$. $(-25 < 28)$.

(c) $\dfrac{1}{3} < \dfrac{7}{12}$ because $1(12) < 3(7)$. $(12 < 21)$.

(d) If $n > 0$, then $\dfrac{2n}{4n} < \dfrac{5}{6}$,   because $2n(6) < 4n(5)$.

$(12n < 20n)$.

(e) If $n > 0$, then $\dfrac{-5n}{7n} < \dfrac{-1}{3}$ because $-5n(3) < 7n(-1)$.

$(-15n < -7n)$.

(f) $\dfrac{2}{-3} < \dfrac{1}{1}$. But   in   this   form, $2(1) \not< -3(1)$ or $2 \not< -3$.

Therefore, we must restate $\dfrac{2}{-3}$ as $\dfrac{-2}{3}$ and proceed as

above.

12.2 FUNDAMENTAL CONCEPTS AND DEFINITION OF ADDITION

Problems involving addition of fractions, and consequently Rational Numbers, are introduced to elementary school pupils through fractions that have a *common* denominator.

EXAMPLE

Find the sum $\frac{1}{3} + \frac{1}{3}$:

On the drawing of the number line, and also by using equal portions of 1 unit area, the sum is found to be $\frac{2}{3}$.

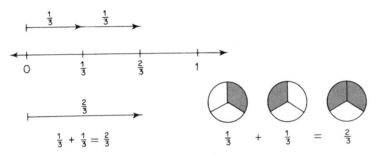

$$\frac{1}{3} + \frac{1}{3} = \frac{2}{3}$$

Figure 12.3

EXAMPLE

Find the sum $\frac{2}{3} + \frac{1}{6}$.

In this case, we see that the denominators are different. When this occurs we resort to the use of equivalent fractions and proceed in the usual manner.

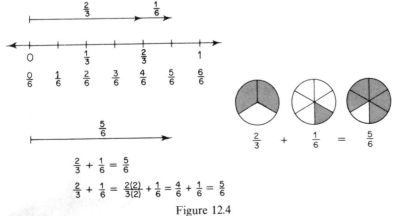

$$\frac{2}{3} + \frac{1}{6} = \frac{5}{6}$$

$$\frac{2}{3} + \frac{1}{6} = \frac{2(2)}{3(2)} + \frac{1}{6} = \frac{4}{6} + \frac{1}{6} = \frac{5}{6}$$

Figure 12.4

We see that since   1 third + 1 third = 2 thirds, and that   2 thirds + 1 sixth is equivalent to the sum   4 sixths + 1 sixth = 5 sixths, we have an excellent basis for forming the sum of two Rational Numbers.

Definition 12.3—Addition for Rational Numbers If   each   of a/b and c/d is a fraction that represents a Rational Number, then

$$\frac{a}{b} + \frac{c}{b} = \frac{a+c}{b}.$$

By the above, we see that the representative of the class $\left[\frac{a}{b}\right]$ added to the representative of the class $\left[\frac{c}{d}\right]$ is a representative of the class $\left[\frac{a+c}{b}\right]$. For   example,   let $\frac{9}{12}$ represent $\left[\frac{3}{4}\right]$ and $\frac{10}{12}$ represent the class $\left[\frac{5}{6}\right]$. Then their sum is the class represented by $\frac{9+10}{12}$:

$$
\left\{\frac{3}{4}, \frac{6}{8}, \boxed{\frac{9}{12}}, \frac{12}{16}, \frac{15}{20}, \frac{18}{24}, \cdots\right\}
$$

$$
\left\{\frac{5}{6}, \boxed{\frac{10}{12}}, \frac{15}{18}, \frac{20}{24}, \frac{25}{30}, \cdots\right\}
$$

$$
\left\{\boxed{\frac{19}{12}}, \frac{38}{24}, \frac{57}{43}, \frac{76}{62}, \frac{95}{81}, \cdots\right\}.
$$

Figure 12.5

But Definition 12.1 does not indicate what tactics should be undertaken when fractions $\frac{a}{b}$ and $\frac{c}{d}$ have different denominators $(b \neq d)$.

This question is easily resolved by expressing the two fractions in their equivalent forms, since it is possible that any two different Rational Numbers can be represented by fractions which have the same denominator:

$$\frac{3}{4} \sim \frac{6(3)}{6(4)} = \frac{18}{24}.$$

$$\frac{5}{6} \sim \frac{5(4)}{6(4)} = \frac{20}{24}.$$

Then their sum:

$$\frac{3}{4} + \frac{5}{6} = \frac{18}{24} + \frac{20}{24} = \frac{38}{24}$$

is illustrated in the following figure:

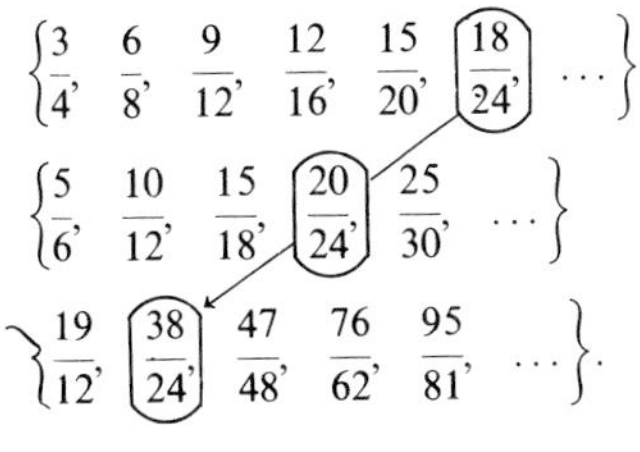

Figure 12.6

We see that the same class, $\left[\dfrac{19}{12}\right]$ has been determined by two different methods. In the first instance, we denoted the class to be $\left[\dfrac{19}{12}\right]$ and in the second instance to be $\left[\dfrac{38}{24}\right]$. But $\dfrac{19}{12} = \dfrac{38}{24}$ because $19(24) = 12(38)$, and hence $\left[\dfrac{38}{24}\right] = \left[\dfrac{19}{12}\right]$. This illustrates that the names of fractions are immaterial, for any representative of $\left[\dfrac{a}{b}\right]$ added to any representative of the class $\left[\dfrac{c}{b}\right]$ is in the class $\left[\dfrac{a+c}{b}\right]$. This is illustrated below:

(a) $\dfrac{2}{3} + \dfrac{1}{5} = \dfrac{10}{15} + \dfrac{3}{15} = \dfrac{13}{15}.$

(b) $\dfrac{2}{3} + \dfrac{1}{5} = \dfrac{20}{30} + \dfrac{6}{30} = \dfrac{26}{30}.$

(c) $\dfrac{2}{3} + \dfrac{1}{5} = \dfrac{30}{45} + \dfrac{9}{45} = \dfrac{39}{45}.$

(d) $\dfrac{-2}{-3} + \dfrac{-1}{-5} = \dfrac{-10}{-15} + \dfrac{-3}{-15} = \dfrac{-10 + (-3)}{-15} = \dfrac{-13}{-15}.$

(e) $\dfrac{-2}{-3} + \dfrac{-1}{-5} = \dfrac{-20}{-30} + \dfrac{-6}{-30} = \dfrac{-20 + (-6)}{-30} = \dfrac{-26}{-30}.$

Each of $\dfrac{13}{15}, \dfrac{26}{30}, \dfrac{39}{45}, \dfrac{-13}{-15},$ and $\dfrac{-26}{-30}$ is a representative of $\left[\dfrac{13}{15}\right]$.

The method of finding equivalent fractions and then finding their sum by Definition 12.1 is called the method of common denominators. The following Theorem does essentially the same thing, although the process is not so evident. It will be referred to as the Theorem for Extended Addition.

Theorem 12.1—Extended Addition   If each of a/b and c/d is a fraction that represents a Rational Number, then

$$\frac{a}{b} + \frac{c}{d} = \frac{ad + bc}{bd}.$$

It should be noted that the basic definition for addition is not violated by Theorem 12.1 Theorem 12.1 is actually an algorithm to shorten our work. In (a) below, we rename $\dfrac{a}{b}$ and $\dfrac{c}{d}$ and then use Definition 12.1 to form their sum:

(a) $\dfrac{a}{b} = \dfrac{da}{db}, \dfrac{c}{d} = \dfrac{bc}{bd},$

$\dfrac{a}{b} + \dfrac{c}{d} = \dfrac{da}{db} + \dfrac{bc}{bd} = \dfrac{da + bc}{bd},$ by Definition 12.1.

(b) By Theorem 12.1:

$$\frac{a}{b} + \frac{c}{d} = \frac{ad + bc}{bd}.$$

Note. Theorem 12.1 is particularly useful when denominators b and d are relatively prime.

EXAMPLES

(a) $\dfrac{1}{2} + \dfrac{-1}{5} = \dfrac{1(5) + 2(-1)}{2(5)} = \dfrac{5 + (-2)}{10} = \dfrac{3}{10},$ ($\frac{3}{10}$ is reduced to lowest terms).

(b) $\dfrac{2}{4} + \dfrac{-4}{20} = \dfrac{2(20) + 4(-4)}{4(20)} = \dfrac{40 + (-16)}{80} = \dfrac{24}{80}$, (sum is not expressed

in lowest terms, but is still a member of $[\frac{3}{10}]$).

PROBLEM SET 12.1

1. Which of the following pairs of Rational Numbers are equal?

(a) $\left\{\dfrac{-1}{3}, \dfrac{-2}{6}, \dfrac{-3}{9}, \ldots\right\}$ and $\left[\dfrac{1}{-3}\right]$.

(b) $\left\{\ldots, \dfrac{1}{1}, \dfrac{2}{2}, \dfrac{3}{3}, \ldots\right\}$ and $\left\{\ldots, \dfrac{-4}{-4}, \dfrac{-3}{-3}, \dfrac{-2}{-2}, \ldots\right\}$.

(c) $\left[\dfrac{-6}{4}\right]$ and $\left[\dfrac{-3}{-2}\right]$.

(d) $\left[\dfrac{5}{-6}\right]$ and $\left\{\dfrac{-5}{6}, \dfrac{-10}{12}, \dfrac{-15}{18}, \ldots\right\}$.

(e) $\left[\dfrac{-2n}{-4n}\right]$ and $\left[\dfrac{n}{2n}\right]$, $n \neq 0$.

2. Let $\frac{1}{-2}$ represent $[\frac{-1}{2}]$ and $\frac{3}{-4}$ represent $[\frac{-3}{4}]$. Show that the Definition for Inequality is not true when these nonstandard forms are used to represent Rational Numbers.

3. The fractions below are fractions that represent Rational Numbers. Using Theorem T11.1, express each pair of fractions so that they have a common denominator. Reminder—every definition is reversible. All letters represent Counting Numbers.

(a) 3/4,   1/7   (b) 21/99,   8/66.
(c) 6x/12x,   36y/24y.   (d) 60/72,   75/90.
(e) 12/96,   45/120.   (f) x/y,   a/d.
(g) (n + 1)/x,   2z/y.   (h) na/xy,   4/z.
(i) a/(a + c),   a/(x + y).   (j) (x + 1)/a,   (a + 1)/(n + 1).

4. Find the following indicated sums. All letters represent Counting Numbers. Leave each sum so that the numerator and denominator contain no common factors.

(a) $\dfrac{-1}{2} + \dfrac{3}{2}$.

(b) $\dfrac{6}{x} + \dfrac{-7}{x}$.

(c) $\dfrac{-4}{2a} + \dfrac{10}{2a}$.

(d) $\dfrac{-6}{n + 1} + \dfrac{7}{n + 1}$.

(e) $\dfrac{1}{2xy} + \dfrac{3}{2xy}$.

(f) $\dfrac{1}{2x} + \dfrac{3x}{4}$.

(g) $\dfrac{12}{x+1} + \dfrac{-3}{4}$.

(h) $\dfrac{3}{2y} + \dfrac{-2}{y+1}$.

(i) $\dfrac{(x+1)}{2} + \dfrac{x}{3}$.

(j) $\dfrac{x+3}{x+4} + \dfrac{3}{5}$.

(k) $\dfrac{1}{x} + \dfrac{-1}{x+y}$.

(l) $\dfrac{n+1}{x+1} + \dfrac{-3}{n+2}$.

(m) $\dfrac{m+3}{m+4} + \dfrac{m+2}{m+1}$.

(n) $\dfrac{12(x+1)}{3} + \dfrac{2x+2}{2}$.

5. Recall that every definition is reversible. Find two fractions whose sum is given below. Reduce each individual fraction so that the numerator and denominator are Relatively Prime.

(a) $\dfrac{12+15}{18}$.

(b) $\dfrac{18+20}{24}$.

(c) $\dfrac{7+8}{z}$

(d) $\dfrac{7x+8y}{23}$.

(e) $\dfrac{(a+b)+c}{3}$.

(f) $\dfrac{(n+x)+10}{20}$.

(g) $\dfrac{4x+9x}{6x^2}$.

(h) $\dfrac{(a^2+ab)+b^2}{ab}$.

6. The following problems involve the Theorem for Extended Addition. Find two fractions that form the given sums.

(a) $\dfrac{1(3)+2(4)}{2(3)}$.

(b) $\dfrac{2(6)+3(-5)}{3(6)}$.

(c) $\dfrac{16(x)+8z}{16(8)}$.

(d) $\dfrac{5x+8(-4)}{8x}$.

(e) $\dfrac{(n+1)z+qr}{qz}$.

(f) $\dfrac{2(n+1)+7(3+r)}{(3+r)(n+1)}$.

7. Show that the relation $=$ for the set of Rational Numbers is an Equivalence Relation.

8. Using fractions $\frac{3}{4}$, $\frac{5}{8}$, $\frac{7}{16}$ illustrate that addition is (a) commutative and (b) associative.

9. Show that the relation $<$ for the set of Rational Numbers is (a) not reflexive, (b) not symmetrical, but (c) is transitive.

10. Determine if the first Rational Number is less than the second Rational Number. All letters represent Counting Numbers.

(a) 5/6,   6/7.

(b) 3/10,   6/19.

(c) $2n/x$, $3n/2x$.

(d) $(n+1)/2$, $(2n+1)/4$.

(e) $6/3n$, $4/2n$.   (f) $10/(n + 12)$, $5/(n + 6)$.
(g) $4/7$, $(n + 1)/(2n + 2)$.   (h) $(3n + 1)/2$, $(x + 4)/3$.
(i) $(x + 1)/3$, $(x + 1)/2$.   (j) $(5x + 2)/3$, $(x + 9)/2$.

12.3   MIXED NUMERALS

It was previously stated that appropriate definitions could be made so that the subset of Rational Numbers

$$\left\{ \ldots, \left[\frac{-2}{1}\right], \left[\frac{-1}{1}\right], \left[\frac{0}{1}\right], \left[\frac{1}{1}\right], \left[\frac{2}{1}\right], \ldots \right\}$$

would preserve characteristics studied for the Integers

$$\{ \ldots, -2, -1, 0, 1, 2, \ldots \}.$$

It is the purpose of this section to do this, for in division of Integers,

(a) $\dfrac{1}{1} = 1$ because $1 = 1(1)$.

(b) $\dfrac{-2}{1} = -2$ because $-2 = 1(-2)$.

(c) $\dfrac{3}{-1} = -3$ because $3 = -1(-3)$, etc.

The reader should recall that we are dealing with numerals, and he should clearly understand that:

> *Under no circumstances can an Integer be added to a Rational Number, nor can any of the four basic operations "mix the different kinds of numbers."*

Because of the ease in dropping the "1" in the Rational Number representatives $\ldots, -2/1, -1/1, 0/1, 1/1, 1/2, \ldots,$ and since "division by 1   does not affect the value of a number," the Integer numerals $\ldots,$ $-2, -1, 0, 1, 2, \ldots$ are frequently used in place of the numerals $\ldots,$ $-2/1, -1/1, 0/1, 1/1, 2/1, \ldots.$ In this sense, Integer numerals are used to represent Rational Numbers:

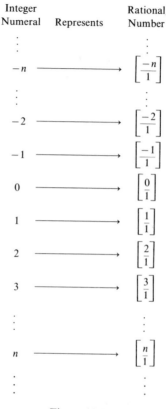

Figure 12.7

In Figure 12.7, is illustrated the existence of a complete one-to-one correspondence between the set of Integers and the subset of Rational Numbers $\{\ldots, \frac{-2}{1}, \frac{-1}{1}, \frac{0}{1}, \frac{1}{1}, \frac{2}{1}, \ldots\}$.

Definition 12.4 If n is an Integer, then the numeral   "n"   represents the Rational Number

$$\left\{\ldots, \frac{-3n}{-3n}, \frac{-2n}{-2n}, \frac{-n}{-1n}, \frac{n}{1}, \frac{2n}{1}, \frac{3n}{3}, \frac{4n}{4}, \ldots\right\}.$$

Similarly, the correspondence between the set of Integers $\{\ldots, -2,$ $-1, 0, 1, 2, 3, \ldots\}$ and   the   subset   of   Rational   Numbers $\{\ldots, [\frac{-2}{1}],$ $[\frac{-1}{1}], [\frac{0}{1}], [\frac{1}{1}], [\frac{2}{1}], \ldots\}$ preserves addition.* For example, if $a \in$ Integers

---

* This correspondence also preserves multiplication; it will be studied in a later chapter.

and $\quad \alpha \in$ Rational Numbers, and $\quad b \in$ Integers and $\quad \beta \in$ Rational Numbers, then when $\quad a + b \quad$ and $\quad \alpha + \beta \quad$ are formed, it will turn out that under this correspondence, $\quad a + b \quad$ corresponds to $\quad \alpha + \beta$:

(a) $2 + 3 = 5.$ $\qquad \dfrac{2}{1} + \dfrac{3}{1} = \dfrac{2+3}{1} = \dfrac{5}{1}.$

(b) $7 + 2 = 9.$ $\qquad \dfrac{7}{1} + \dfrac{2}{1} = \dfrac{7+2}{1} = \dfrac{9}{1}.$

(c) $0 + 4 = 4.$ $\qquad \dfrac{0}{1} + \dfrac{4}{1} = \dfrac{0+4}{1} = \dfrac{4}{1}.$

Figure 12.8

Many physical situations lead to the idea of expressing an improper fraction as a "mixed numeral." In Figure 12.9, below

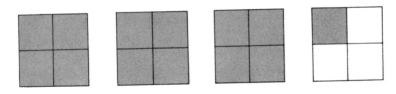

Figure 12.9

we can correctly state that the shaded area is $\quad \frac{13}{4}$, but if each large square represents $\quad 1 \quad$ square yard of cloth, it would be awkward to tell a clerk that you wanted "thirteen-fourths square yards of cloth." Instead, you would probably state "3 $\quad$ and $\quad 1/4 \quad$ square yards of cloth." To denote this area, you would probably write "3 1/4 $\quad$ square yards." The numeral $\quad$ "3 1/4" is referred to as a mixed numeral, since $\quad$ "3" $\quad$ is a numeral for an Integer and $\quad$ "$\frac{1}{4}$" is a numeral for a Rational Number.

In order for the numeral $\quad$ "$3\frac{1}{4}$" $\quad$ to have meaning, we define $3\frac{1}{4} = 3 + \frac{1}{4} = \frac{3}{1} + \frac{1}{4}.$ Similarly:

$$5\frac{1}{3} \quad \text{means} \quad \tfrac{5}{1} + \tfrac{1}{3}.$$

$$6\frac{2}{7} \quad \text{means} \quad \tfrac{6}{1} + \tfrac{2}{7}.$$

$$8\frac{5}{8} \quad \text{means} \quad \tfrac{8}{1} + \tfrac{5}{8}.$$

Hence we resort to Rational Number addition to form the sum $8 + \frac{5}{8}$, for we interpret 8 to represent $[\frac{8}{1}]$. Then for the Hindu-Arabic numerals, the following connections are established:

(a) $8\frac{5}{8}$ means $\frac{8}{1} + \frac{5}{8} = \dfrac{8(8) + 5(1)}{8} = \dfrac{69}{8}$.

(b) $5\frac{1}{3}$ means $\frac{5}{1} + \frac{1}{3} = \dfrac{5(3) + 1(1)}{3} = \dfrac{16}{3}$.

(c) $6\frac{2}{7}$ means $\frac{6}{1} + \frac{2}{7} = \dfrac{6(7) + 1(2)}{7} = \dfrac{44}{7}$.

By resorting to the Rational Number interpretation of addition and the fact that we could interpret the Integer n as a Rational Number, we have the following definition.

Definition 12.5 If n is an Integer numeral that represents a Rational Number and if a/b is a fraction which represents a Rational Number, then

$$n + \frac{a}{b} = \frac{n}{1} + \frac{a}{b}.$$

(a) $4\frac{1}{7} = 4 + \frac{1}{7}$.
(b) $-3\frac{1}{4} = -(3 + \frac{1}{4}) = -3 + (\frac{-1}{4})$.
(c) $-5\frac{1}{8} = -(5 + \frac{1}{8}) = -5 + (\frac{-1}{8})$.
(d) $-6\frac{2}{3} = -(6 + \frac{2}{3}) = -6 + (\frac{-2}{3})$.

By applying the Theorem for extended addition of Rational Numbers, we can express $\frac{n}{1} + \frac{a}{b}$ as $\dfrac{n(b) + a}{b}$. To express the number $5\frac{1}{3}$ as $\frac{5}{1} + \frac{1}{3} = \frac{16}{3}$ is generally defined as "expressing a mixed numeral as an improper fraction which represents the Rational Number represented by $5 + \frac{1}{3}$." This is the fraction $\frac{16}{3}$, found by the above Definition and Theorem 12. To express an improper fraction as a mixed numeral, we use the fact that $n + \dfrac{a}{b} = \dfrac{n(b) + a}{b}$ and the Definition for addition:

(a) $\dfrac{17}{3} = \dfrac{5(3) + 2}{3} = \dfrac{5(3)}{3} + \dfrac{2}{3} = \dfrac{5}{1} + \dfrac{2}{3} = 5\frac{2}{3}$.

(b) $\dfrac{18}{7} = \dfrac{2(7) + 4}{7} = \dfrac{2(7)}{7} + \dfrac{4}{7} = \dfrac{2}{1} + \dfrac{4}{7} = 2\frac{4}{7}$.

(c) $\dfrac{22}{3} = \dfrac{7(3) + 1}{3} = \dfrac{7(3)}{3} + \dfrac{1}{3} = \dfrac{7}{1} + \dfrac{1}{3} = 7\frac{1}{3}$.

(d) $\dfrac{-22}{7} = \dfrac{-(21 + 1)}{7} = \dfrac{-3(7) + (-1)}{7} = -3 + \left(\dfrac{-1}{7}\right) = -3\frac{1}{7}.$

(e) $\dfrac{-42}{8} = \dfrac{-(40 + 2)}{8} = \dfrac{-40 + (-2)}{8} = -5 + \dfrac{-2}{8} = -5\frac{1}{4}.$

Addition which involves mixed numerals may be performed by two different methods. The first of these is the method usually taught at elementary levels:

(a) $5\frac{2}{3} + 6\frac{4}{5} = (5 + \frac{2}{3}) + (6 + \frac{4}{5}),$

$\qquad = (5 + 6) + (\frac{2}{3} + \frac{4}{5}),$

$\qquad = 11 + \left(\dfrac{10 + 12}{15}\right),$

$\qquad = 11 + \frac{22}{15},$

$\qquad = 11 + \left(\dfrac{1(15) + 7}{15}\right),$

$\qquad = 11 + (\frac{15}{15} + \frac{7}{15}),$

$\qquad = (11 + 1) + \frac{7}{15},$

$\qquad = 12 + \frac{7}{15} = 12\frac{7}{15}.$

In (a) above, we see the reason for the "vertical form" algorithm for addition:

$$\begin{aligned}
5\frac{2}{3} &= & 5 + \frac{10}{15} \\
+\ 6\frac{4}{5} &= & 6 + \frac{12}{15} \\
\hline
&= & + \quad 11 + \frac{22}{15}.
\end{aligned}$$

We must restate $11 + \frac{22}{15}$ as

$$\begin{aligned}
11 + \tfrac{22}{15} &= 11 + (1 + \tfrac{7}{15}), \\
&= (11 + 1) + \tfrac{7}{15}, \\
&= 12 + \tfrac{7}{15}, \\
&= 12\tfrac{7}{15}.
\end{aligned}$$

The second method to find the sum of two numbers denoted by mixed numerals is that of first converting each to an improper fraction:

(b) $5\frac{2}{3} + 6\frac{4}{5} = \frac{17}{3} + \frac{34}{5}$,

$$= \frac{17(5) + 3(34)}{15},$$

$$= \frac{85 + 102}{15},$$

$$= \frac{187}{15},$$

$$= \frac{12(15) + 7}{15},$$

$$= 12\frac{7}{15}.$$

As previously defined,*

$-1\frac{1}{3}$ means $-(1 + \frac{1}{3}) = -1 + \frac{-1}{3}$,

$-4\frac{5}{6}$ means $-(4 + \frac{5}{6}) = -4 + \frac{-5}{6}$,

$-6\frac{7}{8}$ means $-(6 + \frac{7}{8}) = -6 + \frac{-7}{8}$.

Therefore,

$$4\frac{5}{8} + (-4\frac{3}{8}) = (4 + \frac{5}{8}) + (-4 + \frac{-3}{8}),$$

$$= [4 + (-4)] + (\frac{5}{8} + \frac{-3}{8}),$$

$$= 0 + \frac{5 + (-3)}{8},$$

$$= \frac{2}{8} = \frac{1}{4}.$$

$$-7\frac{3}{4} + -6\frac{1}{4} = (-7 + \frac{-3}{4}) + (-6 + \frac{-1}{4}),$$

$$= (-7 + (-6)) + (\frac{-3}{4} + \frac{-1}{4}),$$

$$= -13 + \frac{-4}{4},$$

$$= -14.$$

$$-6\frac{1}{8} + 5\frac{5}{8} = (-6 + \frac{-1}{8}) + (5 + \frac{5}{8}),$$

$$= (-6 + 5) + (\frac{-1}{8} + \frac{5}{8}),$$

$$= -1 + \frac{4}{8} = \frac{-1}{2}.$$

* One recalls that in the set of Integers, $a - b = a + (-b)$ which property will transfer directly to the set of Rational Numbers.

PROBLEM SET 12.2

1. Verify each step in (a) and (b) above with some definition, Theorem, or property for Rational Numbers.

2. The Commutative and Associative properties are true for addition which involves numbers denoted by mixed numerals. The following is a proof that $n + \dfrac{a}{b} = \dfrac{a}{b} + n$.

Verify each step within the proof. Assume that n is an Integer numeral which represents a Rational Number and that a/b is a fraction which represents a Rational Number. Then:

$$n + \frac{a}{b} = \frac{nb + a}{b},$$

$$\frac{nb + a}{b} = \frac{a + nb}{b},$$

$$\frac{a + nb}{b} = \frac{a}{b} + \frac{nb}{b},$$

$$\frac{a}{b} + \frac{nb}{b} = \frac{a}{b} + n,$$

$$\frac{a}{b} + n = n + \frac{a}{b}.$$

3. Express each of the following as an improper fraction. All letters represent Counting Numbers.

(a) $4\frac{3}{4}$.

(b) $3\frac{3}{8}$.

(c) $7\frac{4}{5}$.

(d) $3 + \dfrac{1}{x}$

(e) $y + \dfrac{1}{x}$.

(f) $3 + \dfrac{2}{x + 1}$

(g) $x + \frac{2}{3}$.

(h) $(x + 1) + \frac{2}{3}$.

(i) $\dfrac{x + 2}{3} + 6$.

4. Express each of the following improper fractions in the form $n + \dfrac{a}{b}$. All letters represent Counting Numbers.

(a) $\frac{14}{3}$.

(b) $\dfrac{2n + 1}{n}$.

(c) $\dfrac{5c + b}{c}$.

(d) $\dfrac{14 + 7c}{7}$.

(e) $\dfrac{x^2 + x + 3}{x + 1}$.

(f) $\dfrac{x + 4}{x + 2}$.

5. Using the methods outlined in (a) and (b) of the preceding section, add $2\frac{5}{8}$ and $7\frac{1}{4}$. Justify each step.

6. Express each of the following in the form $n + \dfrac{a}{b}$:

(a) $-2\frac{1}{2}$.

(b) $-6\frac{7}{6}$.

(c) $-3\frac{1}{7}$.

7. Add each of the following, leaving answers in Standard Form and reduced to lowest terms.

(a) $-7\frac{3}{4} + 5\frac{3}{8}$. (b) $6\frac{5}{8} + (-4\frac{1}{8})$. (c) $4\frac{1}{3} + (-6\frac{2}{3})$.
(d) $7\frac{1}{8} + (-4\frac{5}{8})$. (e) $-5\frac{2}{7} + (-3\frac{4}{7})$. (f) $-4\frac{5}{9} + (-6\frac{7}{18})$.

12.4 SUBTRACTION

In order to preserve a correspondence between the operations of Integers and those of the Rational Numbers, subtraction for the set of Rational Numbers is defined in terms of addition.

Definition 12.6—Subtraction for Rational Numbers If each of a/b, c/d, and e/f is a fraction that represents a Rational Number, then

$$\frac{a}{b} - \frac{c}{d} \quad \text{is the Rational Number} \quad \frac{e}{f} \quad \text{if and only if} \quad \frac{a}{b} = \frac{c}{d} + \frac{e}{f}.$$

Hence we can state that $\frac{18}{3} - \frac{4}{3} = \frac{14}{3}$ because $\frac{18}{3} = \frac{4}{3} + \frac{14}{3}$.

The reader should note that subtraction is neither commutative nor associative:

(a) $\frac{1}{2} - \frac{1}{3} \neq \frac{1}{3} - \frac{1}{2}$.
(b) $\frac{5}{6} - (\frac{3}{6} - \frac{2}{6}) \neq (\frac{5}{6} - \frac{3}{6}) - \frac{2}{6}$.

Since subtraction is defined in terms of addition, a preservation of those topics studied in addition is made, including those topics pertaining to mixed numerals. Hence, to show that

$$2\frac{3}{4} - 1\frac{1}{4} = 1\frac{1}{2},$$

we may illustrate the problem by using two different methods. The first of these is to express each as an Improper fraction and then use Definition 12.4:

$$2\frac{3}{4} - 1\frac{1}{4} = \frac{11}{4} - \frac{5}{4},$$

$$\frac{11}{4} - \frac{5}{4} = \frac{6}{4} \quad \text{because} \quad \frac{11}{4} = \frac{5}{4} + \frac{6}{4}.$$

The problem can also be represented in terms of "take away subtraction:"
Given $2\frac{3}{4}$ objects (represented as areas below). Take away $1\frac{1}{4}$ of these areas. Then the remaining area is $1\frac{1}{2}$:

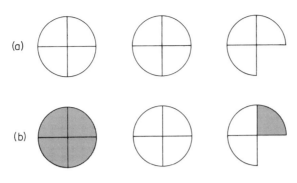

Figure 12.10

$2\frac{3}{4} - 1\frac{1}{4} = 1\frac{2}{4}$ OR $1\frac{1}{2}$. THE BLACKENED AREAS
REPRESENT THE $1\frac{1}{4}$ AREAS TAKEN AWAY.

The following represents the method usually used in elementary programs, and illustrates another parallel between Rational Numbers and Integers. One recalls that in discussing the algorithm for subtraction of Integers, such as $284 - 162$, subtraction was performed by renaming this problem:

$$284 + 162 = (200 + 80 + 4) - (100 + 60 + 2),$$

$$= (200 - 100) + (80 - 60) + (4 - 2),$$

or the fact that for Whole Numbers, a, b, c, and d, $a > c$, $b > d$,

$$(a + b) - (c + d) = (a - c) + (b - d)^*.$$

The subtraction algorithm is then reduced to:

(a) $2\frac{3}{4} - 1\frac{1}{4} = (2 + \frac{3}{4}) - (1 + \frac{1}{4}),$
      $= (2 - 1) + (\frac{3}{4} - \frac{1}{4}),$
      $= 1 + \frac{2}{4} = 1\frac{2}{4} = 1\frac{1}{2}.$
(b) $6\frac{1}{4} - 4\frac{1}{2} = (6 + \frac{1}{4}) - (4 + \frac{1}{2}),$
      $= (5 + \frac{5}{4}) - (4 + \frac{1}{2}),$
      $= (5 - 4) + (\frac{5}{4} - \frac{2}{4}),$
      $= 1 + \frac{3}{4} = 1\frac{3}{4}.$

Note that numbers have many names, for this principle must be used in (b) above. Particularly note that $6\frac{1}{4}$ was renamed $5 + \frac{5}{4}$ and

---

* It was proven for Whole Numbers. This property is assumed for Rational Numbers only to illustrate the subtraction algorithm.

that $\frac{1}{2}$ was renamed $\frac{2}{4}$. This was done in order that $b > d$ in the above algorithm.

The ability to express each mixed numeral as an improper fraction allows us to define subtraction in another manner. This is illustrated below:

(a) $2\frac{3}{4} - 1\frac{1}{2} = \frac{11}{4} - \frac{3}{2} = \frac{11}{4} - \frac{6}{4} = \frac{(11 - 6)}{4} = \frac{5}{4} = 1\frac{1}{4}$,

(b) $5\frac{1}{3} - 4\frac{2}{3} = \frac{16}{3} - \frac{14}{3} = \frac{(16 - 14)}{3} = \frac{2}{3}$,

(c) $6\frac{7}{8} - 1\frac{3}{8} = \frac{55}{8} - \frac{11}{8} = \frac{(55 - 11)}{8} = \frac{44}{8} = 5\frac{1}{2}$.

Through illustrations such as the ones above, we are led to two definitions that parallel those for addition of Rational Numbers.

Definition 12.7 If each of a/b and c/b is a fraction that represents a Rational Number, $a > c$, then

$$\frac{a}{b} - \frac{c}{b} = \frac{a - c}{b}.$$

From Definition 12.7, we can immediately prove the following Theorem. The proof of this Theorem is left as an exercise and parallels that for Addition.

Theorem 12.2—Extended Subtraction If each of a/b and c/d is a fraction that represents a Rational Number, $a/b > c/d$, then

$$\frac{a}{b} - \frac{c}{d} = \frac{ad - bc}{bd}.$$

Theorem 12.2 forms a basis for any problem that involves subtraction of Rational Numbers, for it provides an algorithm that supplements Definition 12.5 The two methods are illustrated below:

$$4\frac{1}{3} - 1\frac{1}{4} = \frac{13}{3} - \frac{5}{4} = \frac{13(4) - 3(5)}{3(4)} = \frac{52 - 15}{15},$$

$$= \frac{37}{15} = 2\frac{7}{15},$$

$$4\frac{1}{3} - 1\frac{1}{4} = \frac{13}{3} - \frac{5}{4} = \frac{52}{12} - \frac{15}{12} = \frac{52 - 15}{12} = 2\frac{7}{15}.$$

Illustrations involving subtraction are presented below:

(a) $\frac{5}{3} - \frac{-2}{3} = \dfrac{5 - (-2)}{3} = \dfrac{5 + 2}{3} = \frac{7}{3}$.

(b) $4\frac{1}{3} - 3\frac{2}{3} = (4 + \frac{1}{3}) - (3 + \frac{2}{3})$.

$$= (4 - 3) + (\tfrac{1}{3} - \tfrac{2}{3}),$$

$$= 1 + \dfrac{1 - 2}{3},$$

$$= 1 + \tfrac{-1}{3},$$

$$= \tfrac{2}{3}.$$

or

$$4\tfrac{1}{3} - 3\tfrac{2}{3} = \tfrac{13}{3} - \tfrac{11}{3} = \dfrac{13 - 11}{3} = \tfrac{2}{3}.$$

(c) $5\frac{1}{6} - 8\frac{5}{6} = (5 + \frac{1}{6}) - (8 + \frac{5}{6})$,

$$= (5 - 8) + (\tfrac{1}{6} - \tfrac{5}{6}),$$

$$= -3 + \left(\dfrac{1 - 5}{6}\right),$$

$$= -3 + \tfrac{-4}{6},$$

$$= -3\tfrac{2}{3}.$$

or

$$5\tfrac{1}{6} - 8\tfrac{5}{6} = \tfrac{31}{6} - \tfrac{53}{6} = \dfrac{31 - 53}{6} = \dfrac{-22}{6} = -3\tfrac{2}{3}.$$

PROBLEM SET 12.3

1. Find the value for each problem below. All letters represent Counting Numbers. Combine all like terms and leave answers so that the numerator and denominator contain no common factors.

(a) $\dfrac{7}{8} - \dfrac{5}{8}$.

(b) $\dfrac{5x}{9} - \dfrac{2x}{9}$.

(c) $\dfrac{(2 + n)}{3} - \dfrac{-n}{3}$.

(d) $\dfrac{6}{x} - \dfrac{-3}{y}$.

(e) $\dfrac{-5}{7x} - \dfrac{3}{8x}$.

(f) $\dfrac{c - 5}{9} - \dfrac{2}{3}$.

(g) $\dfrac{x}{x-1} - \dfrac{-x}{x+1}$, $x \neq 1.$ (h) $\left(\dfrac{m}{n} - \dfrac{2}{3}\right) + \dfrac{6}{n}.$

(i) $\left(\dfrac{x}{y} + \dfrac{4}{5}\right) - \dfrac{2}{3}.$ (j) $\dfrac{4}{5} - \left(\dfrac{2}{3} + \dfrac{x}{y}\right).$

(k) $\left(\dfrac{a+b}{c} - \dfrac{-b}{c}\right) + \dfrac{2}{5}.$ (l) $\left(\dfrac{x+y}{4} - \dfrac{x}{5}\right) + \dfrac{2x}{6}.$

(m) $(a+b) - \dfrac{ab}{a}.$ (n) $\dfrac{24}{x+y} - \dfrac{-36}{x-y}.$

(o) $\left(\dfrac{x+y}{2} + \dfrac{x-y}{3}\right) + x.$ (p) $\dfrac{2}{x-2} - \dfrac{2}{x+2}.$

(q) $\left(\dfrac{1}{x-4} + \dfrac{-1}{x-3}\right) + 4.$ (r) $\left(\dfrac{2}{x-3} + \dfrac{-4}{x+3}\right) + 16.$

CHAPTER 13

Rational Numbers: Multiplication; Identities; Inverses; Division

13.1 INTRODUCTION

In arithmetic, multiplication is frequently interpreted in terms of *area*. The area of a region is defined in terms of square units. If a linear unit is defined, such as the one below:

Figure 13.1

1 LINEAR UNIT

then an area of one square unit is defined as the area of a square whose sides are one linear unit in length.

231

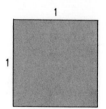

Figure 13.2
1 SQUARE UNIT

To interpret multiplication in terms of area, a rectangle   2   units wide and   3   units long is shown in Figure 13.3

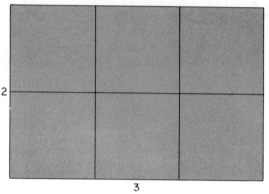

Figure 13.3
2 × 3 REPRESENTED AS   6   SQUARE UNITS

from which we conclude that   2 units × 3 units   are   6 square units.

Similarly, if a square is designated as a particular unit of area, we may partition this square into   6   smaller rectangles and assign to each rectangle an area of $\frac{1}{6}$ square unit.

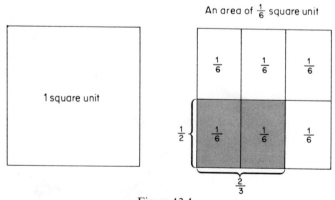

Figure 13.4
$\frac{1}{2} \times \frac{2}{3}$ INTERPRETED AS $\frac{2}{6}$

If we continue using the idea that area is interpreted as "length × width," and the fact that the shaded area in Figure 13.4 is $\frac{2}{6}$, we then define:

$$\tfrac{1}{2} \text{ unit} \times \tfrac{2}{3} \text{ unit} = \tfrac{2}{6} \text{ square units.}$$

A general rule is developed from examples taken from physical interpretations such as the ones above. This rule states that the fraction which names the product of two given fractions is found to be

$$\frac{\text{numerator} \times \text{numerator}}{\text{denominator} \times \text{denominator}}.$$

Hence, $\dfrac{1}{2} \times \dfrac{2}{3} = \dfrac{1(2)}{2(3)} = \dfrac{2}{6}$. This particular idea of multiplication is further reinforced by representing the product $2 \times 3 = 6$ on the drawing of the number line, using rational names for   2,   3, and   6.

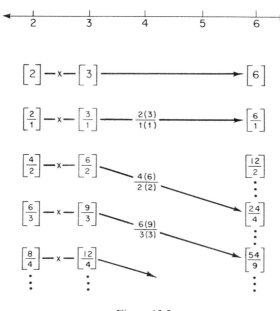

Figure 13.5

By investigation, we see that any representative fraction from $[\frac{2}{1}]$ "times" any representative from $[\frac{3}{1}]$ names a fractional representative for $[\frac{6}{1}]$. Again, the basic idea for defining multiplication is reinforced. For example, each of the names below $[\frac{6}{1}]$:

(a) $\dfrac{2}{1} \times \dfrac{3}{1} = \dfrac{2(3)}{1(1)} = \dfrac{6}{1}.$

(b) $\dfrac{8}{4} \times \dfrac{6}{2} = \dfrac{8(6)}{8} = \dfrac{48}{8}$.

(c) $\dfrac{12}{6} \times \dfrac{9}{3} = \dfrac{12(9)}{6(3)} = \dfrac{108}{18}$.

Similarly, the product $2 \times -2 = -4$ is illustrated in Figure 13.6.

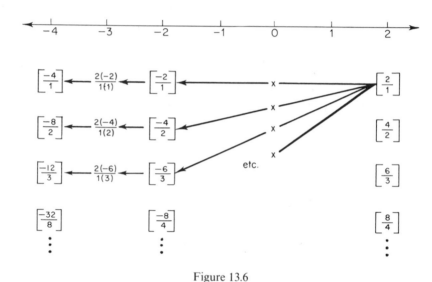

Figure 13.6

From models such as the ones above, we are now able to formally define multiplication.

Definition 13.1—Multiplication for Rational Numbers   If each of a/b and c/d is a fraction that represents a Rational Number,

$$\frac{a}{c} \times \frac{c}{d} = \frac{a(c)}{b(d)}.$$

By the above, we see that the representative of class $\left[\dfrac{a}{b}\right]$ times

the representative of class $\left[\dfrac{c}{d}\right]$ is a representative of class $\left[\dfrac{a(c)}{b(d)}\right]$.

EXAMPLES

(a) $\dfrac{2}{3} \times \dfrac{-8}{3} = \dfrac{2(-8)}{3(3)} \qquad = \dfrac{-16}{9}.$

(b) $\dfrac{n}{n+1} \times \dfrac{4}{3} = \dfrac{n(4)}{(n+1)(3)} = \dfrac{4n}{3n+3}, \qquad (n \neq -1).$

(c) $\dfrac{-n}{5} \times \dfrac{-3}{6} = \dfrac{(-n)(-3)}{5(6)} = \dfrac{3n}{30} = \dfrac{n}{10}.$

(d) $\dfrac{n}{n+1} \times \dfrac{-n}{n-2} = \dfrac{n(-n)}{(n+1)(n-2)} = \dfrac{-n^2}{(n+1)n + (n+1)(-2)},$

$\qquad\qquad\qquad = \dfrac{-n^2}{n^2 - n - 2}, \qquad (n \neq 1 \text{ or } 2).$

13.2 OTHER MODES FOR MULTIPLICATION

Multiplication that involves mixed numerals is easily resolved since we define n to also represent the Rational Number $\left[\dfrac{n}{1}\right]$.

(a) $3 \times \frac{1}{2}$ means $\frac{3}{1} \times \frac{1}{2} = \frac{3}{2}.$
(b) $4 \times \frac{2}{3}$ means $\frac{4}{1} \times \frac{2}{3} = \frac{8}{3}.$

Each of these can be represented pictorially:

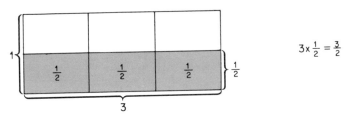

$$3 \times \tfrac{1}{2} = \tfrac{3}{2}$$

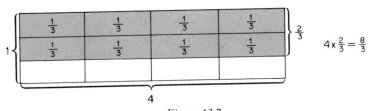

$$4 \times \tfrac{2}{3} = \tfrac{8}{3}$$

Figure 13.7

We may resolve products of the type $2\frac{1}{2} \times 3\frac{1}{4}$ by first expressing each of $2\frac{1}{2}$ and $3\frac{1}{4}$ as improper fractions and multiplying in the usual manner:

(a) $2\frac{1}{2} \times 3\frac{1}{4} = \frac{5}{2} \times \frac{13}{4} = \frac{65}{8} = 8\frac{1}{8}$. Similarly,

(b) $1\frac{5}{8} \times 6\frac{1}{3} = \frac{13}{8} \times \frac{19}{3} = \frac{247}{24} = 10\frac{7}{24}$.

The product $1\,1/2 \times 2\,1/4$ may also be resolved by expressing $1\,1/2$ as $1 + \frac{1}{2}$ and $2\,1/4$ as $2 + \frac{1}{4}$ and then by using the Distributive Property of multiplication over addition:

$$1\,1/2 \times 2\,1/4 = (1 + \tfrac{1}{2})(2 + \tfrac{1}{4}),$$
$$= (1 + \tfrac{1}{2})2 + (1 + \tfrac{1}{2})\tfrac{1}{4},$$
$$= 1(2) + \tfrac{1}{2}(2) + 1(\tfrac{1}{4}) + \tfrac{1}{2}(\tfrac{1}{4}),$$
$$= 2 + 1 + \tfrac{1}{4} + \tfrac{1}{8},$$
$$= 3 + \tfrac{3}{8} = 3\,3/8.$$

Pictorially, each partial sum in the above can be represented as:

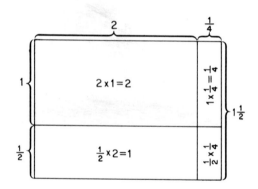

Figure 13.8

$$2(1) + \tfrac{1}{2}(2) + 1(\tfrac{1}{4}) + \tfrac{1}{2}(\tfrac{1}{4}) = 3\tfrac{3}{8}.$$

PROBLEM SET 13.1

1. The following fractions represent Rational Numbers. Find their product. Leave answers so that numerators and denominators are relatively prime.

(a) $\dfrac{3}{4} \times \dfrac{2}{z}$.

(b) $\dfrac{n+1}{x} \times \dfrac{-3}{4}$.

(c) $\dfrac{2x}{3} \times -9$.

(d) $\dfrac{9x^2}{7} \times \dfrac{7}{2}$.

(e) $\dfrac{x+y}{n+1} \times \dfrac{-4}{x+y}$.

(f) $\dfrac{3x^2}{2y^2} \times \dfrac{-8y^2}{6}$.

(g) $\dfrac{6xy^2}{ab^2} \times \dfrac{a^2b}{xy}$.

(h) $\dfrac{(x+y)^2}{xy} \times \dfrac{x^2y^2}{x+y}$.

(i) $\dfrac{(m+n)^2}{m^2n^2} \times \dfrac{m^2n}{(n+n)}$.

(j) $\dfrac{3(x+1)^2}{2(m+n)} \times \dfrac{(m+n)^2}{(x+1)}$.

2. Find *four* fractions, $a/b \times c/d$ and $c/b \times a/d$, whose product is

(a) $\dfrac{5(n+1)}{7x}$.

(b) $\dfrac{(x+y)(n+1)}{2(3+z)}$.

3. A strip of land is   3/4   mile wide and   5/8   mile long. What is the total area of land?

4. What is the cost, in dollars, of   5/16   yard of cotton if the cost is   3   dollars per yard?

5. What is the cost, in cents, of   5/6   pound of meat selling at   79   cents per pound?

6. What is the total cost, in cents, of   12 1/3   pounds of oranges which sell at 29   cents per pound?

7. What is one-half of   5/16?   7/8?

8. What is the perimeter of a room   15 2/3   feet by   20 3/4   feet? What is the area of this room?

9. The picture below represents the product $2\,3/4 \times 1\,1/2$. Label the different areas of this illustration as in Figure 13.8.

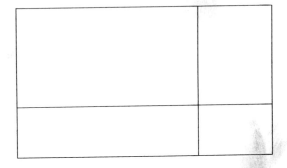

10. Express the following in the form $n + a/b$ and then find their products by repeated application of the Distributive Property of Multiplication over Addition:

(a) $2\,3/4 \times 1\,1/2$.   (b) $6\,7/8 \times 4\,2/3$.

(c) $5\,1/4 \times 2\,3/8$.   (d) $2\,5/7 \times 3\,4/5$.

13.3 IDENTITIES; INVERSES

It was illustrated in prior sections that a complete one-to-one correspondence could be established between the set of Integers and a particular subset of Rational Numbers. Since this complete one-to-one correspondence could be established (and for other reasons), we then defined that Integer numerals could be used as the representative of Rational Numbers:

$$\vdots \qquad\qquad \vdots$$

$$[-2] \quad \text{Represents} \quad \left[\frac{-2}{1}\right]$$

$$[-1] \quad \text{Represents} \quad \left[\frac{-1}{1}\right]$$

$$[0] \quad \text{Represents} \quad \left[\frac{0}{1}\right]$$

$$[1] \quad \text{Represents} \quad \left[\frac{1}{1}\right]$$

$$[2] \quad \text{Represents} \quad \left[\frac{2}{1}\right]$$

$$\vdots \qquad\qquad \vdots$$

Recall that for Whole Numbers, the number 0 was defined as the Additive Identity and that the number 1 was defined as the Multiplicative Identity. Furthermore, we proved that each of these was unique, i.e., there was no other element within the set of Whole Numbers which contained the special properties of 0 or of 1.

In this section, we shall be particularly interested in investigating

$$\left[\frac{0}{1}\right] \quad \text{and} \quad \left[\frac{1}{1}\right]$$

for the possibility that $\left[\dfrac{a}{b}\right] + \left[\dfrac{0}{1}\right] = \left[\dfrac{a}{b}\right]$ and $\left[\dfrac{a}{b}\right] \times \left[\dfrac{1}{1}\right] =$ $\left[\dfrac{a}{b}\right]$. If this is true, then $\left[\dfrac{0}{1}\right]$ will be defined as the *Additive Identity* and $\left[\dfrac{1}{1}\right]$ will be defined as the *Multiplicative Identity Element* for Rational Numbers.

Theorem T13.1 If each of a/b and $\frac{0}{1}$ is a fraction that represents a Rational Number, then

$$\frac{a}{b} + \frac{0}{1} = \frac{a}{b}.$$

Proof: Let each of a/b and $0/1$ be a fraction that represents a Rational Number. Then

$$\frac{a}{b} + \frac{0}{1} = \frac{a(1) + b(0)}{b(1)}$$

$$\frac{a(1) + b(0)}{b(1)} = \frac{a(1) + 0}{b(1)}$$

$$\frac{a(1) + 0}{b(1)} = \frac{a(1)}{b(1)},$$

$$\frac{a(1)}{b(1)} = \frac{a}{b}.$$

By this Theorem, we have shown a correspondence between 0 and $\left[\frac{0}{1}\right]$:

$$a + 0 = a,$$

$$\frac{a}{b} + \frac{0}{1} = \frac{a}{b}.$$

For this reason, we define $\left[\frac{0}{1}\right]$ to be the Additive Identity Element for Rational Numbers.

Definition 13.2—The Additive Identity Element The Rational Number $\left[\frac{0}{1}\right]$ is defined as the Additive Identity Element for the set of Rational Numbers.

Similarly, $\left[\dfrac{a}{b}\right] \times \left[\dfrac{1}{1}\right] = \left[\dfrac{a}{b}\right]$. (Proof of this is left as an exercise for the reader.) For this reason, $\left[\dfrac{1}{1}\right]$ is defined as the Multiplicative Identity Element.

Definition 13.3—Multiplicative Identity Element The Rational Number $\left[\frac{1}{1}\right]$ is defined as the Multiplicative Identity Element for Rational Numbers.

Hence the set of Rational Numbers has also an Additive Identity Element and a Multiplicative Identity Element, and two new correspondences are established between the set of Integers and the set of Rational Numbers:

(a) $a + 0 = a \longleftrightarrow \dfrac{a}{b} + \dfrac{0}{1} = \dfrac{a}{b}$.

(b) $a \times 1 = a \longleftrightarrow \dfrac{a}{b} \times \dfrac{1}{1} = \dfrac{a}{b}$.

The reciprocal of any number $\left[\dfrac{a}{b}\right]$ is the number $\left[\dfrac{c}{d}\right]$ such that

$$\frac{a}{b} \times \frac{c}{d} = \frac{1}{1}.$$

The reciprocal (also called the Multiplicative Inverse) of $\frac{1}{2}$ is $\frac{2}{1}$ because

$$\frac{1}{2} \times \frac{2}{1} = \frac{1(2)}{2(1)} = \frac{2}{2},$$

the reciprocal of $\frac{3}{4}$ is $\frac{4}{3}$ because

$$\frac{3}{4} \times \frac{4}{3} = \frac{12}{12},$$

and the reciprocal of the Rational Number represented by n $(n \neq 0)$ is $1/n$ because

$$n \times \frac{1}{n} \quad \text{means} \quad \frac{n}{1} \times \frac{1}{n} = \frac{n}{n}.$$

This is summarized below.

Definition 13.4—Reciprocals   If a/b is a fraction that represents a Rational Number, $a, b \neq 0$, then b/a is the Reciprocal of a/b.
   Similarly, if "n" is an Integer numeral that represents a Rational Number, $n \neq 0$, then $1/n$ is the Reciprocal of n.

Hence, the reciprocal of a fraction is the fraction obtained by interchanging the numerator and the denominator of the stated fraction. This process is often defined as inverting the fraction. It will be used in the division of Rational Numbers.

13.4 DIVISION

Division of fractions and of Rational Numbers in elementary curricula is sometimes introduced through partitive division or measurement division.

(a) In Measurement Division, to divide $\frac{3}{2}$ by $\frac{1}{4}$ means to find how many fourths are contained in $3/2$:

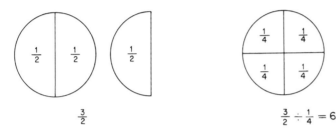

Figure 13.9

In Measurement Division, we see that there are 6 one-fourths in $3/2$; or $\frac{3}{2} \div \frac{1}{4} = 6$.

(b) In Partitive Division, to divide $\frac{3}{2}$ by 6 means to partition $\frac{3}{2}$ into 6 congruent parts, and then determine how large each part is:

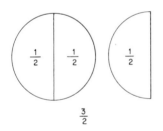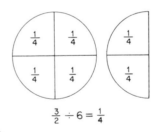

Figure 13.10

Division for Rational Numbers is also defined in terms of Multiplication, as in the case of division for Whole Numbers.

Definition 13.5—Division If each of a/b and c/d is a fraction that represents a Rational Number, $c/d \neq 0$, then

$$\frac{\frac{a}{b}}{\frac{c}{d}} = \frac{x}{y} \quad \text{if and only if} \quad \frac{a}{b} = \frac{c}{d} \times \frac{x}{y}.$$

The notation to indicate division is also written as:

$$\frac{a}{b} \div \frac{c}{d} \quad \text{and} \quad \frac{a/b}{c/d}.$$

The reader should note that since the set of Rational Numbers is closed under multiplication, by Definition 13.5, above, so will this set be closed under Division. This is in contrast to the set of Whole Numbers and the set of Integers, which were *not closed* under division.

Division in terms of multiplication is illustrated below.

(a) If $\dfrac{\frac{1}{2}}{\frac{1}{4}} = \dfrac{x}{y}$, then $\boxed{\dfrac{x}{y} = \dfrac{2}{1}}$ because $\dfrac{1}{2} = \left(\dfrac{1}{4}\right)\left(\dfrac{2}{1}\right).$

(b) If $\dfrac{\frac{-3}{8}}{\frac{1}{2}} = \dfrac{x}{y}$, then $\boxed{\dfrac{x}{y} = \dfrac{-3}{4}}$ because $\dfrac{-3}{8} = \left(\dfrac{1}{2}\right)\left(\dfrac{-3}{4}\right).$

(c) If $\dfrac{\frac{4}{5}}{\frac{1}{10}} = \dfrac{x}{y}$, then $\boxed{\dfrac{x}{y} = \dfrac{8}{1}}$ because $\dfrac{4}{5} = \left(\dfrac{1}{10}\right)\left(\dfrac{8}{1}\right).$

However, all division problems are not as simple, and from the examples of Measurement Division, Partitive Division, and Division defined in terms of Multiplication, we derive the rule: *Invert the advisor and then proceed as in multiplication.* Consider the three examples above and the following ones.

(a) $\dfrac{\frac{1}{2}}{\frac{1}{4}} = \dfrac{1}{2} \times \dfrac{4}{1} = \dfrac{4}{2} = \boxed{\dfrac{2}{1}}.$

(b) $\dfrac{\frac{-3}{8}}{\frac{1}{2}} = \dfrac{-3}{8} \times \dfrac{2}{1} = \dfrac{-6}{8} = \boxed{\dfrac{-3}{4}}.$

(c) $\dfrac{\frac{4}{5}}{\frac{1}{10}} \times \dfrac{4}{5} \times \dfrac{10}{1} \times \dfrac{40}{5} = \boxed{\dfrac{8}{1}}.$

This *Inversion Rule* provides an easy algorithm by which we may find the quotient of two fractions. In order to show how this rule works, an informal proof is given below:

One recalls that for any fraction $\dfrac{a}{b}$ which represents a Rational Number, $\dfrac{a}{b} = \dfrac{na}{nb}, n \neq 0$. One also recalls that for $\dfrac{a}{b}$, $\dfrac{a}{b} \times \dfrac{b}{a} = \dfrac{1}{1}$, is the Multiplicative Identity Element. For the fraction:

$$\frac{\dfrac{a}{b}}{\dfrac{c}{d}}$$

we may multiply by $\dfrac{\dfrac{d}{c}}{\dfrac{d}{c}}$, a form of $\dfrac{1}{1}$:

$$\frac{\dfrac{a}{b}}{\dfrac{c}{d}} = \frac{\dfrac{a}{b}}{\dfrac{c}{d}} \times \frac{\dfrac{d}{c}}{\dfrac{d}{c}} = \frac{\dfrac{a}{b} \times \dfrac{d}{c}}{\dfrac{c}{d} \times \dfrac{d}{c}} = \frac{\dfrac{a}{b} \times \dfrac{d}{c}}{1} = \frac{a(d)}{b(c)},$$

or

$$\frac{\dfrac{a}{b}}{\dfrac{c}{d}} = \frac{a(d)}{b(c)},$$

Note that we make use of the Multiplicative Identity Element represented by $\dfrac{1}{1}$ and also represented by $\dfrac{\dfrac{d}{c}}{\dfrac{d}{c}}$. The idea of Reciprocals is also used in $\dfrac{\dfrac{d}{c}}{\dfrac{d}{c}}$. This algorithm is summarized by the following theorem.

Theorem 13.1—Inversion If each of a/b and c/d is a fraction that represents a Rational Number, $c/d \neq 0$, and if

$$\frac{a/b}{c/d} = \frac{x}{y}, \text{ then } \frac{x}{y} = \frac{a(d)}{b(c)}.$$

Fractions of the form $\dfrac{a/b}{c/d}$ are defined as Complex Fractions. In the fraction,

$$\frac{\dfrac{a}{b}}{\dfrac{c}{d}}$$

numbers a and d are defined as the extremes, numbers b and c are defined as the means. Thus "the quotient of two Rational Numbers is equal to the product of the extremes divided by the product of the means" is another way to state Theorem 13.1.

PROBLEM SET 13.2

1. Find (a) the Multiplicative Inverse and (b) the Additive Inverse for each of the following. All letters represent Counting Numbers.

(a) $\dfrac{1}{2}$.

(b) $\dfrac{-4}{7}$.

(c) $\dfrac{4n}{7n}$.

(d) $-2n$.

(e) $\dfrac{-5}{n}$.

(f) $\dfrac{4}{n+1}$.

(g) $\dfrac{-4}{n+1}$.

(h) $\dfrac{7+n}{n}$.

(i) $\dfrac{c+n}{x}$

2. Each of the following is a Complex Fraction. By using the principle of Inversion, restate each as a proper or improper fraction. Reduce each to lowest terms. All letters represent Counting Numbers.

(a) $\dfrac{\dfrac{3}{4}}{\dfrac{5}{8}}$.

(b) $\dfrac{\dfrac{a}{3}}{\dfrac{b}{6}}$.

(c) $\dfrac{\dfrac{2}{2+x}}{\dfrac{3}{n}}$.

(d) $\dfrac{\dfrac{2-x}{2+x}}{\dfrac{3}{n}}$.

(e) $\dfrac{\dfrac{n+1}{2-n}}{\dfrac{4}{2-n}}$.

(f) $\dfrac{\dfrac{1}{2}}{3}$.

(g) $\dfrac{\dfrac{4}{5}}{7}.$ (h) $\dfrac{\dfrac{1}{n} - 1}{1 + \dfrac{1}{n}}.$ (i) $\dfrac{n - \dfrac{6}{x}}{x - \dfrac{2}{n}}.$

(j) $\dfrac{\dfrac{x+2}{x} + 2}{\dfrac{4x-1}{x} - 3}.$ (k) $\dfrac{\dfrac{4}{x-1} - 2}{4 + \dfrac{8}{x-1}}.$ (l) $1 + \dfrac{1}{1 + \dfrac{1}{x}}.$

3. Verify, in a proof, that $\dfrac{3/4}{7/8} = \dfrac{24}{28}.$ The steps are similar to those of Theorem 13.1 — Inversion.

4. Prove that $\left[\dfrac{a}{b}\right] \times \left[\dfrac{1}{1}\right] = \left[\dfrac{a}{b}\right].$

5. A book is 11 1/2 inches thick and contains 350 pages. What is the thickness, in inches, of each page?

6. If 90 cents was paid for 2/3 pounds of candy, what is the price, in cents, of the candy per pound?

7. A recipe calls for 1 1/2 cups of sugar, 3 1/3 cups of flour, 7/8 teaspoon of vanilla, and 1 5/6 cups of milk. This recipe will feed 10 people. How much of each ingredient should be used if only 4 people are to be fed?

8. Using the data of Problem 7, how much of each ingredient should be used if 6 people are to be fed?

9. How much milk, in quarts, would be required to fill 48 glasses if one glass contains 2/5 quart?

10. "How many thirds are contained in $\frac{7}{8}$" it also means:

$$n \times \frac{1}{3} = \frac{7}{8}. \text{ What is } n?$$

11. How many fourths are contained in $\frac{5}{9}$?

12. Why does $\left[\frac{0}{n}\right]$, $n \neq 0$ not have a reciprocal?

13. Does $\left[\frac{0}{0}\right]$ have a reciprocal? Why?

13.5 SPECIAL PROPERTIES FOR DIVISION

The following are special properties for division and are summarized below.

For every Rational Number $\left[\dfrac{a}{b}\right]$, for every Rational Number

$\left[\dfrac{c}{d}\right]$, and for every Rational Number $\left[\dfrac{e}{f}\right]$, the following can be considered.

$D1$:   Division is not commutative: $\dfrac{a}{b} \div \dfrac{c}{d} \neq \dfrac{c}{d} \div \dfrac{a}{b}.$

$D2$:   Division is not associative: $\left(\dfrac{a}{b} \div \dfrac{c}{d}\right) \div \dfrac{e}{f} \neq \dfrac{a}{b} \div \left(\dfrac{c}{d} \div \dfrac{e}{f}\right).$

$D3$:   Division distributes over addition in a "Right-Hand" manner:

$$\left(\dfrac{a}{b} + \dfrac{c}{d}\right) \div \dfrac{e}{f} = \left(\dfrac{a}{b} \div \dfrac{e}{f}\right) + \left(\dfrac{c}{d} \div \dfrac{e}{f}\right).$$

$D4$: $\dfrac{0}{1} \div \dfrac{a}{b} = \dfrac{0}{1},$ $a \neq 0.$

$D5$: $\dfrac{a}{b} \div \dfrac{0}{1}$ does not exist, $a \neq 0.$

$D6$: $\dfrac{0}{1} \div \dfrac{0}{1}$ is undefined.

In order to show the above to be true statements, assume that each of a/b, c/d, and e/f is a fraction which represents a Rational Number.

$D1$:   Commutativity: Division is not commutative.

EXAMPLE

$$25 \div 5 \neq 5 \div 25   (5 \neq \tfrac{1}{5})$$

$D2$:   Associativity: (Left as an exercise for the reader).

$D3$:   Right-hand distributivity:

$$\left(\dfrac{a}{b} + \dfrac{c}{d}\right) \div \dfrac{e}{f} = \left(\dfrac{ad + bc}{bd}\right) \div \dfrac{e}{f},$$

$$= \left(\dfrac{ad + bc}{bd}\right) \times \dfrac{f}{e},$$

$$= \dfrac{(ad + bd)f}{(bd)e},$$

$$= \dfrac{(ad)f + (bc)f}{(bd)e},$$

$$= \frac{(ad)f}{(bd)e} + \frac{(bc)f}{(bd)e}$$

$$= \frac{(af)d}{(be)f} + \frac{(cf)b}{(de)b}, \quad \text{(by repeated use of Commutative and Associative Properties)}$$

$$= \frac{af}{be} + \frac{cf}{de},$$

$$= \left(\frac{a}{b} \times \frac{f}{e}\right) + \left(\frac{c}{d} \times \frac{f}{e}\right),$$

$$= \left(\frac{a}{b} \div \frac{e}{f}\right) + \left(\frac{c}{d} \div \frac{e}{f}\right).$$

$D4:\quad \dfrac{0}{1} \div \dfrac{a}{b} = \dfrac{0}{1} \times \dfrac{b}{a},$

$$= \frac{0(b)}{1(a)},$$

$$= \frac{0}{1}, a \neq 0.$$

This is parallel to division for Whole Numbers, $\dfrac{0}{n} = 0$, for the above shows

that in Rational Numbers, $\dfrac{0}{1} \div \dfrac{a}{b}$ denotes as always the Rational

Number represented by $\dfrac{0}{1}$.

$D5:\quad \dfrac{a}{b} \div \dfrac{0}{1} = \dfrac{a}{b} \times \dfrac{1}{0} = \dfrac{a(1)}{b(0)}$. There is no Rational Number represented by

$\dfrac{a(1)}{b(0)}$, for by the definition of a fraction, the denominator must never be   0.

Hence $\dfrac{a}{b} \div \dfrac{0}{1}$ does not exist for the set of Rational Numbers.

$D6:\quad \dfrac{0}{1} \div \dfrac{0}{1}$. Assume that there is a Rational Number, represented by $\dfrac{e}{f}$,

so that $\dfrac{0}{1} \div \dfrac{0}{1} = \dfrac{e}{f}$. Then $\dfrac{0}{1} = \dfrac{0}{1} \times \dfrac{e}{f}$. We see that $\dfrac{e}{f}$ may be

the representative of any Rational Number:

$$\frac{0}{1} \times \frac{1}{2} = \frac{0}{2},$$

$$\frac{0}{1} \times \frac{1}{3} = \frac{0}{3},$$

$$\frac{0}{1} \times \frac{4}{5} = \frac{0}{5}, \text{ etc.}$$

Since any Rational Number, represented by $\dfrac{e}{f}$, is a possible candidate to be the quotient $\dfrac{0}{1} \div \dfrac{0}{1} = \dfrac{e}{f}$, we say that $\dfrac{0}{1} \div \dfrac{0}{1}$ is not defined.

PROBLEM SET 13.3

1. Using fractions $\frac{1}{2}$, $\frac{3}{4}$, and $\frac{7}{8}$, illustrate that division is not associative, Using $\frac{1}{2}$ and $\frac{7}{8}$ illustrate that division is not commutative.

2. Illustrate that $\frac{5}{8} \div (\frac{1}{4} + \frac{1}{3}) \neq (\frac{5}{8} \div \frac{1}{4}) + (\frac{5}{8} \div \frac{1}{3})$. This is the left-hand distributive property.

3. Find the following quotients by first expressing each as a problem involving addition, i.e., by using the right-hand distributive property. Leave answers so that numerators and denominators contain no common factors.

(a) $\left(\dfrac{3}{4} + \dfrac{4}{5}\right) \div \dfrac{1}{2} = \left(\dfrac{3}{4} \div \dfrac{1}{2}\right) + \left(\dfrac{4}{5} \div \dfrac{1}{2}\right) =$

(b) $\left(\dfrac{n+1}{2} + \dfrac{1}{4}\right) \div \dfrac{2}{3} =$

(c) $\left(\dfrac{3}{6} + \dfrac{x}{2x+2}\right) \div \dfrac{5}{8} =$

4. Find the value of each expression by first converting each one to a problem involving division of two numbers through use of the Distributive Property of Division over Addition:

(a) $\left(\dfrac{x}{y} \div \dfrac{2}{3}\right) + \left(\dfrac{n+2}{5} \div \dfrac{2}{3}\right) = \left(\dfrac{x}{y} + \dfrac{n+2}{5}\right) \div \dfrac{2}{3} =$

(b) $\left(\dfrac{n+2}{4} \div \dfrac{x}{y}\right) + \left(\dfrac{2}{5} + \dfrac{x}{y}\right) =$

(c) $\left(\dfrac{n+1}{2} \div \dfrac{2n}{5}\right) + \left(\dfrac{n+2}{3} \div \dfrac{2n}{5}\right) =$

5. Explain how the definition for addition of Rational Numbers,

$$\frac{a}{b} + \frac{c}{b} = \frac{a+c}{b},$$

is related to the distributive property of division over addition.

6. State whether each of the following is one, zero, or is undefined.

(a) If $x = 2$, then $\dfrac{6}{x - 2} = $ _____ .

(b) If $x = y$, then $\dfrac{n + 1}{2(x - y)} = $ _____ .

(c) If $x = 2$, then $\dfrac{x - 2}{x^2 - 4x + 4} = $ _____ .

(d) If $x = 2$, then $\dfrac{(x - 2)(x + 2)}{x^2 - 4} = $ _____ .

CHAPTER 14

The System of Rationals

14.1 INTRODUCTION

When defined for the set of Whole Numbers and Integers, properties such as closure, commutativity, associativity, and distributivity were considered to be basic properties. Similarly, we wish to retain these properties for the system of Rational Numbers (**R**). The following is a list of these basic properties for **R**. (Use of the notation [a], [b], and [c] is made for simplicity.)

For every Rational Number [a], for every Rational Number [b], and for every Rational Number [c] (except as denoted below), the following can be considered.

Properties for Equality.

E1: Dichotomy: [a] = [b] or [a] ≠ [b].

E2: Reflexivity: [a] = [a].

E3: Symmetry: If [a] = [b], then [b] = [a].

E4: Transitivity: If [a] = [b] and [b] = [c], then [a] = [c].

Properties for Addition and Multiplication.

$P1$:   Closure:

$$[a] + [b] \in R \qquad \text{and} \qquad [a] \times [b] \in R.$$

$P2$:   Commutativity:

$$[a] + [b] = [b] + [a] \qquad \text{and} \qquad [a] \times [b] = [b] \times [a].$$

$P3$:   Associativity:

$$[a] + ([b] + [c]) = ([a] + [b]) + [c],$$

$$[a] \times ([b] \times [c]) = ([a] \times [b]) \times [c].$$

$P4$:   Existence of Identities:

There exists a unique Rational Number $[0]$ such that for every Rational Number $[a]$, $[a] + [0] = [a]$.

There exists a unique Rational Number $[1]$ such that for every Rational Number $[a]$, $[a] \times [1] = [a]$.

$P5$:   Existence of Inverses:

For every Rational Number $[a]$, there exists a unique Rational Number $[-a]$, such that $[a] + [-a] = [0]$, the Additive Identity.

For every Rational Number $[a] \neq [0]$, there exists a unique Rational Number $\left[\dfrac{1}{a}\right]$ such that $[a] \times \left[\dfrac{1}{a}\right] = [1]$, the Multiplicative Identity.

$P6$:   Distributivity:

$$[a] \times ([b] + [c]) = ([a] \times [b]) + ([a] \times [c]).$$

$P7$:   Uniqueness properties:

If $[a] = [b]$ then $[a] + [c] = [b] + [c]$.

If $[a] = [b]$ then $[a] \times [c] = [b] \times [c]$.

$P8$:   Cancellation properties:

If $[a] + [c] = [b] + [c]$, then $[a] = [b]$.

If $[a] \times [c] = [b] \times [c]$, then $[a] = [b]$, $[c] \neq 0$.

Similarly, the properties for Inequality are stated:

$I1$:   Trichotomy: $[a] = [b]$ or $[a] < [b]$ or $[b] < [a]$.

$I2$:   Transitivity: If $[a] < [b]$ and $[b] < [c]$, then $[a] < [c]$.

$I3$:   Addition: If $[a] < [b]$ then $[a] + [c] < [b] + [c]$.

$I4$:   Multiplication: If $[a] < [b]$ and $[c] > [0]$,   then $[a] \times [c] < [b] \times [c]$. If $[c] < 0$, $[a] \times [c] > [b] \times [c]$.

*I*5:   Cancellation:

If $[a] + [c] < [b] + [c]$ then $[a] < [b]$.
If $[a] \times [c] < [b] \times [c]$ and if $[c] > 0$, then $[a] < [b]$.
If $[c] < 0$,   then $[a] > [b]$.

*I*6:   Property for density: In Chapter 2 an illustration was given of a one-to-one correspondence between the set of Whole Numbers and a subset of points on the drawing of the number line. This was denoted as:

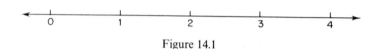

Figure 14.1

Similarly, a one-to-one correspondence was established between the subset of Rational Numbers and a subset of points on the diagram of the Number line:

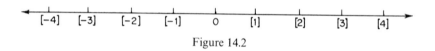

Figure 14.2

But there is an infinite number of Rational Numbers between any two Rational Numbers, say for $\frac{3}{4}$ and $\frac{1}{1}$. Some of these are $\frac{7}{8}$, $\frac{15}{16}$, $\frac{31}{32}$, $\frac{63}{64}$, $\frac{127}{128}$, $\frac{255}{256}$, ... It is easily shown that

$$\frac{3}{4} < \frac{7}{8} < \frac{15}{16} < \frac{31}{32} < \frac{63}{64} < \frac{127}{128} < \cdots < \frac{1}{1}.$$

The discovery that an infinite number of Rational Numbers occurs between any two given Rational Numbers leads to the idea of Density. For example, is there a Rational Number $\left[\dfrac{a}{b}\right]$ so that

$$\frac{999}{1000} + \left[\frac{a}{b}\right] < \frac{1}{1}?$$

In order to find this number, we take the average of $\frac{999}{1000}$ and $\frac{1}{1}$:

$$\frac{\dfrac{999}{1000} + \dfrac{1}{1}}{2} = \frac{1999}{2000}.$$

Using the definition for the Inequality Relation, we can state that

$$\frac{999}{1000} < \frac{1999}{2000} < \frac{1}{1}.$$

By continuing the process of "averaging" we can find a Rational Number $\left[\dfrac{c}{d}\right]$ so that

$$\frac{1999}{2000} < \frac{c}{d} < \frac{1}{1}, \text{ etc.}$$

The idea of infinitely many Rational Numbers occurring between any two Rational Numbers leads to the idea of Density.

Property for Density: If $\left[\dfrac{a}{b}\right] < \left[\dfrac{c}{d}\right]$ then there exists a Rational Number $\left[\dfrac{e}{f}\right]$ so that

$$\left[\frac{a}{b}\right] < \left[\frac{e}{f}\right] < \left[\frac{c}{d}\right].$$

One such number is $\left[\dfrac{e}{f}\right] = \left[\dfrac{\dfrac{a}{b} + \dfrac{c}{d}}{2}\right].$

If we let each of a and b be a Rational Number, then by the process of averages, $\dfrac{a + b}{2}$ satisfies the conditions:

$$a < \frac{a + b}{2} < b.$$

This is represented on the number line:

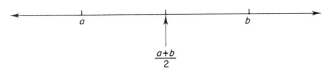

$$\frac{a+b}{2}$$

Figure 14.3

The graphs of certain functions should be reinterpreted because of the idea of density. Consider the examples which follow.

EXAMPLES

(a) The graph of $\{x| \quad x < 10\}$:

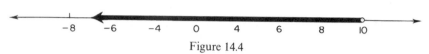

Figure 14.4

(b) Let $M = \{x| \quad |x| > 2\}$. Graph M.

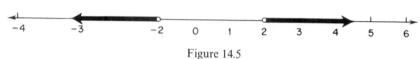

Figure 14.5

(c) Let $M = \{x| \quad |x| < 3\}$. Graph M.

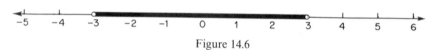

Figure 14.6

(d) Let $M = \{x| \quad -2 \leq x \leq 3\}$. Graph $M \times M$.

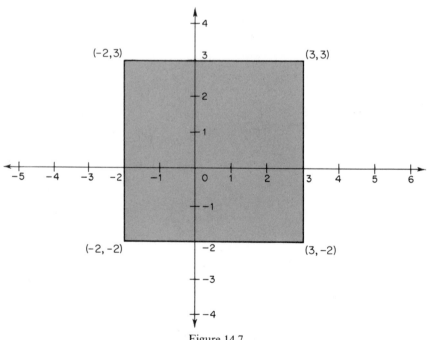

Figure 14.7

(e) Let $M = \{n|\quad n \leq 4\}$. Graph $M \times M$.

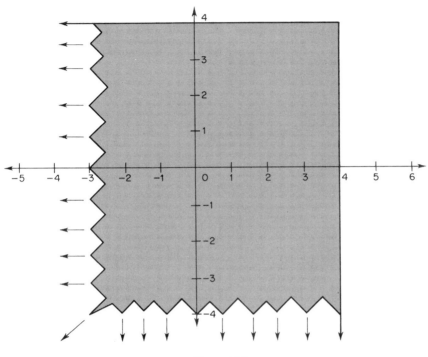

Figure 14.8

PROBLEM SET 14.1

1. Given the following mathematical sentences, state if each sentence is true or false. If the sentence is true, cite the property of Equality or Inequality as a justification for your answer. If false, explain why the sentence is not true by using a short sentence or giving an example. All letters represent Rational Numbers.

(a) If $8n = 5$, then $n = \frac{5}{8}$.
(b) If $4n < 3$, then $4n + 8 < 3 + 8$.
(c) If $4 < n$, then $-16 > -4n$.
(d) If $8n < 24$, then $-n < -3$.
(e) If $14n + 5 < 10$, then $14n < 5$.
(f) If $5n < 10$, then $n < 2$.
(g) If $\dfrac{n}{2} = 20$, then $n = 40$.
(h) If $-n < 20$, then $n > -20$.
(i) If $4 + \dfrac{n}{2} < 16$, then $\dfrac{n}{2} > 12$.

(j) If $a(n) = 5$, then $n = \dfrac{5}{a}$, $(a \neq 0)$.

(k) If $3n + 4y = 6n$, then $4y = 3n$.

(l) If $\dfrac{-n}{2} < 4$, then $\dfrac{n}{2} > -4$.

(m) If $-3 < 12$, then $3a < 12a$, $(a < 0)$.

(n) If $\dfrac{x + y}{a} < 7$, then $(x + y) < 7$, $(a < 0)$.

(o) If $7n + 4 = 3$, then $4 = 3 - 7n$.

(p) If $2x + 2y < 14$, then $(x + y) < 7$.

(q) If $\dfrac{a}{b} < 0$, then $\dfrac{-a}{b} < 0$.

(r) If $-n > 0$, then $-(-n) < 0$.

(s) If $-6 > -7$, then $-6a < -7a$, $(a \neq 0)$.

(t) If $-n < x$, then $(-1)(-n) > (-1)(-x)$.

(u) If $(-1)(-n) > (-1)(-x)$, then $n > x$.

(v) If $-n < 0$, then $(-1)(-n) > 0$.

(w) If $(-1)(-n) > 0$, then $n > 0$.

(x) $|x + y| < |x| + |y|$.

(y) $|a(b)| = |a| \times |b|$.

(z) $|a| - |b| < |a - b|$.

2. Complete the following:

(a) If $\dfrac{1}{2} < \dfrac{a}{b}$ and $\dfrac{a}{b} < \dfrac{c}{d}$, then $\dfrac{1}{2} <$ _____ .

(b) If $\dfrac{3}{4}n < \dfrac{7}{8}$, then $n <$ _____ .

(c) If $\dfrac{3}{4} + n < \dfrac{3}{4} + \dfrac{5}{8}$, then $n =$ _____ .

(d) If $\dfrac{a}{b}\left(\dfrac{x}{y}\right) < \dfrac{a}{b}\left(\dfrac{7}{8}\right)$, and $\dfrac{a}{b} > 0$, then $\dfrac{x}{y} =$ _____ .

3. Place $=$, $<$, or $>$ in the $\bigcirc$ so that each sentence is true. Each letter represents a Counting Number:

(a) $\dfrac{3}{4} \bigcirc \dfrac{5}{8}$.

(b) $\dfrac{a}{b} \bigcirc \dfrac{2a}{2b}$.

(c) $\dfrac{1}{x + 1} \bigcirc \dfrac{1}{1}$.

(d) $\dfrac{2x}{3y} \bigcirc \dfrac{x}{2y}$.

(e) $\dfrac{n + 1}{2n + 1} \bigcirc \dfrac{1}{1}$.

(f) $\dfrac{n}{2n} \bigcirc \dfrac{n + 2}{4 + n}$.

4. If $\mathcal{U} = $ Set of Rational Numbers, find n. Graph n on the drawing of the number line:

(a) $\{n|\quad 2n - 1 < 5\}$.
(b) $\{n|\quad n + 2 < 7\}$.
(c) $\{n|\quad \frac{1}{2}n < 8\}$.

(d) $\left\{n|\quad \dfrac{n}{2} + \dfrac{3}{4} < \dfrac{17}{18}\right\}$.

(e) $\left\{n|\quad 2n - \dfrac{3}{2}n < \dfrac{5}{8}\right\}$.

5. Find a Rational Number between the following:

(a) $\frac{3}{4}$ and $\frac{7}{8}$.   (b) $\frac{1}{2}$ and $\frac{9}{16}$.
(c) $\frac{59}{60}$ and   1.   (d) 0   and $\frac{1}{100}$.

6. Consider $\{n|\quad 0 < n < 1\}$. Is there a Rational Number, $\left[\dfrac{a}{b}\right]$, so that there is no Rational Number $\left[\dfrac{c}{d}\right]$, $\dfrac{a}{b} < \dfrac{c}{d} < \dfrac{1}{1}$? Is there a Rational Number that is the "closest" to   1?   to   0?

7. If $\mathcal{U} = $ Set of Rational Numbers graph $A \times A$ if:

(a) $A = \{n|\quad n < 2\frac{1}{2}\}$.
(b) $A = \{n|\quad n < 10\}$.
(c) $A = \{n|\quad n$ is a Rational Number$\}$.
(d) $A = \{n|\quad 5 < n < 6\}$.
(e) $A = \{n|\quad 4 < n < 5\frac{1}{2}\}$.

8. Cite the property that justifies each step within the following:

(a) If $5n + 6 = 36$, then $5n + 6 = 30 + 6$.
   If $5n + 6 = 30 + 6$, then $5n = 30$.
   If $5n = 30$, then $n = 6$.
(b) If $\frac{4}{3}n + 16 = 20$, then $\frac{4}{3}n + 16 = 4 + 16$.
   If $\frac{4}{3}n + 16 = 4 + 16$, then $\frac{4}{3}n = 4$.
   If $\frac{4}{3}n = 4$, then $4n = 12$.
   If $4n = 12$, then $n = 3$.
(c) If $8n/3 < 15$, then $8n < 45$.
   If $8n < 45$, then $n < \frac{45}{8}$.
(d) If $a + c = b + c$, then $(a + c) + (-c) = (b + c) + (-c)$.
   If $(a + c) + (-c) = (b + c) + (-c)$, then $a + [c + (-c)] = b + [c + (-c)]$.
   If $a + [c + (-c)] = b + [c + (-c)]$, then $a + 0 = b + 0$.
   If $a + 0 = b + 0$, then $a = b$.
(e) If $-n < -x$, then $(-1)(-n) > (-1)(-x)$.
   If $(-1)(-n) > (-1)(-x)$, then $n > x$.
(f) If $-n < 0$, then $(-1)(-n) > (-1)(0)$.
   If $(-1)(-n) > (-1)(0)$, then $(-1)(-n) > 0$.
   If $(-1)(-n) > 0$, then $n > 0$.

9. Evaluate. Leave answers in simplest form. No denominator is zero.

(a) $\dfrac{-5n}{9} + \dfrac{2n}{3} =$

(b) $\left(\dfrac{2-n}{3}\right) + \dfrac{n}{3} =$

(c) $\dfrac{6}{x} - \dfrac{-3}{y} =$

(d) $\dfrac{-5}{7n} - \dfrac{3}{8n} =$

(e) $\dfrac{n-5}{9} + \dfrac{-2}{3} =$

(f) $\left(\dfrac{m}{n} - \dfrac{1}{3}\right) + \dfrac{-6}{n} =$

(g) $\dfrac{n}{n-1} - \dfrac{-n}{n+1} =$

(h) $\dfrac{9n^2}{7} - \left(\dfrac{-9}{n} + \dfrac{n^2}{7}\right) =$

(i) $\left(\dfrac{7}{12y} - \dfrac{3}{44}\right) + \dfrac{4}{18xy} =$

(j) $\left(\dfrac{m}{n} - 2\right) + \dfrac{n}{m} =$

(k) $\left(\dfrac{2}{3} + \dfrac{n}{m}\right) - 4 =$

(l) $\left(\dfrac{6}{n-3} + n\right) - \dfrac{2}{3} =$

(m) $\left(\dfrac{1}{n} - \dfrac{1}{n-m}\right) + \dfrac{2}{5} =$

(n) $\left(n - \dfrac{1}{n-1}\right) + \dfrac{4}{7} =$

(o) $\left(\dfrac{n-2}{3} - 4\right) + n =$

(p) $\left(\dfrac{2}{n-2} + 1\right) - n =$

(q) $\left(n - \dfrac{1}{n-2}\right) + \dfrac{5}{7} =$

(r) $\left(\dfrac{5}{7-n} - \dfrac{n}{7-n}\right) - 4 =$

10. Evaluate. No denominator is zero.

(a) $(-4)(-3) =$

(b) $(-4)(-4)(-4) =$

(c) $(2)(-3)(5) =$

(d) $(-4)(-2)(3) =$

(e) $(5)(2)(-10) =$

(f) $(-6)(8)(6) =$

(g) $\left(\dfrac{-4}{3}\right)\left(\dfrac{5}{4}\right) =$

(h) $\left(\dfrac{-5}{2}\right)\left(\dfrac{-4}{7}\right) =$

(i) $\left(\dfrac{x+1}{y}\right)\left(\dfrac{-2}{3}\right) =$

(j) $\left(\dfrac{n-2}{3}\right)\left(\dfrac{2}{x-1}\right) =$

(k) $\left(\dfrac{3n-1}{2}\right)\left(\dfrac{4}{3n-1}\right) =$

(l) $\left(\dfrac{n-1}{2}\right)\left(\dfrac{n+1}{3}\right) =$

(m) $\left(\dfrac{-m}{n}\right)\left(\dfrac{-m}{n-1}\right) =$

(n) $\left(\dfrac{16}{m}\right)\left(\dfrac{m-1}{4}\right)\left(\dfrac{-m}{4}\right) =$

11. Evaluate by division. No denominator is zero.

(a) $\dfrac{\dfrac{-3}{5}}{\dfrac{5}{8}} =$

(b) $\dfrac{\dfrac{a}{3}}{\dfrac{-m}{n}} =$

(c) $\dfrac{\dfrac{2-n}{2+n}}{\dfrac{-3}{n}} =$

(d) $\dfrac{\dfrac{n+1}{2-n}}{\dfrac{-4}{2-n}} =$

(e) $\dfrac{-n}{\dfrac{2}{3}} =$

(f) $\dfrac{\dfrac{1}{n}-1}{1-\dfrac{1}{n}} =$

(g) $\dfrac{n-\dfrac{6}{n}}{n-\dfrac{2}{n}} =$

(h) $\dfrac{\dfrac{n-2}{n}+2}{\dfrac{n-4}{n}-3} =$

(i) $\dfrac{1-\dfrac{4}{n-3}}{2-\dfrac{2}{n-3}} =$

(j) $\dfrac{\dfrac{4}{n-1}-2}{\dfrac{8}{n-1}-4} =$

12. Evaluate, using the right hand distributive property of multiplication over addition or subtraction:

(a) $\left(\dfrac{-3}{n}+\dfrac{2}{3}\right) \div \dfrac{5}{8} =$

(b) $\left(\dfrac{3}{n-1}-\dfrac{4}{3}\right) \div \dfrac{-2}{9} =$

(c) $\left(\dfrac{-2}{n-1}-\dfrac{4}{3}\right) \div \dfrac{2}{n-1} =$

(d) $\left(\dfrac{4}{n-2}+\dfrac{3}{4}\right) \div \dfrac{-2}{5} =$

(e) $\left(\dfrac{-n}{n+m}+\dfrac{3}{2}\right) \div \dfrac{m}{n} =$

(f) $\left(\dfrac{-m}{m-n}-\dfrac{1}{2}\right) \div \dfrac{-n}{m} =$

13. From a high of   267.3   points, the stock market declined on successive days an average of $\frac{1}{3}$, $\frac{1}{4}$, and $\frac{2}{3}$ points. What is the point value of the stock market after these successive declines?

14. What is   1/2   of   7/8? of   15/16?

15. A recipe calls for   2/3   cup of milk, $2\frac{2}{3}$ cups of flour,   7/8   teaspoon of vanilla, and   5/8   cup of lemon, which will feed   12   people. If   18   people are to be fed using the above recipe, how much of each ingredient should be used?

16. A man's age is   70. Divide the measure of his age by   1/2   and add   35. What number do you get?

17. A tank is   3/5   full of water. Two-thirds of the water is drained from the tank. How much water is left in the tank?

18. "How many thirds are contained in $\frac{7}{8}$" means: $n \times \frac{1}{3} = \frac{7}{8}$. Find n.

19. Graph the following sets of Rational Numbers on the Rational Number Line:

(a) $\{n| \quad n < 2\}$.

(b) $\{n| \quad -2 < n < 6\frac{1}{2}\}$.

(c) $\{n| \quad n < -5\} \cup \{n| \quad n > 5\}$.

(d) $\{n| \quad |n| > 5\}$.

(e) $\{n| \quad n > -2\} \cap \{n| \quad n < 6\}$.

(f) $\{n| \quad n = 4\} \cup \{n| \quad n > 5\}$.

20. On coordinate axes, graph:

(a) $\{n| \quad 0 < n < 4\} \times \{n| \quad 0 < n < 5\}$.

(b) $\{n| \quad 0 < n < 4\} \times \{n| \quad 2 < n < 5\}$.

(c) $\{n| \quad n < 4\} \times \{n| \quad n < 10\}$.

(d) Let $M = \{$Rational Numbers$\}$. Graph $M \times M$.

21. Evaluate. Consider $a > 0$ and $-a < 0$:

(a) $|-7| =$

(b) $|7| + |-10| =$

(c) $|-7| + |6| + |-12| =$

(d) $|-5| + |-8| + |14| =$

(e) $|a| + |b| =$

(f) $|-a| + |-b| =$

CHAPTER 15

Per Cent and Percentage

15.1 INTRODUCTION

Governments, businesses, and industries make extensive use of per cent to describe physical situations to their employees or business associates. For example: the cost-of-living index increased by 6 per cent each year; the stock market rose 2 per cent today; the greatest possible error for this instrument is one tenth of one per cent; my commission on this sale is 6 per cent, or the interest on this loan is 10 per cent per year. Hence we are constantly faced with the *per cent* concept.

Definition 15.1—Per Cent A fraction with denominator 100 is defined as a per cent.*

The fraction $\frac{1}{100}$ means 1 per cent; $\frac{5}{100}$ means 5 per cent; $\frac{6}{100}$ means 6 per cent. In general, if n is a Whole Number, $\frac{n}{100}$ means n per cent.

---

* The term per cent is derived from the Latin percentum, meaning "by the hundred," or "per hundred".

When working with fractions as per cents, it becomes necessary to express per cents as fractions and fractions as per cents. In order to perform this operation, the following definition is made.

Definition 15.2　　The numeral　　"%"　　means a per cent.

To express a per cent as a common fraction we write:

$$1\% \quad \text{means} \quad 1\left(\frac{1}{100}\right) = \frac{1}{100},$$

$$7\tfrac{1}{2}\% \quad \text{means} \quad 7\tfrac{1}{2}\left(\frac{1}{100}\right) = \frac{7\tfrac{1}{2}}{100} = \frac{15}{200},$$

$$125\% \quad \text{means} \quad 125\left(\frac{1}{100}\right) = \frac{125}{100},$$

$$\tfrac{3}{4}\% \quad \text{means} \quad \tfrac{3}{4}\left(\frac{1}{100}\right) = \frac{3}{400}.$$

If　　n　　is a Whole Number,　　$n\%$　　means　　$n\left(\dfrac{1}{100}\right) = \dfrac{n}{100}.$

We have two methods in order to express a fraction as a per cent. The first method is to obtain the equivalent form from the Theorem

$$\frac{a}{b} = \frac{n(a)}{n(b)}, \quad n \neq 0.$$

(a) $\dfrac{2}{5} = \dfrac{2(20)}{5(20)} = \dfrac{40}{100} = 40\%.$

(b) $\dfrac{2}{3} = \dfrac{2(33\tfrac{1}{3})}{3(33\tfrac{1}{3})} = \dfrac{66\tfrac{2}{3}}{100} = 66\tfrac{2}{3}\%.$

(c) $\dfrac{5}{8} = \dfrac{5(12\tfrac{1}{2})}{8(12\tfrac{1}{2})} = \dfrac{62\tfrac{1}{2}}{100} = 62\tfrac{1}{2}\%.$

One also recalls from the study of Rational Numbers, that if　　$\dfrac{a}{b} = \dfrac{c}{d},$

then　　$a(d) = b(c)$. To express the fraction　　$\dfrac{a}{b}$　　with denominator 100　　we use the particular form:

$$\frac{a}{b} = \frac{c}{100},$$

$$a(100) = b(c),$$

$$\frac{a(100)}{b} = c.$$

For example:

(a) If $\dfrac{12}{25} = \dfrac{c}{100}$, $\dfrac{12(100)}{25} = c = 48$. Therefore, $\dfrac{12}{25} = \dfrac{48}{100} =$

48%.

(b) If $\dfrac{2}{15} = \dfrac{c}{100}$, $\dfrac{2(100)}{15} = c = 13\frac{1}{3}$. Therefore, $\dfrac{2}{15} = \dfrac{13\frac{1}{3}}{100} =$

$13\frac{1}{3}$%.

(c) If $\dfrac{9}{8} = \dfrac{c}{100}$, $\dfrac{9(100)}{8} = c = 112\frac{1}{2}$. Therefore, $\dfrac{9}{8} = \dfrac{112\frac{1}{2}}{100} =$

$= 112\frac{1}{2}$%.

PROBLEM SET 15.1

1. Express each of the following per cents as a simple fraction:

(a) 25%.
(b) 32 1/2%.
(c) 85 3/4%.
(d) 130%.
(e) 23 2/3%.
(f) 1/2%.
(g) 1 1/2%.
(h) 175%.
(i) 1/4%.
(j) 3/5%.
(k) $\frac{7}{10}$%.
(l) 8/9%.

2. Express each of the following common fractions as a per cent. Use either of the two methods described above.

(a) $\frac{3}{5}$.
(b) $\frac{7}{50}$.
(c) $\frac{3}{7}$.
(d) $\frac{7}{8}$.
(e) $\frac{30}{200}$.
(f) $\frac{25}{150}$.
(g) $\frac{61}{75}$.
(h) $\frac{4}{1}$.
(i) $\frac{300}{88}$.
(j) $1\frac{7}{8}$.
(k) $5\frac{2}{3}$.
(l) $4\frac{5}{9}$.

15.2 APPLICATIONS OF PER CENT

Applications for fractions as per cents fall generally into three categories. These categories are outlined below, and are generally referred to as problems that involve percentages.

Definition 15.3—Percentage If each of a/b and $c/100$ is a fraction, $a/b = c/100$, then number a is defined as the percentage of b, $b \neq 100$.

To illustrate this definition, consider the following.

(a) John has   150   marbles. He gives   10 *per cent* of these marbles to his friend, James. How many marbles did John give to James?

Solution. The number of marbles James receives is the *percentage* of the total number of marbles. If for each   100   marbles, John gave   10 to James:

$$\frac{10}{100} = \frac{n}{150},$$

$$n = 15 \text{ marbles.}$$

The *percentage* of marbles given to James is   15   marbles.

(b) The converse of this problem is stated: John has   150   marbles. He gives   15   marbles (the percentage of marbles) to James. What *per cent* of the marbles did John give to James?

Solution. If for each   150   marbles, John gives   15, we are essentially asked how many marbles he would give to James if he had   100 marbles:

$$\frac{15}{150} = \frac{n}{100}, \qquad n = 10.$$

Therefore, John gave away   10   per cent of his marbles.

(c) The problem can be stated in still another manner. John gave   10 per cent of his marbles to James. If John gave James   15   marbles (the percentage of marbles), how many marbles did John have originally? Since for each   100   marbles John gave away   10, then if John gave away   15   marbles:

$$\frac{10}{100} = \frac{15}{n}, \qquad n = 150.$$

John originally had   150   marbles.

The following problems involve per cent and percentage. Solutions are also included.

EXAMPLE

Eighty boys attended summer school last season, and   75%   of these boys passed arithmetic. How many boys passed arithmetic?

Solution. In this case, we want the *percentage* of boys who passed arithmetic. Since 75 per cent of the boys passed arithmetic, this means that if 100 boys had attended summer school, 75 of them would have passed. However, only 80 boys attended school:

$$\frac{75}{100} = \frac{x}{80}, \qquad x = 60.$$

Therefore, 60 boys passed arithmetic.

EXAMPLE

Eighty boys attended summer school and 60 of these boys passed arithmetic. What *per cent* of the boys passed arithmetic?

Solution. Since 60 of the 80 boys passed arithmetic, the per cent of the boys who passed arithmetic would be the same as finding how many boys would pass arithmetic if 100 has attended summer school:

$$\frac{60}{80} = \frac{n}{100}, \qquad n = 75.$$

Therefore, 75 per cent of the boys passed arithmetic.

EXAMPLE

In school, last summer, 75 per cent of the boys passed arithmetic. Sixty boys passed. How many boys attended school?

Solution. If 75% of the boys passed, this means that on a basis of 100 boys, 75 would pass. However, only 60 boys passed:

$$\frac{75}{100} = \frac{60}{n}, \qquad n = 80.$$

Therefore, 80 boys attended school.

The method of solving per cent and percentage problems as outlined above is by *ratio* and *proportion*. Each example makes use of the principle:

$$\frac{75}{100} \text{ is proportional to } \frac{60}{80}.$$

15.3   PER CENT INCREASE AND PER CENT DECREASE

Another type of per cent problem is the type that involves a "per cent increase" or a "per cent decrease," a per cent that indicates a *rate of change*.

In solving problems of this type, the per cent change is always determined from the first given quantity. The following examples illustrate this principle.

PER CENT INCREASE

In the fall semester,   25   students enrolled for Supervised Rest 209. The next spring,   30   students enrolled for Supervised Rest 209. On the basis of the fall enrollment, what was the per cent increase in students?

The increase in students is represented below.

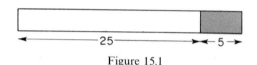

Figure 15.1

Since we desire to know the per cent increase, *based on the fall enrollment*, we should ask the question: If   100   students had enrolled in the fall, how many more (than   100)   students would be enrolled in the spring?

We see that for each   25   students, in the fall,   5   additional students enrolled in the spring. Therefore, if   100   students had enrolled in the fall,

$$\frac{5}{25} = \frac{x}{100},$$

$$x = 20.$$

Hence, the per cent increase, based on the fall enrollment, is   20%.

PER CENT DECREASE

In the fall semester,   30   students enrolled for Advanced Supervised Rest 310. In the spring,   24   students were enrolled for this course. On the basis of the fall enrollment, what was the per cent decrease in students?

Since we desire to know the per cent decrease, based on the fall enrollment, we should first ask this question: If   100   students had enrolled in the fall, how many fewer (than   100) students would be enrolled in the spring?

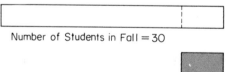

Number of Students in Fall = 30

6 = Number of Student Decrease

Figure 15.2

For each 30 students, 6 dropped. Therefore, if 100 students had enrolled in the fall,

$$\frac{6}{30} = \frac{n}{100}, \qquad n = 20.$$

Hence, on the basis of the fall enrollment, the per cent decrease was 20%.

PROBLEM SET 15.2

1. Find the following percentages, using ratio and proportion.

(a) 28 per cent of   750.
(b) 1/2 per cent of   290.
(c) 155 per cent of   80.
(d) $15\frac{1}{2}$ per cent of   120.
(e) $120\frac{3}{4}$ per cent of   110.

2. Find the specified per cents.

(a) 8   is what per cent of   20?
(b) 22   is what per cent of   10?
(c) 3   inches is what per cent of   3   feet?
(d) 60   cents is what per cent of   3   dollars?
(e) 1   dollar is what per cent of   25   cents?

3. Find the desired number if:

(a) 5   per cent of the number is   75.
(b) 1/2   per cent of the number is   10.
(c) 110   per cent of the number is   120.
(d) $12\frac{1}{2}$ per cent of the number is   1000.
(e) 1/4   per cent of the number is   20.

4. Find the per cent increase or decrease if:

(a) 450   pounds is increased to   500   pounds.
(b) 600   dollars is decreased to   500   dollars.
(c) 15,000   students is increased to   18,000   students.
(d) 20   cents is decreased to   15   cents.
(e) 33   pounds is decreased to   27   pounds.
(f) $1.25   is increased to $1.50.

5. In 1960, the enrollment of a certain university was   10,000. In 1965, the enrollment of this same school was   12,500. What was the per cent increase in enrollment?

6. School taxes in 1960 were $1.35   per $100   of evaluation. In 1965, taxes on the same property were $1.50   per $100   of evaluation. What was the per cent increase in taxes?

7. A class in mathematics originally enrolled thirty-three pupils. By the end of the twelfth class day, the enrollment was twenty-five pupils. What was the per cent decrease in pupils?

8. In September, 1965, fourteen Cub Scouts were enrolled in Den 44. In January, 1966, the enrollment was twenty Cub Scouts. What was the per cent increase in enrollment of this Den?

9. If the state sales tax is   2   per cent, how much tax must be paid on an article that costs $199.50?

10. A state sales tax is   2   per cent. If $1.20   is paid as tax on a certain item, how much did the item cost?

11. A river tested   3000   parts of salt in 1960. In 1965, this same river tested 3500   parts of salt. What was the per cent increase in parts of salt?

CHAPTER 16

Decimals:
Basic Definitions

16.1 INTRODUCTION

The purpose of this chapter is to introduce the decimal notation for fractions that represent Rational Numbers and to show how our place value numeration system can be extended to encompass this new notation. In the following chapter, an investigation of the four basic operations—addition, multiplication, subtraction, and division will be conducted.

In order to introduce decimal fractions, it is necessary for the reader to understand the meaning of *base*, *power of the base*, and *exponent*.

Definition 16.1 If each of a and b is an Integer, then a^b means $\underbrace{(a)(a)(a)\ldots(a)}_{b \text{ factors}}$. The number a is called the base, a^b is called the b'th power of the base a, and b is the exponent of the power.

For example:

    (a) In $10^3 = (10)(10)(10) = 1000$,   the base   is   10, 10^3 is called the third power of   10, and   3   is the exponent.

    (b) In $8^2 = (8)(8) = 64$,   the   base   is   8, 8^2 is called   the second power of   8, and   2   is the exponent.

    (c) In $3^3 = (3)(3)(3) = 27$,   the base   is   3, 3^3 is called   the third power of   3, and   3   is the exponent.

16.2   PLACE VALUE AND DECIMALS

A numeration system is a system for naming numbers. In our culture, we use a *base* and *place* system with Hindu-Arabic numerals and a base of ten. To undertake a study of decimals, a quick review of place value is appropriate, for decimals are a logical extension of the place value concept.

    Within our numeration system, any number may be expressed in expanded form:

    (a) $72 = 7(10) + 2$.

    (b) $836 = 8(10^2) + 3(10) + 6$.

    (c) $2653 = 2(10^3) + 6(10^2) + 5(10) + 3$.

This shows that the value of each digit within a numeral is uniquely determined by its relative position according to the following place value chart.

	Ten thousands	Thousands	Hundreds	Tens	Ones
- - - -	10^4	10^3	10^2	10^1	10^0
		4	4	4	4

4444 means $4(10^3) + 4(10^2) + 4(10^1) + 4$

Figure 16.1

    The chart illustrates that the value of any digit within a numeral has a value that is   10   times the value of the digit immediately to its right.

The reader is familiar with this pattern when extended *to the left* but in order to study decimals, it becomes necessary to extend this chart *to the right*.

To explain this extension *to the right*, Definition 16.1 suggests the following rules for multiplication and division when using exponents:

(a) $(a^4)(a^2) = (a \cdot a \cdot a \cdot a)(a \cdot a) = a \cdot a \cdot a \cdot a \cdot a \cdot a = a^6$.

(b) $(2^4)(2^2) = (2 \cdot 2 \cdot 2 \cdot 2)(2 \cdot 2) = 2 \cdot 2 \cdot 2 \cdot 2 \cdot 2 \cdot 2 = 2^6 = 64$.

(c) $a^5 \cdot a^3 = a^8$.

(d) $\dfrac{a^7}{a^5} = \dfrac{a \cdot a \cdot a \cdot a \cdot a \cdot a \cdot a}{a \cdot a \cdot a \cdot a \cdot a} = a \cdot a = a^2$.

(e) $\dfrac{2^7}{2^3} = \dfrac{2 \cdot 2 \cdot 2 \cdot 2 \cdot 2 \cdot 2 \cdot 2}{2 \cdot 2 \cdot 2} = 2 \cdot 2 \cdot 2 \cdot 2 = 2^4 = 16$.

(f) $\dfrac{3^5}{3^2} = \dfrac{3 \cdot 3 \cdot 3 \cdot 3 \cdot 3}{3 \cdot 3} = 3 \cdot 3 \cdot 3 = 3^3 = 27$.

These examples suggest the following definitions regarding Multiplication and Division.

Definition 16.2   If each of a, b, and c is a numeral which represents an Integer, then

(a) $a^b \cdot a^c = a^{b+c}$.

(b) $\dfrac{a^b}{a^c} = a^{b-c}$, $a \neq 0$.

(c) $a^{-b} = \dfrac{1}{a^b}$, $a \neq 0$.

(d) $a^0 = 1$, $a \neq 0$.

This Definition provides relatively simple methods to perform Multiplication and Division.

(a) $100(1000) = (10^2)(10^3) = 10^{2+3} = 10^5 = 100,000$.

(b) $8(4) = (2^3)(2^2) = 2^{3+2} = 2^5 = 32$.

(c) $(a^7)(a^3) = a^{7+3} = a^{10}$.

(d) $\dfrac{1000}{100} = \dfrac{10^3}{10^2} = 10^{3-2} = 10^1 = 10$.

(e) $\dfrac{125}{5} = \dfrac{5^3}{5^1} = 5^{3-1} = 5^2 = 25$.

(f) $\dfrac{a^7}{a^4} = a^{7-4} = a^3, \qquad a \neq 0.$

Parts (b) and (c) of Definition 16.2 present two important concepts. It is these concepts that we shall need in order to extend the place value chart in Figure 16.2.

(a) $\dfrac{100}{100} = \dfrac{10^2}{10^2} = 10^{2-2} = 10^0 = 1.$

(b) $\dfrac{8}{8} = \dfrac{2^3}{2^3} = 2^{3-3} = 2^0 = 1.$

(c) $\dfrac{a^7}{a^7} = a^{7-7} = a^0 = 1,\ a \neq 0.$

(d) $\dfrac{10}{100} = \dfrac{10^1}{10^2} = 10^{1-2} = 10^{-1} = \dfrac{1}{10}.$

(e) $\dfrac{10}{1000} = \dfrac{10^1}{10^3} = 10^{1-3} = 10^{-2} = \dfrac{1}{100}.$

(f) $\dfrac{10}{10000} = \dfrac{10^1}{10^4} = 10^{1-4} = 10^{-3} = \dfrac{1}{1000}.$

(g) $\dfrac{10^n}{10^{2n}} = 10^{n-2n} = 10^{-n} = \dfrac{1}{10^n}.$

Fractions with denominators expressed as a power of   10   as in (a), (d), (e), (f), and (g) above, are called decimal fractions.

Definition 16.3—Decimal Fraction   If a/b is a fraction that represents a Rational Number and if b is expressed as a power of   10, then a/b is a *decimal fraction*.

For example, $\dfrac{3}{10},\ \dfrac{45}{100},\ \dfrac{75}{10},$ and $\dfrac{3}{1000}$ is each a decimal

fraction because $\dfrac{3}{10} = \dfrac{3}{10^1},\ \dfrac{45}{100} = \dfrac{45}{10^2},\ \dfrac{75}{10} = \dfrac{75}{10^1},$ and $\dfrac{3}{1000} =$

$\dfrac{3}{10^3}.$ By using equivalent forms to denote the same Rational Number

$\dfrac{2}{5}$ can be expressed as the decimal fraction $\dfrac{4}{10}.$

$\dfrac{4}{25}$ can be expressed as the decimal fraction $\dfrac{16}{100}$,

$\dfrac{3}{8}$ can be expressed as the decimal fraction $\dfrac{37\frac{1}{2}}{100}$.

Decimal Numerals (called Decimals) are used to denote *decimal fractions*. This is made possible through use of the *decimal point* (dot .) and is illustrated below:

Decimal Fraction		Decimal Numeral
$\dfrac{1}{10^1} = \dfrac{1}{10}$	is denoted by	0.1
$\dfrac{1}{10^2} = \dfrac{1}{100}$	is denoted by	0.01
$\dfrac{1}{10^3} = \dfrac{1}{1000}$	is denoted by	0.001

$$\vdots \qquad \vdots \qquad \longleftrightarrow \qquad \vdots$$

If one digit occurs to the right of the decimal point, we say that the decimal numeral is expressed to *one decimal place*; if two digits occur to the right of the decimal point, then the decimal numeral is expressed to *two decimal places*. In general, a decimal numeral is expressed in n decimal places.

Definition 16.4 For $n \geq 1$, the decimal fraction $\dfrac{1}{10^n}$ is expressed as a decimal numeral:

$$\underbrace{0.000\ldots01}$$

$$n \quad \text{decimal places.}$$

or

$$n \quad \text{digits } \textit{after} \text{ the decimal point.}$$

The fractions $\dfrac{75}{1000}$, $\dfrac{8}{100}$, and $\dfrac{781}{10000}$ are expressed as follows.

(a) $\dfrac{75}{1000} = 0.075$.

(b) $\dfrac{8}{100} = 0.08$.

(c) $\dfrac{781}{10000} = 0.781$.

Since $0.075 = \frac{75}{1000}$,   "0.075" is read "seventy-five thousandths."
Similarly, since $0.37 = \frac{37}{100}$, "0.37" is read "thirty-seven hundredths;"
"0.009" is read "nine thousandths," because $0.009 = \frac{9}{1000}$.

As in the case for mixed numerals $22\frac{1}{2}$, $17\frac{1}{4}$, and $22\frac{2}{3}$, so can
numerals and decimals be "mixed." The expanded form for   22.3   is
$22 + 0.3 = 22 + \frac{3}{10}$, and is read "twenty-two and three tenths;"   200.009
$= 200 + \frac{9}{1000}$ and is read "two-hundred *and* nine thousandths;"
$1.06 = 1 + \frac{6}{100}$ and is read "one *and* six hundredths."

By investigating the above examples of division, we find that a parallel
has been established with the definition for decimals:

$$10^0 = 1,$$

$$10^{-1} = \frac{1}{10} = 0.1,$$

$$10^{-2} = \frac{1}{100} = 0.01,$$

$$10^{-3} = \frac{1}{1000} = 0.001,$$

$$\vdots$$

$$10^{-n} = \frac{1}{10^n} = 0.\underbrace{000\ldots01}.$$

(n digits after
the decimal point)

Since our system of numeration requires that the value of each digit
within a numeral denote a value that is   10   times the value of the digit
immediately to its right, we now can establish a basis for extending the place
value chart *to the right*. This basis is illustrated below:

100   is ten times as large as   10   because $10(10) = 100,$

10   is ten times as large as   1   because $10(1) = 10,$

1   is ten times as large as $\frac{1}{10}$ because $10\left(\frac{1}{10}\right) = 1,$

$\frac{1}{10}$ is ten times as large as $\frac{1}{100}$ because $10\left(\frac{1}{100}\right) = \frac{1}{10},$

$\dfrac{1}{100}$ is ten times as large as $\dfrac{1}{1000}$ because $10\left(\dfrac{1}{100}\right) = \dfrac{1}{1000}$,

$\vdots$

$\dfrac{1}{10^n}$ is ten times as large as $\dfrac{1}{10^{n+1}}$ because $10\left(\dfrac{1}{10^{n+1}}\right) = \dfrac{1}{10^n}$,

etc.

We denote the place values to the right of the "ones" position as "tenths," "hundredths," and "thousandths," etc.

Thousands	Hundreds	Tens	Ones	Tenths	Hundredths	Thousandths
$\cdots$ 1000	100	10	1	$\frac{1}{10}$	$\frac{1}{100}$	$\frac{1}{1000}$ $\cdots$
10^3	10^2	10^1	10^0	10^{-1}	10^{-2}	10^{-3} $\cdots$

Figure 16.2

The Hindu-Arabic system of numeration requires that by custom the last digit within a numeral be the "ones" digit. But by combining the concepts of (a) denoting fractions with denominators as powers of 10 with (b) the place value concept, the decimal point is introduced. This, (dot.) is used to denote that the number has a Whole Number portion and a decimal fraction portion. We have three forms to denote the same Number:

(a) $453\frac{27}{100}$ means $453 = \frac{27}{100}$, (Mixed Form).
(b) 453.27 means $453 + 0.27$, (Decimal Form).
(c) 453.27 means $4(10^2) + 5(10) + 2(\frac{1}{10}) + 7(\frac{1}{100})$, (Expanded Form).

           Whole Number   Fractional
              Portion   Portion

PROBLEM SET 16.1

1. Express   64   as:

(a) a power of   2.   (b) a power of   4.
(c) a power of   8.

2. Express $\dfrac{16 \times 64}{32 \times 8}$ as a power of   2.

3. Express $\dfrac{3^7 \times 3^3}{3^4 \div 3}$ as a power of   3.

4. Is $a^b = b^a$? Is $a^b + a^c = a^{b+c}$? Justify your answers by citing an example.

5. Express each of the following in decimal form:

(a) $3(100) + 0(10) + 7 + 3(\frac{1}{10}) + 0(\frac{1}{100}) + 5(\frac{1}{1000})$.
(b) $6(10) + 3(\frac{1}{1000})$.
(c) $7(\frac{1}{100}) + 4(\frac{1}{1000})$.

6. Express each of the following in mixed form:

(a) 234.02.   (b) 38.701.   (c) 0.098.
(d) 7.008.   (e) 1.0901.   (f) 4.080.

7. Express each of the following in decimal form:

(a) $\frac{3}{10} + \frac{7}{100} =$ (b) $21 + \frac{8}{10} + \frac{5}{100} =$
(c) $25 + \frac{8}{100} =$ (d) $\frac{8}{100} + \frac{16}{1000} =$
(e) $13 + \frac{7}{10} + \frac{17}{100} =$ (f) $22 + \frac{9}{1000} =$

16.3 TERMINATING DECIMALS

Any fraction, proper or improper, has a decimal representation (can be expressed with a denominator of   10   or a denominator as a power of 10). In some cases, this is rather easy, particularly so for fractions such as $\frac{1}{5}$ or $\frac{1}{2}$:

$$\frac{1}{5} = \frac{1(2)}{5(2)} = \frac{2}{10} = 0.2,$$

$$\frac{1}{5} = \frac{1(20)}{5(20)} = \frac{20}{100} = 0.20,$$

$$\frac{1}{5} = \frac{1(200)}{5(200)} = \frac{200}{1000} = 0.200,$$

$$\frac{1}{5} = \frac{1(2000)}{5(2000)} = \frac{2000}{10000} = 0.2000,$$

$$\frac{1}{5} = 0.2 = 0.20 = 0.200 = 0.2000 = \ldots.$$

Similarly,

$$\frac{1}{2} = 0.5 = 0.50 = 0.500 = 0.5000 = \ldots.$$

$$\frac{1}{4} = 0.25 = 0.250 = 0.2500 = 0.25000 = \ldots.$$

This illustrates that fractions may be expressed as infinite decimals. The set of infinite decimals may be partitioned into two subsets, (a) terminating decimals and (b) nonterminating decimals.

Definition 16.5—*Terminating Decimals* A terminating decimal is a decimal in which, after a finite number of digits, each succeeding digit is zero.

If a decimal is not a terminating decimal, then it is a nonterminating decimal.

As illustrated above, $\frac{1}{2}$, $\frac{1}{5}$, and $\frac{1}{4}$ are terminating decimals. Terminating decimals generally go by their shortest name:

$$0.200000 \ldots \text{ is abbreviated } \quad 0.2,$$
$$0.500000 \ldots \text{ is abbreviated } \quad 0.5,$$
$$0.250000 \ldots \text{ is abbreviated } \quad 0.25.$$

A convenient way to distinguish terminating decimals from nonterminating decimals is by investigating the prime factors of the denominator:

$$\frac{1}{5} = \frac{1(2)}{5(2)} = \frac{2}{10} = 0.2$$

$$\frac{1}{2} = \frac{1(5)}{2(5)} = \frac{5}{10} = 0.5,$$

$$\frac{3}{4} = \frac{3(25)}{4(25)} = \frac{75}{100} = 0.75,$$

$$\frac{1}{20} = \frac{1(5)}{20(5)} = \frac{5}{100} = 0.05.$$

The above illustrates the important concept: *If the prime factors of n are 2 or 5 or both 2 and 5, then there is some Counting*

Number,   x, such that $n \times x$ is   10   or is a power of   10.
If this is so, then the fraction can be expressed as a terminating decimal:

(a) $8 = (2)(2)(2)$. Therefore, $\frac{7}{8}$ can be expressed in terminating
decimal form by multiplying both numerator and denominator by the
Counting Number   125:

$$\frac{7}{8} = \frac{7(125)}{8(125)} = \frac{875}{1000} = 0.875.$$

(b) $20 = (2)(2)(5)$. Therefore, $\frac{14}{20}$ can be expressed in terminating
decimal form by multiplying both numerator and denominator by the
Counting Number   5:

$$\frac{14}{20} = \frac{14(5)}{20(5)} = \frac{70}{100} = 0.70.$$

(c) $25 = (5)(5)$; $\frac{9}{25} = \frac{9(4)}{25(4)} = \frac{36}{100} = 0.36.$

But if the prime factors of n are not   2 or 5   or   2 and 5,
then there is no Counting Number x such that $n(x)$ is   10
or is a power of   10:

(d) $\dfrac{1}{3} = \dfrac{(1)(3\frac{1}{3})}{(3)(3\frac{1}{3})} = \dfrac{3\frac{1}{3}}{10} = 0.3\frac{1}{3},$

(e) $\dfrac{1}{3} = \dfrac{(1)(33\frac{1}{3})}{(3)(33\frac{1}{3})} = \dfrac{33\frac{1}{3}}{100} = 0.33\frac{1}{3},$

(f) $\dfrac{1}{3} = \dfrac{(1)(333\frac{1}{3})}{(3)(333\frac{1}{3})} = \dfrac{333\frac{1}{3}}{1000} = 0.333\frac{1}{3},$

(g) $\frac{1}{3} = 0.3\frac{1}{3} = 0.33\frac{1}{3} = 0.333\frac{1}{3} = \ldots.$

By inspection of (d)–(g) above, we may intuitively conclude that $\frac{1}{3}$
may not be expressed as a terminating decimal and that the set of prime
factors of the denominator is not from $\{2, 5\}$. We make the following
observation.

If a/b is a fraction that represents a Rational Number and the set
of prime factors of b is $\{2, 5\}$, then a/b may be expressed
as a terminating decimal.

In summary, any Rational Number $\left[\dfrac{a}{b}\right]$ can be represented by
either a terminating decimal or a nonterminating decimal. Conversely,
every terminating decimal number is a Rational Number, but not every

Rational Number is a terminating decimal number. An investigation of nonterminating decimals will be made in a following chapter.

PROBLEM SET 16.2

1. Express each of the following as a terminating decimal.

(a) $8\frac{4}{20}$.   (b) $5\frac{6}{25}$.   (c) $3\frac{6}{20}$.

(d) $8\frac{17}{50}$.   (e) $5\frac{16}{25}$.   (f) $3\frac{7}{125}$.

2. By investigating the set of prime factors of each denominator, determine if each of the following can be represented as a terminating decimal. If so, express as a terminating decimal.

(a) $\frac{7}{300}$.   (b) $\frac{3}{22}$.   (c) $\frac{3}{200}$.

(d) $\frac{7}{150}$.   (e) $\frac{3}{80}$.   (f) $\frac{9}{60}$.

(g) $\frac{3}{500}$.   (h) $\frac{3}{140}$.   (i) $\frac{7}{110}$.

3. Express each of the following terminating decimals as a fraction $\frac{a}{b}$.

(a) 6.38.   (b) 7.023.   (c) 8.31.

(d) 10.01.   (e) 14.007.   (f) 8.0032.

CHAPTER 17

Decimals:
Basic Operations

17.1 INTRODUCTION

The basic operations of addition, subtraction, and multiplication are generally defined for terminating decimals. To divide the terminating decimal number a by the terminating decimal number b may, or may not, produce a quotient, that is a terminating decimal. For this reason, division is not discussed in this chapter.

Addition and Subtraction   One recalls from previous elementary experience that to form the sum or difference of two numbers represented as terminating decimals one "lined up the decimal point" and then proceeded to find the sum in the usual manner of column addition or of column subtraction, keeping the decimal points in its same relative position. This is made possible by retaining the place value system of numeration:

$$
\begin{array}{r}
8.32 \\
+\ 1.67 \\
\hline
9.99\ \text{(sum)}
\end{array}
$$

An investigation of this process will further explain decimal addition:

$$8.32 = 8 + 3(\tfrac{1}{10}) + 2(\tfrac{1}{100})$$
$$\underline{+\ 1.67 = 1 + 6(\tfrac{1}{10}) + 7(\tfrac{1}{100})}$$
$$= [8 + 1] + [3(\tfrac{1}{10}) + 6(\tfrac{1}{10})] + [2(\tfrac{1}{100}) + 7(\tfrac{1}{100})],$$
$$= 9 + (3 + 6)\tfrac{1}{10} + (2 + 7)\tfrac{1}{100},$$
$$= 9 + 9(\tfrac{1}{10}) + 9(\tfrac{1}{100}) = 9.99.$$

The above illustrates the principle for "lining up the decimal point" and then proceeding as in column addition for Whole Numbers, retaining the relative position of the decimal point in the sum.

This method is also appropriate for finding a sum when the number of digits following the decimal point varies among the summands:

$$
\begin{array}{r}
8.9 \\
1.008 \\
+\ 7.04 \\
\hline
\end{array}
$$

because

$$8.9 = 8.90 = 8.900 = 8.9000 = \ldots,$$
$$1.008 = 1.0080 = 1.00800 = 1.008000 = \ldots,$$
$$7.04 = 4.040 = 7.0400 = 7.04000 = \ldots.$$

By selecting names so that each summand has the same number of digits following the decimal point, addition is performed in the usual manner:

$$
\begin{array}{r}
8.900 \\
1.008 \\
+\ 7.040 \\
\hline
16.948
\end{array}
$$

Since the sum $n + 0 = n$, for any n, the practice of naming each number with the same number of digits is generally not performed:

$$
\begin{array}{r}
8.9 \\
1.008 \\
+\ 7.04 \\
\hline
16.948
\end{array}
$$

Addition that involves the "carrying" or regrouping process is still applicable because of place values:

$$8.9 \ = 8 + 9(\tfrac{1}{10}),$$
$$+ \ 0.78 = 0 + 7(\tfrac{1}{10}) + 8(\tfrac{1}{1000}),$$

$$= [8 + 0] + [9(\tfrac{1}{10}) + 7(\tfrac{1}{10})] + 8(\tfrac{1}{100}),$$
$$= 8 + (9 + 7)\tfrac{1}{10} + 8(\tfrac{1}{100}),$$
$$= 8 + 16(\tfrac{1}{10}) + 8(\tfrac{1}{100}).$$

By renaming $16(\tfrac{1}{10})$ as:

$$16(\tfrac{1}{10}) = (10 + 6)\tfrac{1}{10},$$
$$= 10(\tfrac{1}{10}) + 6(\tfrac{1}{10}),$$
$$= 1 + 6(\tfrac{1}{10}),$$

the sum now becomes:

$$8.9$$
$$+ \ 0.78$$
$$= 8 + [1 + 6(\tfrac{1}{10})] + 8(\tfrac{1}{100}),$$
$$= [8 + 1] + 6(\tfrac{1}{10}) + 8(\tfrac{1}{100}),$$
$$= 9.68.$$

This illustrates that "carrying" can be performed for addition of decimals just as in addition for Whole Numbers.

Subtraction   As in the case for addition, subtraction is performed by "lining up the decimal point" and proceeding in the usual manner. This is possible because of retention of place value.

One recalls that upon occasion, "borrowing" must be done. This is another regrouping procedure and is used in the manner established for column subtraction of Whole Numbers:

$$7.9 \ = 7 + 9(\tfrac{1}{10}) + 0(\tfrac{1}{100}),$$
$$- \ 4.72 = 4 + 7(\tfrac{1}{10}) + 2(\tfrac{1}{100}),$$

$$= (7 - 4) + (9 - 7)(\tfrac{1}{10}) + (0 - 2)(\tfrac{1}{100}),$$
$$= 3 + 2(\tfrac{1}{10}) + (0 - 2)(\tfrac{1}{100}),$$

from which we see immediately that $(0 - 2)(\tfrac{1}{100})$ has no meaning in the decimal notation. This illustrates the need for "borrowing" or renaming of the minuend. By expressing 7.9 as:

$$7.9 = 7 + 9(\tfrac{1}{10}),$$
$$= 7 + (8 + 1)\tfrac{1}{10},$$
$$= 7 + 8(\tfrac{1}{10}) + 1(\tfrac{1}{10}),$$
$$= 7 + 8(\tfrac{1}{10}) + 10(\tfrac{1}{100}).$$

The problem is now restated as:

$$7.9 = 7 + 8(\tfrac{1}{10}) + 10(\tfrac{1}{100}),$$
$$- 4.72 = 4 + 7(\tfrac{1}{10}) + 2(\tfrac{1}{100}),$$

$$= 3 + 1(\tfrac{1}{10}) + (10 - 2)(\tfrac{1}{100}),$$
$$= 3 + 1(\tfrac{1}{10}) + 8(\tfrac{1}{100}),$$
$$= 3.18.$$

Multiplication   Multiplication may be performed without regard to the relative position of the decimal point within the numerals. The following product illustrates this principle:

$$1.6 = 1 + 6(\tfrac{1}{10}),$$
$$\times 0.02 = \times 2(\tfrac{1}{100}).$$

By expressing each in expanded form and by using the distributive property of multiplication over addition, the product is found to be:

$$[1 + 6(\tfrac{1}{10})] \times 2(\tfrac{1}{100}) = 1[2(\tfrac{1}{100})] + [6(\tfrac{1}{10})][2(\tfrac{1}{100})],$$
$$= 2(\tfrac{1}{100}) + 12(\tfrac{1}{1000}).$$

By regrouping the partial product $12(\tfrac{1}{1000})$ as:

$$1(\tfrac{1}{100}) + 2(\tfrac{1}{1000}),$$

the product is expressed as:

$$= 2(\tfrac{1}{100}) + 1(\tfrac{1}{100}) + 2(\tfrac{1}{1000}),$$
$$= 3(\tfrac{1}{100}) + 2(\tfrac{1}{1000}),$$
$$= 0.032.$$

This example is consistent with the rule that the number of digits following the decimal in the product equals *"the sum of the number of digits following the decimal points in the factors."* This rule is explained by reconsidering the example $1.6 \times 0.002 = 0.032$. The number   1.6   contains "tenths" and   0.032   contains "hundredths." The product must contain

tenths	$\times$ hundredths	thousandths
$\tfrac{1}{10}$	$\tfrac{1}{100}$ $=$	$\tfrac{1}{1000}$
1.6	0.002 $=$	0.032,

1 decimal + 2 decimals = 3 decimals.

Since the concept of place value is preserved, this rule for multiplication allows us to multiply as in the case of Whole Number multiplication and then to "count off the number of decimals from the right:"

> 1.5   [Involves tenths, 1 digit following decimal.]
> × 0.16   [Involves hundredths, 2 digits following decimal.]
>
> ———
>
> 90
> .15
>
> ———
>
> 0.240   [Involves product tenths × hundredths = thousandths,
>   3 decimals following decimal point.]

Division may involve nonterminating decimal numerals. For this reason, division is not discussed until a later chapter.

17.2   DECIMALS AND PER CENTS

One recalls that a fraction with denominator 100 was defined as a per cent. Hence 5 per cent meant $\frac{5}{100}$, 2 per cent meant $\frac{2}{100}$, etc. One also recalls that the numeral "%" meant $\frac{1}{100}$. Fractions that are expressed as per cents are a subset of the set of decimal fractions:

(a) $0.2 = \frac{2}{10} = \frac{20}{100} = 20\%$.
(b) $0.33 = \frac{33}{100} = 33\%$.
(c) $1.2 = \frac{12}{20} = \frac{120}{100} = 120\%$.
(d) $0.0025 = \frac{0.25}{100} = 0.25\%$.

The concept of ratio is retained for solving problems involving per cent as illustrated below. In general, per cent fractions are expressed in their decimal equivalent.

(a) $33\frac{1}{2}\% = 33\frac{1}{2}(\frac{1}{100}) = 33.5(\frac{1}{100}) = 33.5\%$.
(b) $254\frac{1}{4}\% = 254\frac{1}{4}(\frac{1}{100}) = 254.25(\frac{1}{100}) = 254.25\%$.
(c) $\frac{1}{4}\% = \frac{1}{4}(\frac{1}{100}) = 0.25(\frac{1}{100}) = 0.25\%$.
(d) $\frac{2}{5}\% = \frac{2}{5}(\frac{1}{100}) = 0.4(\frac{1}{100}) = 0.4\%$.

PROBLEM SET 17.1

1. Express in expanded form:

(a) 82.16.   (b) 6.0008.
(c) 0.07.   (d) 2.408.
(e) 6.08.   (f) 71.081.

2. Express in decimal form:

(a) $1(1) + 8(\frac{1}{10}) + 3(\frac{1}{100}) =$
(b) $8(\frac{1}{10}) + 9(\frac{1}{100}) =$

(c) $7(10^2) + 4(10) + 7 + 8(\frac{1}{10}) + 9(\frac{1}{1000}) =$

(d) $3(10) + 5 + 5(\frac{1}{100}) + 8(\frac{1}{1000}) =$

(e) $7(10^2) + 2(\frac{1}{1000}) =$

3. Perform the indicated operation:

(a) $1.80 + 2.9 + 3.002 =$ (b) $23.04 + 9.1 + 8.06 =$

(c) $84.02 - 7.85 =$ (d) $48.007 - 8.06 =$

(e) $22.3 \times 1.07 =$ (f) $18.05 \times 2.92 =$

4. Change the following per cents to their equivalent decimal forms.

(a) 25%.   (b) 130%.   (c) 175%.   (d) 210%.   (e) $32\ 1/2\%$.

(f) $85\frac{3}{4}\%$.   (g) $23\frac{1}{5}\%$.   (h) $\frac{3}{4}\%$.   (i) $1\frac{1}{2}\%$.   (j) $4\frac{1}{4}\%$.

5. Express each of the following as a per cent:

(a) 2.   (b) 1.   (c) $1/2$.   (d) $3/4$.   (e) 1.25.

(f) 3.2.   (g) 0.25.   (h) 0.2175.   (i) 0.034.   (j) 0.0801.

6. Find n if:

(a) n is $1/2\%$ of   120.

(b) n is $1\ 1/2\%$ of   120.

(c) n is 200% of   35.

7. A state sales tax is $2\frac{1}{2}$ per cent of each dollar. If an item costs   380 dollars, what is the state sales tax?

8. In 1960, school taxes for a certain piece of property were   100 dollars. If the tax in 1968 was   120 dollars, what was the per cent increase in taxes?

9. The cost of living index rose   0.09 per cent between September and October. If a person made $1000 in September, how much should he make in October to have the same purchasing power?

10. It is estimated that   35.9 per cent of every person's income is paid in federal, state, and hidden taxes. If a person makes $12,500 in a year, how much is paid in taxes?

11. Assume that in 1933, the purchasing power of a dollar was   100 pennies. Presently, assume that the purchasing power of a dollar is   34 pennies. If a person made $4000 in 1933, how much must he make now in order to have the same purchasing power?

12. A person makes $250 per week. If   25.5 per cent of the salary goes to food,   13.8 per cent goes to savings, and   10.4 per cent goes to clothes, what per cent is left for other purchases? How much of each week's salary can go to other purchases?

CHAPTER 18

Decimals: Terminating and Nonterminating Repeating

18.1 INTRODUCTION

The decimal representation for nonintegral Rational Numbers was introduced in previous chapters. The reader should note that in every instance the decimal representation had a finite number of nonzero digits to the right of the decimal point. For this reason, the decimal was said to *terminate*.

It should be noted that every terminating decimal is a Rational Number, and may be expressed in the form a/b:

(a) $0.012 = \frac{12}{1000}$.

(b) $1.077 = \frac{1077}{1000}$.

(c) $2.001 = \frac{2001}{1000}$.

(d) $2.8686 = \frac{28686}{10000}$.

The reader can appropriately state that every terminating decimal may be expressed in the fractional form a/b. But is the converse of this sentence true, i.e., can every Rational Number expressed in the form a/b also be expressed as a terminating decimal? In order to answer this question, an investigation of the division algorithm for decimals is undertaken.

Division has been previously defined in terms of multiplication, and this same definition is applicable to decimals:

(a) If $\frac{1}{2} = x$, then $x = 0.5$ because $1 = 2(0.5)$.

(b) If $\frac{3}{4} = x$, then $x = 0.75$ because $3 = 4(0.75)$.

(c) If $\frac{62}{125} = x$, then $x = 0.496$ because $62 = 125(0.496)$.

The three examples above make use of the *definition* of division (division being defined in terms of multiplication). However, there is an algorithm that may be used to determine the value of x in each example. The algorithm is very similar to the one encountered in long division, except for the introduction of the decimal point and the location of this decimal point within the quotient.

EXAMPLE

If $\frac{3}{4} = x$, then $x = 0.75$ because $3 = 4(0.75)$.

One recalls that $3 = 3.0 = 3.00 = 3.000 = \ldots$. Hence the fraction $\frac{3}{4} = \frac{3.0}{4} = \frac{3.00}{4} = \frac{3.000}{4} = \ldots$. The algorithm for converting a fraction to a decimal proceeds as for Whole Numbers except for the location of the decimal point. The decimal point is located in the quotient directly above the decimal point of the dividend. Division is continued until a remainder of zero is obtained:

$$
\begin{array}{r}
.75 \\
4\overline{)3.0000\ldots} \\
28 \\
\hline
20 \\
20 \\
\hline
0
\end{array}
\qquad
\begin{aligned}
\tfrac{3}{4} &= 3 \div 4, \\
&= 3 \times \tfrac{1}{4}, \\
&= \tfrac{300}{100} \times \tfrac{1}{4}, \\
&= \tfrac{75}{100} = \boxed{0.75}.
\end{aligned}
$$

EXAMPLE

$$
\begin{array}{r}
.496 \\
125\overline{)62.0000\ldots} \\
500 \\
\hline
1200 \\
1125 \\
\hline
750 \\
750 \\
\hline
0
\end{array}
\qquad
\begin{aligned}
\tfrac{62}{125} &= 62 \div 125, \\
&= 62 \times \tfrac{1}{125}, \\
&= \tfrac{62000}{1000} \times \tfrac{1}{125}, \\
&= \tfrac{496}{1000} = \boxed{0.496}.
\end{aligned}
$$

In each of the above examples, both the numerator and denominator of the fraction were a Whole Number. We then expressed the numerator as a decimal and proceeded as in division of Whole Numbers. In general, the division algorithm provides that *only the denominator* be a Whole Number. This is done only for simplification purposes.

EXAMPLE

$$\begin{array}{r} \boxed{2.625} \\ 2{\overline{\smash{\big)}\,5.250}} \\ \underline{4} \\ 12 \\ \underline{12} \\ 5 \\ \underline{4} \\ 10 \\ \underline{10} \\ 0 \end{array}$$

$$\frac{5.25}{2} = 5.25 \div 2,$$
$$= 5.25 \times \tfrac{1}{2},$$
$$= \tfrac{5250}{100} \times \tfrac{1}{2},$$
$$= \tfrac{2625}{1000} \times \boxed{2.625}.$$

In the event both numerator and denominator are decimals, division is performed using an equivalent form with Whole Number denominator. An example of this is the following:

$$\frac{5.25}{0.2} = n.$$

In order to find an equivalent fraction with Whole Number denominator, one recalls that many other fractions are within the same equivalence class of fractions:

$$\left\{ \ldots, \frac{5.25}{0.2}, \frac{52.5}{2}, \frac{525}{20}, \frac{5250}{200}, \ldots \right\}.$$

By observation, we see that when the denominator of a fraction is expressed as a decimal, then there are many equivalent fractions with Whole Number denominators. The division is performed, not with the given fraction, but with *an equivalent fraction with Whole Number denominator.*

$$\frac{5.25}{0.2} = \frac{52.5}{2},$$

$$\begin{aligned} \frac{5.25}{0.2} &= 5.25 \div 0.2, \\ &= 5.25 \div \tfrac{2}{10}, \\ &= \tfrac{5250}{1000} \times \tfrac{10}{2}, \\ &= \boxed{26.25}. \end{aligned} \qquad \begin{aligned} \frac{52.5}{2} &= 52.5 \div 2, \\ &= \tfrac{5250}{100} \times \tfrac{1}{2}, \\ &= \tfrac{2625}{100}, \\ &= \boxed{26.25}. \end{aligned}$$

Using the equivalent form, the division algorithm is performed in the usual manner:

$$
\begin{array}{r}
\boxed{26.25} \\
2)\overline{52.50} \\
\underline{4} \\
12 \\
\underline{12} \\
5 \\
\underline{4} \\
10 \\
\underline{10} \\
0
\end{array}
$$

Another algorithm is used to find equivalent forms. This is done by "moving the decimal point a desired number of places to the right in both numerator and denominator."

To move the decimal point one place to the right is to multiply by 10; 2 places is to multiply by 100; 3 places by 1000, etc.

$$0.256 = 2.56; \qquad 0.256(10) = 2.56,$$

$$0.256 = 25.6; \qquad 0.256(100) = 25.6,$$

$$0.256 = 256; \qquad 0.256(1000) = 256.$$

Thus, any fraction with denominator a terminating decimal can be changed to an equivalent form by *moving the decimal points the desired number of places to the right*:

$$\frac{0.9}{0.2} \sim \frac{0.9(10)}{0.2(10)} = \frac{9}{2},$$

$$\frac{5.214}{0.7} \sim \frac{5.214(10)}{0.7(10)} = \frac{52.14}{7},$$

$$\frac{0.003}{22.14} \sim \frac{0.003(10)}{22.14(100)} = \frac{0.3}{2214},$$

$$\frac{212.000}{0.132} \sim \frac{212(1000)}{0.132(1000)} = \frac{212000}{132}.$$

Figure 18.1

18.2 NONTERMINATING, REPEATING DECIMALS

By using the division algorithm as studied in the preceding section, we are now ready to investigate the possibility that every Rational Number of the form a/b *cannot* be expressed as a terminating decimal.

EXAMPLE

Let $\frac{5}{12}$ be a fraction that represents a Rational Number and which can be expressed as a decimal.

One recalls from the definition of division that we are searching for the number n so that $5 = 12(n)$. In order to find n, we make use of the division algorithm:

(a)
$$\begin{array}{r} 0.4 \\ 12\overline{)5.00000} \\ 48 \\ \hline 2 \end{array}$$

$$5 = 0.4(12) + 0.2$$
$$= 4.8 + 0.2$$

Continuing the division and expressing the dividend as the product of the divisor times the quotient plus the remainder, we find the following.

(b)
$$\begin{array}{r} 0.41 \\ 12\overline{)5.00000} \\ 48 \\ \hline 20 \\ 12 \\ \hline 8 \end{array}$$

$$5 = 0.41(12) + 0.08$$
$$= 4.92 + 0.08$$

(c)
$$\begin{array}{r} 0.416 \\ 12\overline{)5.00000} \\ 48 \\ \hline 20 \\ 12 \\ \hline 80 \\ 72 \\ \hline 8 \end{array}$$

$$5 = 0.416(12) + 0.008$$
$$= 4.992 + 0.008$$

$$
\begin{array}{r}
0.4166 \\
\text{(d)} \quad 12\overline{)5.00000} \\
48 \\
\hline
20 \\
12 \\
\hline
80 \\
72 \\
\hline
80 \\
72 \\
\hline
8
\end{array}
$$

$$
\boxed{
\begin{aligned}
5 &= 0.4166(12) + 0.0008 \\
&= 4.9992 + 0.0008
\end{aligned}
}
$$

By continuing the division process, we find there will *always be a partial remainder of* 8, and consequently, the remainder will never be zero and the division does not terminate.

(e) $5 = 0.41666(12) + \boxed{0.00008}$.

(f) $5 = 0.416666(12) + \boxed{0.000008}$.

(g) $5 = 0.4166666(12) + \boxed{0.0000008}$.

(h) etc.

From the above, we see that the difference between the partial quotients $0.4, 0.41, 0.416, 0.4166, \ldots$ and $\frac{5}{12}$ becomes smaller as the number of digits increase following the decimal point. Thus these decimals are each *approximately* $\frac{5}{12}$:

Difference

(a) $\frac{5}{12} - 0.4 \longrightarrow \frac{1}{60}$.

(b) $\frac{5}{12} - 0.41 \longrightarrow \frac{1}{150}$.

(c) $\frac{5}{12} - 0.416 \longrightarrow \frac{1}{1500}$.

(d) $\frac{5}{12} - 0.4166 \longrightarrow \frac{1}{15000}$.

It is easily established that

$$
1/60 > 1/150 > 1/1500 > 1/15000 > \ldots
$$

which illustrates that the decimal approximations $\frac{5}{12}$ become closer to $\frac{5}{12}$ as the number of digits increase following the decimal point. We define the actual value of $\frac{5}{12}$ to be

$$
\frac{5}{12} = 0.41666\ldots,
$$

where the "6's" go on without end. This is generally shortened to:

$$
\frac{5}{12} = 0.41666\ldots = 0.41\overline{6}.
$$

The decimal representation for $\frac{5}{12}$ is called a nonterminating, repeating decimal (the 6's repeat without termination).*

Many other fractions must be expressed as a nonterminating, repeating decimal. In some of these representations, repeating groups of digits occur:

$$
\begin{array}{r}
0.3535\ldots \\
99\overline{)35.0000} \\
297 \\
\hline
530 \\
495 \\
\hline
350 \\
297 \\
\hline
530 \\
\vdots
\end{array}
\qquad
\begin{array}{r}
0.1212\ldots \\
99\overline{)12.0000} \\
99 \\
\hline
210 \\
198 \\
\hline
120 \\
99 \\
\hline
210 \\
198 \\
\hline
120 \\
\vdots
\end{array}
$$

When repeating groups of digits occur, they are defined as the period of the decimal. In the above, the periods are "35" and "12", respectively.

It can be easily shown that if the decimal representation for a Rational Number is nonterminating, then the decimal is repeating. Consider $\frac{2}{7} =$ n. In the division algorithm, the only possible remainders at each step can be a number from $\{0, 1, 2, 3, 4, 5, 6\}$ $(n = bq + R, \quad 0 \le R < b)$. Seven cannot be a remainder.

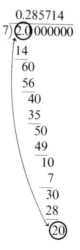

After at most six steps in the above division, one of the remainders must appear for the second time. But since we are "bringing down" zeros to associate with the remainders at each step, the digits within the quotient must begin repeating.

Repetition may begin prior to exhausting the complete set of possible remainders. In the illustration below, the complete set of possible remainders is $\{0, 1, 2, 3, 4, \ldots, 998\}$.

$$
\begin{array}{r}
0.013\overline{013} \\
999\overline{)13.00000} \\
999 \\
\hline
3010 \\
2997 \\
\hline
1300 \\
999 \\
\hline
3010 \\
2997 \\
\hline
13 \\
\vdots
\end{array}
$$

In summary, we find the two following important concepts: Every fraction that represents a Rational Number can be expressed as follows.

1. As a terminating decimal, or
2. As a nonterminating, repeating decimal.

18.3   FRACTION REPRESENTATIONS FOR NONTERMINATING, REPEATING DECIMALS

Next, we need to investigate if every nonterminating, repeating decimal can be expressed as a fraction a/b. In order to investigate this, we must assume two properties. The first of these properties is an "infinite" distributive property of multiplication over addition. An illustration of this "infinite" distributive property is illustrated by letting $n = 1.66\overline{6}$ and then finding $10n$.

EXAMPLE

Let $n = 1.66\overline{6}$. Then

$$n = 1 + \tfrac{6}{10} + \tfrac{6}{100} + \tfrac{6}{1000} + \tfrac{6}{10000} + \tfrac{6}{100000} + \cdots,$$

$$10n = 10[1 + \tfrac{6}{10} + \tfrac{6}{100} + \tfrac{6}{1000} + \tfrac{6}{10000} + \tfrac{6}{100000} + \ldots],$$

$$= 10 + \tfrac{60}{10} + \tfrac{60}{100} + \tfrac{60}{1000} + \tfrac{60}{10000} + \tfrac{60}{100000} + \ldots,$$

$$= 10 + 6 + \tfrac{6}{10} + \tfrac{6}{100} + \tfrac{6}{1000} + \tfrac{6}{10000} + \tfrac{6}{100000} + \ldots,$$

$$= 16.66\overline{6}.$$

The second property that must be assumed is one involving subtraction. We must assume that to subtract one repeating, nonterminating decimal from a like decimal, that each decimal representation has the same number of digits following the decimal point. Let us define the difference $16.66\overline{6} - 1.66\overline{6}$ to be:

$$10n = 16 + \tfrac{6}{10} + \tfrac{6}{100} + \tfrac{6}{1000} + \tfrac{6}{10000} + \tfrac{6}{100000} + \ldots$$

$$\underline{n = 1 \; + \tfrac{6}{10} + \tfrac{6}{100} + \tfrac{6}{1000} + \tfrac{6}{10000} + \tfrac{6}{100000} + \ldots}$$

$$10n - n = [16 - 1] + [\tfrac{6}{10} - \tfrac{6}{10}] + [\tfrac{6}{100} - \tfrac{6}{100}] + \ldots,$$

$$9n = 15 + 0 + 0 + 0 + \ldots,$$

$$9n = 15.$$

By assuming the two properties above, we can express any nonterminating, repeating decimal in the fractional form $\dfrac{a}{b}$.

EXAMPLE

If $n = 1.6\overline{6}$, express n in fraction form. There is 1 digit in the period and repetition begins by the tenths position, so multiply n by 10:

$$n = 1.6\overline{6}$$
$$10n = 16.6\overline{6}.$$

If n is subtracted from $10n$, we obtain the desired fraction:

$$10n = 16.6\overline{6}$$
$$- \quad n = 1.6\overline{6}$$
$$\overline{9n = 15,}$$
$$n = \tfrac{15}{9}.$$

The reader should verify that $\tfrac{15}{9} = 1.6\overline{6}$ by using the division algorithms.

EXAMPLE

If $n = 12.\overline{675}$, express n in fraction form.

There are 3 digits in the period and repetition begins by the thousandths position, so multiply n by 1000:

$$1000n = 12675.\overline{675}$$
$$- \quad n = \quad 12.\overline{675}$$
$$\overline{999n = 12663,}$$
$$n = \tfrac{12663}{999}.$$

The reader should verify that $\tfrac{12663}{999} = 12.\overline{675}$.

EXAMPLE

If $n = 4.05\overline{12}$, express n in fraction form.

This example is different from the two preceding examples because there are two nonrepeating digits, 0 and 5, and 2 digits in the period. Repetition begins by the ten thousandths position, so multiply n by 10000:

$$10000n = 40512.\overline{12}.$$

The nonrepeating digits terminate by the hundredths position. Multiply n by 100 and proceed with subtraction as before.

$$10000 = 40512.1\overline{212}$$
$$- \quad 100n = \quad 405.1\overline{212}$$
$$\overline{9900n = 40107,}$$
$$n = \tfrac{40107}{9900}.$$

This will conclude the introductory study of terminating and non-terminating, repeating decimals. We have shown a few examples that lead to the following generalization.

Any decimal may be expressed as a fraction that represents a Rational Number if its decimal is

(a) repeating and nonterminating, and
(b) terminating.

Conversely, the set of Rational Numbers may be separated into the disjoint subsets

(a) {Terminating decimals}, and
(b) {Non-terminating, repeating decimals}.

PROBLEM SET 18.1

1. Find the quotient for each of the following.

(a) 0.0075/3.   (b) 0.125/0.05.

(c) 3/0.075.

(d) 273/0.03.

(e) 0.0064/0.08.

(f) 0.005/0.025.

2. A piece of wood is   13.25   feet long. If this piece is cut into five equal lengths, how many feet, to the nearest one-hundredth foot, is in each piece?

3. A dictionary is   3.5   inches thick. If a page in the book is   0.002   inches thick, how many pages are in the book?

4. If   5.2   pounds of meat cost $6.25, find to the nearest cent, the cost of 7   pounds of meat.

5. Flour costs $0.065   per pound. How many pounds of flour can be purchased for $19.50?

6. Express each fraction as a terminating or nonterminating decimal.

(a) $\frac{3}{7}$.

(b) $\frac{5}{12}$.

(c) $\frac{3}{8}$.

(d) $\frac{7}{9}$.

(e) $\frac{2}{11}$.

(f) $\frac{7}{8}$.

7. Express each decimal as a fraction $\dfrac{a}{b}$. Reduce fractions to lowest terms.

(a) 0.33.

(b) 1.648.

(c) 33.02.

(d) 1.$\overline{67}$.

(e) 0.$\overline{33}$.

(f) 20.$\overline{51}$.

(g) 8.$\overline{55}$.

(h) 4.120$\overline{120}$.

(i) 8.40$\overline{167}$.

(j) 23.0$\overline{612}$.

(k) 0.01$\overline{23}$.

(l) 5.01$\overline{68}$.

8. The following are decimals that are nonterminating repeating:

(a) 1.01$\overline{01}$.

(b) 2.541$\overline{541}$.

Each of these can be made a nonterminating, nonrepeating decimal by inserting after each period some different value:

(a) 1.01301330133301333301 ....

(b) 2.541054100541000541 ....

Express each of the following as a nonterminating, nonrepeating decimal.

(a) 7.$\overline{12}$.

(b) 6.0$\overline{54}$.

(c) 4.0$\overline{74}$.

(d) 8.00$\overline{1}$.

9. If $n = 0.99\overline{9}$, does $n = 1$? Is n a nonterminating decimal?

10. If $n = 0.349\overline{9}$, does $n = 0.35$?

11. If $n = 0.39\overline{9}$, does $n = 0.4$?

18.4   APPROXIMATIONS

In this section, we shall undertake studies regarding closure, commutativity, and associativity for addition and multiplication, order relations, and some operations involving nonterminating, repeating decimals.

First, recall that we established that every fraction could be expressed as a terminating, or nonterminating, repeating decimal. Second, recall that we established that every terminating or nonterminating, repeating decimal could be expressed as a fraction a/b. Since this is the case, all properties including the closure, commutative, and associative properties for multiplication and addition will be true for the set of terminating or nonterminating repeating decimals. In general, since the set containing all terminating, or nonterminating, repeating decimals is the set of Rational Numbers, all properties pertaining to the set of Rational Numbers are also true for these two sets of decimals. Particularly, since each terminating, or nonterminating, repeating decimal is a Rational Number, properties for the relation $=$ and the relation $<$ are true for these two sets.

In order to determine equality or inequality for nonterminating, repeating decimals, we may first express each as a fraction a/b and proceed in the usual manner, using the same tests as before.

(a) $0.99\bar{9} = 1$. This is so because

$$10n = 9.99\bar{9}$$
$$n = 0.99\bar{9}$$
$$\overline{9n = 9,}$$
$$n = 1.$$

(b) $0.33\bar{3} < 0.34$. This is true because $\frac{1}{3} < \frac{34}{100}$.

(c) $1.6\bar{6} < 1.7$. $(1\frac{2}{3} < 1\frac{7}{10}$ or $\frac{5}{3} < \frac{17}{10})$.

(d) $1.3 < 1.3\bar{3}$. $(\frac{13}{10} < \frac{4}{3})$.

The above illustrates that properties of order are retained within the Rational Numbers, regardless of the symbols used to represent these numbers. Hence we introduce new names for the Rational Numbers. Consider the following equivalence classes of fractions that denote the particular Rational Numbers:

$$[\tfrac{1}{4}] = \{\tfrac{1}{4}, 0.25, \tfrac{2}{8}, \tfrac{3}{12}, \ldots\}.$$

$$[\tfrac{1}{3}] = \{\tfrac{1}{3}, 0.33\bar{3}, \tfrac{2}{6}, \tfrac{3}{9}, \ldots\}.$$

$$[\tfrac{5}{12}] = \{\tfrac{5}{12}, 0.41\bar{6}, \tfrac{10}{24}, \tfrac{15}{36}, \ldots\}.$$

$$[\tfrac{5}{3}] = \{\tfrac{5}{3}, 1.6\bar{6}, \tfrac{10}{6}, \tfrac{15}{9}, \ldots\}.$$

$$[\tfrac{7}{4}] = \{\tfrac{7}{4}, 1.75, \tfrac{14}{8}, \tfrac{21}{12}, \ldots\}.$$

$$[2] = \{\tfrac{2}{1}, 1.99\bar{9}, \tfrac{4}{2}, \tfrac{6}{3}, \ldots\}.$$

From the above, we see that both terminating and nonterminating, repeating decimals may be used to denote Rational Numbers.

18.5 BASIC OPERATIONS

Operations such as addition, subtraction, multiplication, and division may be performed by each decimal as a fraction that represents the same Rational Number. The examples below illustrate this principle.

Addition and Subtraction

EXAMPLE

$1.6\overline{6} + 2.87 = n.$ Find $n.$

$$1.6\overline{6} = 1\tfrac{2}{3} \quad \text{and} \quad 2.87 = \tfrac{287}{100}.$$

We use these equivalent forms to perform the addition:

$$n = 1.6\overline{6} + 2.87 = \tfrac{5}{3} + \tfrac{287}{100},$$

$$= \frac{5(100) + 3(387)}{3(100)},$$

$$= \tfrac{1361}{300} = 3\tfrac{161}{300}.$$

EXAMPLE

$n = 2.87\overline{87} - 1.6\overline{6}$ Find $n.$

$$n = 2.87\overline{87} - 1.6\overline{6} \quad \tfrac{285}{99} - \tfrac{5}{3} = 1.21\overline{21}.$$

Multiplication and Division

EXAMPLE

$n = 1.6\overline{6} \times 0.3\overline{3}.$ Find $n.$

$$n = 1.6\overline{6} \times 0.3\overline{3} = \tfrac{5}{3} \times \tfrac{1}{3} = \tfrac{5}{9} = 0.5\overline{5}.$$

EXAMPLE

$n = 12 \times 0.99\overline{9}.$ Find $n.$

$$n = 12 \times 0.99\overline{9} = 12 \times 1 = 12.$$

EXAMPLE

$n = 1.6\overline{6} \div 0.3\overline{3}.$ Find $n.$

$$n = 1.6\overline{6} \div 0.3\overline{3} = \tfrac{5}{3} \div \tfrac{1}{3} = 5.$$

EXAMPLE

$n = 0.6\overline{6} \div 0.3\overline{3} = \frac{2}{3} \div \frac{1}{3} = 2.$

PROBLEM SET 18.2

1. The following problems deal with terminating, or nonterminating, repeating decimals that represent Rational Numbers. In all problems, express these decimals in an equivalent form a/b. Then perform the indicated operation. Leave your answer as a terminating or nonterminating, repeating decimal.

(a) $3.58\overline{58} + 2.23\overline{23}.$
(b) $1.2\overline{2} + 3.7.$
(c) $8.6\overline{3} + 2.5\overline{1}.$
(d) $1.4 - 0.8\overline{7}.$
(e) $32.5\overline{11} - 17.8\overline{23}.$
(f) $2.3\overline{1} \times 2.78.$
(g) $8.0\overline{4} \times 4.6\overline{7}.$
(h) $2.0\overline{01} \div 0.2\overline{3}.$

CHAPTER 19

Measurement

19.1 INTRODUCTION

On many occasions approximate numbers are used to denote properties such as weight, distance, time, or area. For example, "the distance from the earth to the moon is 200,000 miles," and "the population of New York City is 9,000,000 people" is each an approximation for a particular distance or a particular population.

Contrasted to *approximate* numbers are *exact* numbers. Consider the following statements which illustrate the use of *exact* or approximate numbers.

(a) There are exactly 172 apples in the bushel and the weight of these apples is approximately 86 pounds.
(b) It took exactly 102 strokes for 18 holes of golf and he walked approximately 7200 yards on the golf course.

We can count the exact number of students in this classroom or count the exact number of people in the United States. However, we do not count the length of a room, we *measure* the length. Neither do we count the distance between Los Angeles and New York City, we *measure* the distance.

When numbers are used in the exact sense, such as to denote the individual objects in a finite set, we say that the number is defined as a *discrete* or an *exact* number. The set of Counting Numbers is used in a discrete manner when "counting the days in January," "counting the steps in the staircase," or "counting the number of days until Christmas."

Measurement is used to associate the number with the *magnitude* of an object or of a set of objects. Estimates of weight, height, length, distance, capacity, or time are placed into the general category of *measurements*. This is so because *none of the above can be described exactly*. It is primarily true because the instruments used to measure weights, heights, etc. cannot be made to be exactly   1   ft. in length or exactly   1   lb. in weight. Therefore, we have two processes: the process of *counting* (exact), and the process of *measuring*.

However, the set of Counting (exact) Numbers may be used in such a manner that they indicate an *approximate* value. For example, if we start with the two separate notions of a foot and an inch, then we discover that there are exactly   12   inches in a foot, but that *foot* is an approximate measure.

Approximations for nonterminating decimals are sometimes used in calculations. Therefore, the ideas of "rounding off" and of "error" are introduced. When a number is rounded off to some particular value, all digits to the right of the stated value are discarded. To round of   41.8751 to tenths,

Discarded

41.8|7518751875

Figure 19.1

to round off   82.05007   to hundredths,

Discarded

82.05|007

Figure 19.2

and to round off   1875   to thousands,

Discarded

1|875.

Figure 19.3

A rule is generally established regarding a change of the digit to which a number is rounded off. Almost everyone defines this rule as follows.

   (a) The digit to which the number is rounded off is *unchanged* if the first digit to its right is less than or equal to   4.
   (b) The digit to which the number is rounded off is *increased by*   1 if the first digit to its right is greater than or equal to   5.

Using this rule, we have the following examples.

   (a) 41.$\overline{8451}$ rounded off to tenths is   41.8;
   (b) 41.$\overline{8451}$ rounded off to hundredths is   41.85;
   (c) 41.$\overline{8451}$ rounded off to thousandths is   41.845;
   (d) 41.$\overline{8451}$ rounded off to ten-thousandths is   41.8452.

When either a terminating or a nonterminating decimal is rounded off to various place values, an   *n-place*   decimal approximation is obtained.

   (a) When a decimal is rounded off to tenths, a one-place decimal approximation is obtained.
   (b) When a decimal is rounded off to hundredths, a two-place decimal is obtained.
   (c) When a decimal is rounded off to thousandths, a three-place decimal is obtained, etc.

If a number is rounded off to   1   digit, a one-digit approximation is obtained.

   (a) 187.23   rounded off to a one-digit approximation is   200.
   (b) A two-digit approximation of   187.23   is   190.
   (c) A three-digit approximation is   187.23   is   187.
   (d) A four-digit approximation of   187.23   is   187.2.

Thus we have   *n-place*   decimal approximation and   *n-place* digit approximations. The notation $\approx$ is used to denote approximations.

$$14 \approx 14.1$$
$$0.3 \approx 0.3\overline{3}$$
$$20 \approx 19.6$$
$$17.6 \approx 18.$$

Many problems use   *n-place*   decimal approximations to perform calculations. Since these calculations involve approximate numbers, the calculations (in most cases) will give approximate values. This introduces the concept of Absolute Error, generally referred to as Error.

Definition 19.1—Absolute Error   If A is an approximate value
and V is an exact value, then the Absolute Error, E is defined
as:

$$E \quad = \quad A \quad - \quad V$$

$$\text{Error} = \text{Approximate} - \text{Exact}$$
$$\text{value} \qquad \text{value}$$

To illustrate Absolute Error, or more simply *Error*, consider the follow-
ing: Find the product of $0.3\overline{3}$ and $1.7\overline{7}$ by using three different
methods:

(a) Expressing $0.3\overline{3}$ and $1.7\overline{7}$ as fractions that represent
   their respective Rational Numbers (this will be the Exact Value).
(b) Rounding off each to a one-place decimal approximation.
(c) Rounding off each to a two-place decimal approximation.
(d) Find the Error in (a)–(c), above.

Solution.

(a) $(0.3\overline{3})(1.7\overline{7}) = (\frac{1}{3})(\frac{16}{9}) = \frac{16}{27}$. This is the exact value. $\frac{16}{27} = 0.59\overline{2592}$.
(b) $(0.3)(1.8) = 0.54$. The Absolute Error is $0.54 - 0.592592 =$
   -0.052592.
(c) $(0.33)(1.78) = 0.5874$. The Absolute Error is $0.5874 - 0.592\overline{592} =$
   $-0.005192\overline{592}$.

If we wished to continue in this manner, we would find that the   3-place,
4-place, and   5-place   decimal approximations produce smaller and
smaller Absolute Errors.

		Absolute Error
(d) $0.333(1.778) = 0.592074$	$\longleftarrow$	$0.000518\overline{592}$.
(e) $0.3333(1.7778) = 0.59254074$	$\longleftarrow$	$0.000052252\overline{592}$.
(f) $0.33333(1.77778) = 0.5925894074$	$\longleftarrow$	$0.000003185192\overline{592}$.

Note that in each case, except for (a), the product does not equal the
exact value for $(\frac{1}{3})(\frac{16}{9})$, but that the products more closely approximate
the exact value. This is so because each succeeding factor more nearly
approximates the exact values of $\frac{1}{3}$ and $\frac{16}{9}$,   respectively.

Absolute Errors occur also when forming the sum of approximate Values.
For example, consider the sum of $0.3\overline{3}$ and $1.7\overline{7}$:

	Approximate Value	True Value		Absolute Error of Sum
(a)	0.3	$0.3\overline{3}$		$-0.03\overline{3}$
	$\dfrac{+0.7}{1.0}$ $(-)$	$\dfrac{0.7\overline{7}}{1.1\overline{1}}$ $=$		$\dfrac{(+)-0.07\overline{7}}{-0.11\overline{1}}$
(b)	0.33	$0.3\overline{3}$		$-0.003\overline{3}$
	$\dfrac{0.77}{1.10}$ $(-)$	$\dfrac{0.7\overline{7}}{1.1\overline{1}}$ $=$		$\dfrac{(+)-0.007\overline{7}}{-0.011\overline{1}}$
(c)	0.333	$0.3\overline{3}$		$-0.0003\overline{3}$
	$\dfrac{0.777}{1.110}$ $(-)$	$\dfrac{0.7\overline{7}}{1.1\overline{1}}$ $=$		$\dfrac{(+)-0.0007\overline{7}}{-0.0011\overline{1}}$

The above also illustrates a very important concept.

The sum of the absolute errors is the error of the sum. This is stated in mathematical terms: let E_1, V_1, and A_1 be the Error, Exact Value, and Approximate Value for a given set of data. Let E_2, V_2, A_2, be the Error, Exact Value, and Approximate Value for a second set of data:

$$
\begin{array}{ccccc}
E_1 & = & A_1 & - & V_1 \\
E_2 & = & A_2 & - & V_2 \\
\hline
E_1 + E_2 & = & (A_1 + A_2) & - & (V_1 + V_2)
\end{array}
$$

(Sum of errors) = (Approximate − (Exact Value = (Error of sum)
                    value of sum)   of sum)

PROBLEM SET 19.1

1. Classify each of the following statements as to whether they involve exact or approximate numbers.

(a) The number of students in school.
(b) The weight of your car.
(c) The number of days in January.
(d) The thickness of a board.
(e) The number of eggs in one dozen.
(f) The diameter of a circle.
(g) The number of feet in one yard.
(h) The length of a room in yards.
(i) The temperature in Nome, Alaska.
(j) The volume of a gas tank.
(k) The number of beans in a jar.

2. Round off each of   97.8399   and   85.5472   to a (a) one-digit approximation, (b) two-digit approximation, and (c) a four-digit approximation.

3. By rounding off each of   0.3\overline{3}   and   0.6\overline{6}   to a (a)   1-place, and (b)
4-place, decimal approximation, find their product and the Absolute Errors of (a) and
(b), respectively.

4. Show, in a manner similar to that of the previous section, that Error decreases as
n increases in an n-digit   approximation by finding the product $(0.6\overline{5})(0.2\overline{3})$
by using (a) a   2-digit   approximation, and (b) a   4-digit   approximation.

5. In a county fair,   120   beans are placed in a jar. Lady A guesses   110
beans; lady B guesses   130   beans. Show that the sum of the errors is zero.

6. The exact dimensions of a room are   12   by   14   ft. A carpenter
estimates the room to be   11   by   15   ft and orders flooring material.
Show that the sum of the errors is zero. Will the carpenter have exactly enough material
to floor the room?

19.2 PRECISION

As stated previously, measurements are used to denote the magnitude of
objects. Measurements deal with properties such as time, length, speed,
pounds, and area. In each, the measure (a number) represents a number of
units. Many different standards can be used to establish a unit:

$$12 \text{ inches } = 1 \text{ foot (the unit is } foot\text{),}$$
$$24 \text{ hours } = 1 \text{ day (the unit is } day\text{),}$$
$$12 \text{ eggs } = 1 \text{ dozen eggs (the unit is } dozen\text{),}$$
$$16 \text{ ounces } = 1 \text{ pound (the unit is } pound\text{).}$$

On this basis, if we wish to find how many "dozen" eggs a grocer has, we
must first establish the criterion for a "dozen." Similarly, if we wish to
measure the distance between two points, in feet, we must establish the
criterion for a "foot." In general, if we desire to "measure" an object we
must first establish the criterion of a *unit*. The selection of a particular unit
will depend entirely upon the physical situation we wish to describe. We
might select the unit "inch" to measure the length of a table, but we probably
would not use this unit to measure the distance from the earth to the sun.

If we think of the line segment $\overline{AB}$, below, as satisfying the requirements
for a unit,

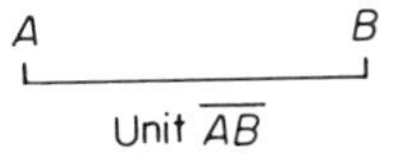

Unit $\overline{AB}$

Figure 19.4

we can think of the *measure* of other line segments *in terms of this defined unit.*

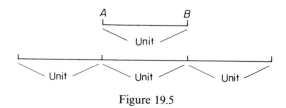

Figure 19.5

We define the measure* of line segment $\overline{CE}$ to be the number 3 and write

$$m(\overline{CE}) = 3.$$

As a parallel to the above, if we state that "the length of your desk is 3 ft," we mean that the foot has been established as the unit, and the measure of the length of the desk in terms of this unit is the number 3:

$$m(\text{length of the desk}) = 3.$$

If we state that the distance between Los Angeles and New York City is 5000 miles, we mean that the "mile" has been established as the unit and that the measure of the distance between these two cities in terms of this unit is the number 5000.

But not all measures are as simple. Suppose we establish the "inch" as the unit and then attempt to find the measure of the distance between points *A* and *B* on the line segment $\overline{AB}$:

Figure 19.6

By using the previously defined unit of "inch" we see that $m(\overline{AB})$ is not exact (is not a Whole Number).

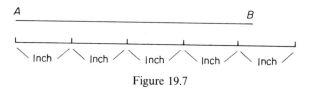

Figure 19.7

* Physical machines will never let us establish that $m(\overline{CE})$ is exactly three units.

When this situation occurs, we define then the measure of $\overline{AB}$ to be greater than 4 and less than 5:

$$4 < m(\overline{AB}) < 5.$$

Furthermore, if we estimate that the measure of $\overline{AB}$ is nearer to 4 than to 5, we say that *to the nearest unit*, 4 is a more precise approximate measure of $\overline{AB}$ than is 5:

$$m(\overline{AB}) \approx 4.$$

To say that $m(\overline{AB}) \approx 4$ means that the actual measure of $\overline{AB}$ lies somewhere in the interval $3.5 \le m(\overline{AB}) < 4.5$.

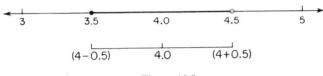

Figure 19.8

Any value greater than or equal to 3.5 and less than 4.5 will be rounded off to 4. The *greatest possible error* in the measure of $\overline{AB}$ is 1/2 of an inch.

Definition 19.2—Greatest Possible Error   The greatest possible error of an approximate measure is 1/2 the *unit* of the measure.

If we state that $m(\overline{AB}) = 4.2$, and the unit is $\frac{1}{10}$, then the greatest possible error is $\frac{1}{2} \times \frac{1}{10} = \frac{1}{20} = 0.05$, and

$$4.2 - 0.05 \le (\text{actual measure}) < 4.2 + 0.05,$$

$$4.15 \le (\text{actual measure}) < 4.25.$$

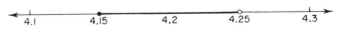

Figure 19.9

Some measurements describe a situation more precisely than other measurements simply because of the size of the unit involved. The *more precise* of two measures is the measure involving the *smaller unit*. This is so because the interval in which the actual measure must fall becomes smaller (and therefore more precise as the unit becomes smaller).

Suppose that carpenter A states that the length of a fence is   42   ft. Carpenter B says that the length of the same fence is   42.3   ft. Carpenter C states that the length of this fence is   42.84   ft.

(a) For carpenter A,   42   ft are interpreted to be precise to the nearest foot. (The unit is   1   foot.) The actual measure of the fence is greater than or equal to   41.5   ft but less than   42.5   ft.

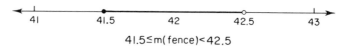

$$41.5 \leq m(\text{fence}) < 42.5$$

Figure 19.10

Since the approximate measure of the fence is stated to be   42   ft, the *actual measure* is greater than or equal to   41.5   and less than 42.5. Using the unit "1   foot" we see that the *greatest possible error* is 1/2   of   1   foot.

(b) For carpenter B,   42.3   ft is interpreted to be precise to the nearest   1/10   of a foot. (The unit is   1/10   of a foot.) We can now state that the actual measure of the fence is greater than or equal to   42.25   but less than   42.35. The actual measure then must fall in a much smaller interval.

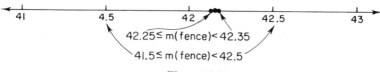

Figure 19.11

(c) For carpenter C, the actual measure must fall in still a smaller interval, $42.335 \leq m(\text{Fence}) < 42.345$.

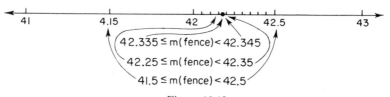

Figure 19.12

As illustrated above, the smaller the unit involved, the smaller the interval in which the actual measure must fall. This is the basis for *Precision*.

Definition 19.3—*Precision*   Measure A is said to be more precise than Measure B if the units of Measure A are smaller than the units of Measure B.

We see that the precision of a measure is dependent upon the unit, for as the unit decreases, the greatest possible error of the measure decreases. We also use the greatest possible error to determine the interval in which the actual measure lies:

EXAMPLE 1.

The most precise measure, to the nearest tenth, of a certain object A is   10.2.

    (a) The greatest possible error is $(\frac{1}{2})(\frac{1}{10}) = 0.05$.
    (b) $10.15 \le$ (exact measure) < 10.25.

EXAMPLE 2.

The most precise measure, to the nearest thousandth, of a certain object A is   10.200.

    (a) The greatest possible error is $(\frac{1}{2})(\frac{1}{1000}) = 0.0005$.
    (b) $10.1995 \le$ (exact measure) < 10.2005.

Since the unit of Example 2 is smaller than that of Example 1 the measure of object A in Example 2 is more precise than the measure of Example 1.

PROBLEM SET 19.2

1.   Round off each measure to the place indicated.

(a) 885.7 (tens).   (b) 8.723 (tenths).
(c) 9.477 (hundredths).   (d) 10.1256 (thousandths).
(e) 3766.5 (ones).   (f) 3746.5 (hundredths).
(g) 3746.5 (tens).   (h) 3746.5 (thousandths).

2.   Give a one-place, two-place, and a three-place decimal approximation for the following.

(a) $8.\overline{346}$.   (b) $10.7\overline{525}$.
(c) $9.8\overline{18}1$.   (d) $22.4\overline{89}$.
(e) $0.\overline{33}$.   (f) $0.\overline{66}$.

3. Are the numbers used in the exact or approximate sense in the following statements?

(a) There are ten people per table.
(b) The measurements of this room are   36   by   50   ft.
(c) There are   31   days in March.
(d) The decimal value for   3/7   is   0.42.
(e) The population of California is   24 million.
(f) The price of steak is one dollar per pound.
(g) Two thousand pounds is a short ton.
(h) The average weekly payroll is $225.
(i) The number of students is   15,583.

4. The following are measures, and each measure is precise to the unit indicated. Find the greatest possible error of each measure, and then determine the interval in which the exact measure lies.

(a) 56 (ones).   (b) 12.7 (tenths).
(c) 12.418 (thousandths).   (d) 8965.505 (thousandths).
(e) 3.808 (hundredths).   (f) 9.981 (tenths).

5. It is estimated, to the nearest   1000   miles, that the distance to the moon is 239,000   miles. Find the interval in which the exact distance lies.

6. It is estimated, to the nearest foot, that the length of a pool is   38   ft and the width of this same pool is   27   ft. Find the interval in which the exact area lies.

7. If the length and width of the pool of Problem 6 is estimated to the nearest inch, find the interval in which the exact area lies.

8. A toolmaker must make a certain part A that is precise to $\frac{13}{1000}$ of an inch. Part B must be precise to $\frac{1}{100}$ of an inch. Which part requires greater precision for manufacturing purposes?

19.3 ACCURACY

Some measures demand that for successful results, they be more precise than other measures. For example, consider rifleman X, who misses the bull's eye at   500   yds by   1   in. Rifleman Y misses the bull's eye at   50   yds by   1   in. On this basis, which rifleman do you consider the better shot?

Although we can state that each rifleman missed the bull's eye by only 1   in., we see that *on this basis*, at   500   yds, rifleman Y would miss the bull's eye by   10   in. :

$$\frac{1}{50} = \frac{10}{500}.$$

Suppose that councilman X estimated the population of his town to the nearest   1000   as   5000   people. In another town, councilman Y estimated the population of his city, to the nearest   1000   as 8,500,000. Which councilman do you believe to be better informed?

When estimating to the nearest   1000   people the population of a town as   5000   people, the greatest possible error is $\frac{1}{2} \times 1000 =$ 500. Similarly, the greatest possible error for the population of the city is 500:

$$4500 \leq \text{(population of town)} < 5500;$$

$$8,499,500 \leq \text{(population of city)} < 8,500,500.$$

Note that the greatest possible error in each of the above was   500. But which was the better estimate, that is, which guess had the less relative error.

$$\text{Relative Error} = \frac{\text{greatest possible error}}{\text{measure}}.$$

By dividing the greatest possible error by the measure, we obtain the following.

(a) $\frac{500}{5000} = 0.1 = 10$ per cent (the estimate was missed in a ratio of   1 for every   10). This is the Relative Error for councilman X.

(b) $\frac{500}{8,500,000} \approx 0.00006 = 0.006$ per cent (the estimate was missed in a ratio of   1   for every   6000). This is the relative error for councilman Y.

Although the unit in each of the above remained the same, it is readily established that   0.1   is approximately   1666   times as large as 0.00006. From this, we conclude that councilman Y's guess was   1666 times as *accurate* as the guess of councilman X.

Definition 19.4—Accuracy   The more accurate of two measures is that measure which has the *smaller* Relative Error.

In order to compare accuracy, the Relative Error is frequently expressed as per cent error. This is done for ease in understanding the seriousness of an error. The machinist whose error in cutting a part is   1/1000   "may be in far more serious trouble than the astronomer who misses the distance of a galaxy by   1/1000." In summary:

1. The more *precise* of two measures is the measure established from the smaller unit.

2. The more *accurate* of two measures is the measure with the smaller *relative* error.

PROBLEM SET 19.3

1. Denote which of the following is more accurate, when the conditions mentioned prevail.

(a) A measure of   8000   is estimated to the nearest   200   and a measure of 0.006   is estimated to the nearest   0.001.

(b) A measure of   3   is estimated to the nearest   1   and a measure of   100 is estimated to the nearest   10.

(c) A measure of   500   is missed by   4   and a measure of   20,000   is missed by   300.

(d) A measure of   0.5   is missed by   0.01   and a measure of   0.01   is missed by   0.005.

19.4   SIGNIFICANT DIGITS, SCIENTIFIC NOTATION

The discussions of unit, greatest possible error, and relative error lead to the importance of the digits that offer data regarding the exact value of an approximated value:

Definition 19.5—Significant Digit   Any digit that can provide information regarding the exact value of an estimated value is a *significant digit*.

Obviously, the next step is to find how digits provide information regarding exact values. Let us assume we are given the measure   10.2, precise to   1/10   (the unit is   1/10). Then *the number of units of measure determines the number of significant digits in   10.2.*

Under the conditions established above, there are   102   units in 10.2. We see that each of the   "1," the   "0," and the   "2"   provide information regarding the true value of an estimated value. By counting the number of digits in   102, we conclude that there are   *3 significant digits*   in   10.2, precise to   1/10.

Using this idea, we see that the number of significant digits is dependent only upon the number of units in a measure.

(a) Assume we are given the measure   0.0017, precise to   1/10000 (the unit is   1/10000). From this, there are   17   units in   0.0017   and the number of significant digits is   2.

(b) In the measure   8,500,000, precise to   100,000, the number of units is   85. Therefore, the number of significant digits is   2. This is summarized by the following.

Definition 19.6—Number of Significant Digits Given a measure n
which represents an estimated value, and the number of *units* of measure,
m then the number of significant digits of n is the number of
digits of m. The following chart illustrates this principle:

n	Unit	Number of units in n	Significant digits of n
8,500,000	10,000	850	3
8,500,000	1000	8500	4
8,500,000	100	85,000	5
8,500,000	10	850,000	6
8,500,000	1	8,500,000	7
7.0005	1/10000	70,005	5
7.0005	1/1000	7000	4
7.0005	1/100	700	3
7.005	1/10	70	2
7.005	1	7	1

Figure 19.13

As long as we know the unit of measure, we can always establish the
number of significant digits of n by determining the number of units
in n. The reader need not wonder whether or not "zeros" are significant
or insignificant, for the number of units in n determines their signifi-
cance.

With the introduction of significant digits completed, a method of
prominently displaying these significant digits is defined as *Scientific Notation,*
or Standard Notation.

If we were given the distance   16,070,000,000, precise to the nearest
1,000,000   then the significant digits are:

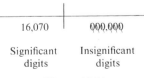

Figure 19.14

As illustrated below, we can express any number as:

Whole Number × Power of 10;

and in particular,

$$16,070,000,000 = 1,607,000,000.0(\underline{10}),$$

$$16,070,000,000 = 160,700,000.00(\underline{10^2}),$$

$$16,070,000,000 = 16,070,000.000(\underline{10^3}),$$

$$\vdots \qquad\qquad \vdots$$

$$16,070,000,000 = 1.6070000000(\underline{10^{10}}).$$

The above illustrates the principle of expressing a Whole Number as "a power of   10." If we wish to express a number as a power of   10 and exhibit only the significant digits, then the number is said to be expressed in Scientific Notation. In order to express a number in Scientific Notation, the following steps are followed.

1. Record *only* the significant digits, retaining their relative positions.
2. Insert a decimal point in the significant digits of (1) so that only *one* digit is to the *left* of this point, and
3. Multiply the number of (2) by the appropriate power of   10   so that the digits are restored to the proper positional value as stated in the given number.

To illustrate the rules above, let us assume that the estimated distance to the moon from the earth is   239,000, precise to the nearest   1000 miles. Then there are   3   significant digits in   239,000. By (1) above, record these significant digits in their relative positions

$$239,$$

Next, by (2), insert the decimal point so that only one digit is to the left of this point

$$2.39,$$

lastly, multiply   2.39   by the power of   10   that restores the digits to their proper positional value

$$2.39(10^5) = 239,000.$$

Scientific   Given
Notation   Number

We have then expressed   239,000   precise to the nearest   1000, in Scientific Notation.

Similarly, numbers less than   1   may be expressed in Scientific Notation, using the same procedures outlined above. However, the reader should recall that the value of digits to the right of the decimal point is determined by negative powers of   10:

$$0.1 = \tfrac{1}{10} = 10^{-1},$$

$$0.01 = \tfrac{1}{100} = 10^{-2};$$

$$0.001 = \tfrac{1}{1000} = 10^{-3}; \text{ etc.}$$

We can represent the measure   0.0214, precise to the nearest 1/10000, by recording the significant digits:

214,

inserting the decimal,

2.14,

and then multiplying by the appropriate power of 10:

$$2.14 \times 10^{-2} = 2.14 \times \tfrac{1}{100} = 0.0214.$$

Scientific   Given

Notation   Number

PROBLEM SET 19.4

1. Complete the following table for the following measures, each precise to the unit indicated. Find (a) the greatest possible error, (b) the relative error, and (c) the number of significant digits. Express each in Scientific Notation.

n	Precise to the nearest	Greatest possible error	Relative error	Significant digits	Scientific notation
8400	100				
30	1				
30	10				
1	1/10				
423	1				
0.2	1/10				
0.081	1/1000				
80.41	1/100				
8040	10				
8040	1				

Figure 19.15

19.5   CALCULATIONS WITH APPROXIMATE MEASURES

If two measures of the same precision are combined by addition, it was shown in Section 1 that the absolute error of the sum is the algebraic sum of the absolute errors of the given measures. To illustrate this, and to aid in stating rules for computations that involve measures of different precision, consider the following example.

EXAMPLE 1

Two boards,   11.2   ft and   13.5   ft, precise to the nearest   1/10 of a foot are placed end-to-end. What is the minimum length and the maximum length when the boards are placed end-to-end? Show that the sum   11.2 + 13.5 = 24.7, precise to the nearest   1/10   is not a true representative of the sum.

  Case I:

$$\begin{array}{l} \text{Board 1: } 11.15 \le \quad \text{(actual length)} \quad < 11.25. \\ \text{Board 2: } 13.45 \le \quad \text{(actual length)} \quad < 13.55. \\ \hline 24.60 \le \text{(actual end-to-end length)} < 24.80. \end{array}$$

Case II: But 11.2 + 13.5 = 24.7, precise to   1/10   means

$$24.65 \le \text{(actual end-to-end length)} < 24.75,$$

which is a contradiction of Case I. The discrepancies are represented on the number line.

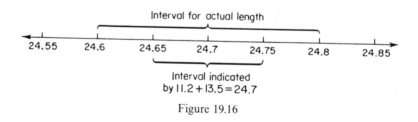

Figure 19.16

This illustrates that the absolute error of the sum must be the sum of the absolute errors. Hence the rule is established for finding the sum of two measures each precise to the same degree.

EXAMPLE 2

Three boards are measured and their lengths are recorded, along with their precision.

Board 1: 5   ft, precise to nearest foot.
Board 2: 13.7   ft precise to nearest   1/10   foot.
Board 3: 12.75   ft, precise to nearest   1/100   foot.
If the boards are placed end-to-end, find:

Case I: The interval in which the actual length falls.

$$
\begin{array}{lll}
\text{Board 1:} & 4.5 \leq & \text{(actual length)} & < \ 5.5 \\
\text{Board 2:} & 13.65 \leq & \text{(actual length)} & < 13.75. \\
\text{Board 3:} & 12.745 \leq & \text{(actual length)} & < 12.755
\end{array}
$$

$$30.895 \leq \text{(actual end-to-end length)} < 32.005.$$

Case II: The interval into which the end-to-end length would fall if each measure were rounded off to   1/10. The rounded values are   5, 13.7, and 12.8, and their sum is $5 + 13.7 + 12.8 = 31.5$. The interval defined by this measure:

$$31.45 \leq 31.5 < 31.55.$$

Case III: The interval into which the end-to-end length would fall if each measure were rounded off to   1. The rounded values are   5, 14, and 13, and their sum is $5 + 14 + 13 = 32$. The interval defined by this measure is

$$31.5 \leq 32 < 32.5.$$

These three intervals are represented on the number line.

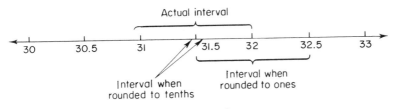

Figure 19.17

We see that by rounding off, we do not get the exact interval into which the end-to-end length would terminate. However, we would obtain the same approximate result by rounding off each measure to *within one position of the least precise measure* and then rounding off their sum to the *lowest degree of precision*:

$$
\begin{array}{r}
5. \\
13.7 \\
+ \ 12.8 \\
\hline
31.5,
\end{array}
$$

the measure   31.5   rounded off to ones is   32   and we obtain exactly the answer of Case III above:

$$31.5 \le 32 < 32.5.$$

Although rounding off will (almost) never give the exact interval when finding the sum of two or more measures, the error of the least precise measure will be *at least*   10   *times as big* as the error for the more precise measures. Because of this magnitude, the errors for the more precise measures become insignificant. Using this approach to obtain a justifiable answer, the following definition is given.

Definition 19.7—Addition for Measures of Different Degree   Round off each measure to within one position of the least precise measure, add, round off the sum to the lowest degree of precision found within the addends.

EXAMPLE

Each of the following is a measure, with each digit significant:

$$2.48, 323, 2.18. 18.6, 4.24,$$

and their sum is illustrated as:

$$
\begin{array}{rcl}
2.475 \le & 2.48 & < \quad 2.485 \\
231.5 \;\; \le & 232. & < 323.5 \\
2.175 \le & 2.18 & < \quad 2.185 \\
18.55 \;\le & 18.6 & < \quad 18.65 \\
4.235 \le & 4.24 & < \quad 4.245 \\
\hline
258.925 \le & \text{(Actual Measure)} & < 260.065.
\end{array}
$$

By rounding off each measure to within one place of the least precise measure:

$$
\begin{array}{r}
2.5 \\
232. \\
12.2 \\
18.6 \\
4.2 \\
\hline
259.5
\end{array}
$$

$$259.5 \le 260 < 260.5,$$

which is approximately the interval in which the actual measure will fall.

If a measure has two significant digits, the measure is said to have two-digit accuracy; three significant digits, three-digit accuracy*, etc. In

---

* Note that this is different from accuracy based on relative error.

multiplication, we use the idea of *n*-digit accuracy to devise rules in computation.

Suppose that we wish to find the area of a rectangle with dimensions of 5.4 ft (2-digit accuracy) by 22.4 ft (3-digit accuracy). We know that the area of this rectangle falls somewhere in the interval

$$119.5725 \leq \text{(actual area)} < 122.3525.$$

From the above, we cannot determine the area for certain to *2-digit accuracy*, even though the measures have 2-digit and 3-digit accuracy, respectively. In general, a product will not be more *n-digit accurate* than the least accurate factor.

By rounding off each factor to *one more significant digit* than the factor of least *n*-digit accuracy, we obtain an interval which is approximately that for the actual area:

$$
\begin{array}{r}
33.4 \text{ (3-digit accuracy)} \\
\times \ 5.4 \text{ (2-digit accuracy)} \\
\hline
896 \\
1120 \\
\hline
120.96.
\end{array}
$$

If we assume that each digit is significant, then the interval defined by 120.96 is:

$$120.955 \leq 120.96 < 120.965.$$

If we round off 120.96 to the same digit accuracy as the least accurate factor, then the interval as defined by 121.0 is:

$$120.5 \leq 121.0 < 121.5$$

which more nearly approximates the actual interval.

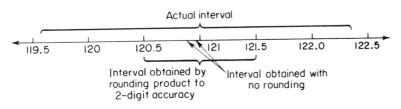

Figure 19.18

Hence by rounding off the product to the *n*-digit accuracy of the least *n*-digit accurate factor, we obtain an interval that is approximately that of the actual interval.

Definition 19.8—Multiplication for Approximate Measures Round off each measure within one digit of the least   *n*-digit accurate factor, multiply, round off the product to the accuracy of the least accurate factor.

For illustration, consider the product of the measures 3×1.64. The product falls in the interval

$$4.0875 < \text{(actual product)} < 5.7575.$$

By following the rules outlined in Definition 19.7, we obtain:

$$\begin{array}{r} 1.6 \\ \times\ 3 \\ \hline 4.8 \end{array}$$

and by rounding off to   1-digit accuracy, we establish the interval

$$4.5 \le 5 < 5.5.$$

Similarly, the same rule will be true for division, because division is defined in terms of multiplication. Therefore, the quotient should be rounded off to the same   *n*-digit accuracy as the least accurate of the divisor or dividend.

PROBLEM SET 19.5

1. Explain the difference in   *n*-digit accuracy for the measurements   9   yds, 9.0   yds, and   9.00   yds. Each digit is significant.

2. Explain the difference in accuracy of the measures   12   ft   3   in. and $4\frac{1}{4}$ yds.

3.   What is the unit in each measure?

(a) 13   ft   4   in.   (b) 4   lb   6   oz.
(c) 14   min   3   sec.   (d) 2   bu   3   pk.
(e) 1128   miles   (f) 128.5   miles.
(g) 4   yds   3   in.   (h) 10.00   mm.
(i) 9   cm.   (j) $1\frac{1}{4}$ oz.

4.   In the following measures, which is (a) the more precise, and (b) which is the more accurate?

(a) 50   in. or   4   ft   2   in.
(b) 144   in. or   12   ft.
(c) 100   miles or   100.0   miles.
(d) 29   lbs or   0.29   lb.

(e) 28   ft or   28   miles.
(f) 15   min or   900   sec.
(g) 42   gallons or   168   qts.
(h) 3   in. or   1/12   yd.
(i) 1   hr. or   60   min.

5. Using Definition 19.6, find the perimeter of the following closed polygons if the conditions mentioned prevail.

(a) The sides of a triangle are   12.23   ft,   19.0   ft, and   21   ft.
(b) An equilateral triangle, each of whose sides is   21.08   in.
(c) A square, each of whose sides is   16.98   in.

6. Find the greatest possible error, the relative error, and the per cent error in the following:

(a) 120, if the unit is   10.
(b) 120, if the unit is   1.
(c) 120, if the unit is   1/10.

7. Determine the number of significant digits in each.

(a) 85,000   is precise to the nearest   100.
(b) 85,000   is precise to the nearest   10.
(c) 0.0030   is precise to the nearest   1/1000.
(d) 0.0030   is precise to the nearest   1/10,000.

8. Round off the following to two significant digits.

(a) 2794.   (b) 3051.
(c) 0.007046.   (d) 0.00783.
(e) 38.525.   (f) 2.901.

9. Write in scientific notation the following.

(a) 318.05.   (b) 0.0213.
(c) 0.0245.   (d) 2385.
(e) 1.007.   (f) 0.0872.

10. Use scientific notation to find the values of the following. Leave answers in scientific notation with each rounded off to the correct number of significant digits. The last digit in each problem established the unit.

(a) $(4 \cdot 10^2)(3 \cdot 10^3) =$
(b) $(1.2 \cdot 10^2)(2 \cdot 10^2) =$
(c) $(2.9 \cdot 10^{-2})(3.8 \cdot 10^4) =$
(d) $(1.6 \cdot 10^{-21})(8.6 \cdot 10^{10}) =$
(e) $(2.05 \cdot 10^{-5})(3.1 \cdot 10^6) =$

11.   The following are respectively, the lengths and widths of certain rectangles.

(a) Determine the interval in which the actual area falls.

(b) Using the rounding methods described in this chapter, find the area of each. Round off your answer to the least accurate of the two factors.

(a) 500   and   20.5.   (b) 2   ft   4   in. and   1   ft   3   in.

(c) 5   miles and   527   ft.   (d) 6   ft   4   in. and   2   yds.

The Real Numbers.
Number Theory

PART FIVE

CHAPTER 20

The Real Numbers

20.1 INTRODUCTION

It was illustrated in earlier chapters that on the drawing of the number line, a complete one-to-one correspondence could be established between the set of Whole Numbers and a subset of points on this line. We then conclude that each Whole Number was matched with one, and only one, point on this line.

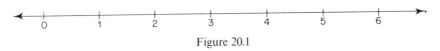

Figure 20.1

We then "extended" the number line by defining the set of Integers and Rationals, using the idea that every positive number had an Opposite, or Additive Inverse. From this, the set of Negative Integers and the set of Negative Rationals were defined. The idea of denseness was also established.

Every Rational Number, either positive or negative, could be matched with a point on the number line.

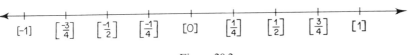

Figure 20.2

From the idea of *denseness*, it would seem that every point on the number line has a number associated by a one-to-one correspondence, thereby exhausting the supply of points. However, this is not the case. *There remain infinitely many points on the number line that are not associated by a one-to-one correspondence with a Rational Number.* The purpose of this chapter is to conduct an investigation of these "nonassociated" points and to define numbers that can be associated with these "unmatched" points.

20.2 NONTERMINATING, NONREPEATING DECIMALS

One recalls that any terminating decimal of the form

$$0.x_1x_2x_3 \ldots x_n0000 \ldots$$

or that any nonterminating, repeating decimal of the form

$$0.x_1x_2x_3 \ldots x_n\overline{x_1x_2x_3 \ldots x_n}$$

could be expressed as a fraction in the form a/b.

However, there are infinitely many more numbers that *cannot* be expressed as a fraction of the form a/b. It is this particular set, we wish to investigate in this section and in order to accomplish it, we undertake a short discussion of trigonometry.

A triangle is a closed polygon of three sides. In particular, a triangle with one angle of $90°$ is called a right triangle. The angle of $90°$ in triangle ABC below is the angle denoted at vertex C. The longer of the three sides is referred to as the hypotenuse.

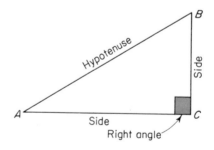

Figure 20.3

The ancient civilizations of Babylonia* and Egypt observed that the sides of a right triangle were related in certain ways. Particularly, it was noted that

* See Eves, Howard P., "An Introduction to the History of Mathematics," Rinehart and Co., N.Y., 1956.

if the measures of sides $a = 3$ and $b = 4$, then the measure of the hypotenuse (side c) will be 5. It was also discovered that the triple numbers $(3, 4, 5)$ were related as $3^2 + 4^2 = 5^2$, or $9 + 16 = 25$. In terms of geometry the relationship is illustrated in Figure 20.4 below.

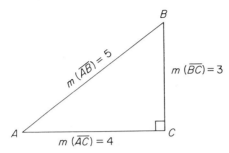

Figure 20.4

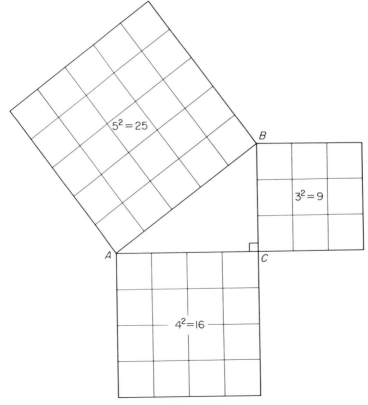

Figure 20.5

GEOMETRIC INTERPRETATION OF $3^2 + 4^2 = 5^2$

If three Whole Numbers can be related to the sides of a right triangle in the manner illustrated above, these three Whole Numbers are referred to as a Pythagorean triple. This is so because the Greek philosopher and mathematician Pythagoras investigated triples of numbers which eventually led to the Pythagorean theorem.

The Pythagorean Theorem   For any right-angled triangle, the sum of the squares of the two sides is equal to the square of the hypotenuse.

Other Pythagorean triples are illustrated.

$$(5, 12, 13) \qquad 5^2 + 12^2 = 13^2,$$
$$25 + 144 = 169.$$
$$(8, 13, 17) \qquad 8^2 + 15^2 = 17^2,$$
$$64 + 225 = 289.$$
$$(9, 40, 41) \qquad 9^2 + 40^2 = 41^2,$$
$$81 \times 1600 = 1681.$$

But the measure of the hypotenuse is not always a Whole Number. In particular, consider the right-angled triangle with sides of measure   1.

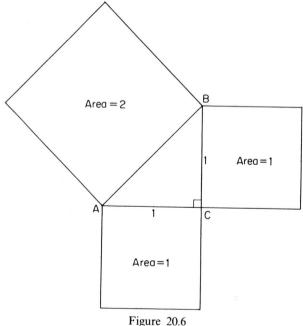

Figure 20.6

GEOMETRIC INTERPRETATION OF $1^2 + 1^2 = 2.$

From the above illustration, we are searching for a number, c, such that

$$c(c) = 2.$$

By the trial and error method, we first investigate the Whole Numbers to provide possible candidates whose square is 2:

$$1 \times 1 = 1; \quad (1 < 2).$$
$$2 \times 2 = 4; \quad (2 < 4).$$

Using properties for inequalities, we can eliminate all other Whole Numbers as possible candidates. From the above, we have established an interval which contains the number whose square is 2.

Too little
$(1 \times 1 < 2)$

Too big
$(2 \times 2 > 2)$

Figure 20.7

Hence we see that the number whose square is 2 lies in the interval between 1 and 2. The next logical step is to investigate the Rational Numbers between 1 and 2. In the illustration below, the column headed "Too Little" indicates those numbers whose square is less than 2; the column headed "Too Big" indicates those numbers whose square is greater than 2.

Too Little						Too Big
1.1^2	$=$	1.21	$< 2 <$	3.24	$=$	1.8^2
1.2^2	$=$	1.44	$< 2 <$	2.89	$=$	1.7^2
1.3^2	$=$	1.69	$< 2 <$	2.56	$=$	1.6^2
1.4^2	$=$	1.96	$< 2 <$	2.25	$=$	1.5^2

Figure 20.8

From the above, we have determined that *1.4 is the biggest number whose square is too little, and that* 1.5 *is the smallest number whose square is too big.* This tells us that we now need to investigate the set of Rationals that lie in the interval between 1.4 and 1.5.

Too
Little

Too
Big

1.41^2 = 1.9981 < 2 < 2.0164 = 1.42^2

Figure 20.9

Again, we have found a largest number whose square is too little   (1.41), and a smallest number whose square is too big   (1.42). Hence the number whose square is   2   lies in the interval between   1.41   and   1.42. Following this pattern, we continue to find a set of numbers, one being the largest number whose square is too little and the other whose square is too big.

Too
Little

Too
Big

1.414^2	=	1.999396	< 2 <	2.00225	= 1.415^2
1.4142^2	=	1.99961644	< 2 <	2.00034449	= 1.4143^2
1.41421^2	=	1.9999899241	< 2 <	2.0000182084	= 1.41422^2

Figure 20.10

We can find any number based on pairs of Rationals, one number being the largest number whose square is too little and the other number whose square is too big, *but we can never find a Rational Number whose square will be exactly   2.*

With the invention of high speed computers that can perform additions and multiplications in billionths of a second, interested programmers have found the largest number whose square is too little to approximately   1000 decimal places. They have determined two characteristics.

(a) *The decimal does not terminate.*

(b) *No digit or groups of digits repeat.*

One recalls that any nonterminating, repeating decimal could be expressed as a fraction of the form $\dfrac{a}{b}$. But no *nonterminating, nonrepeating decimal* can be expressed in the form $\dfrac{a}{b}$, the requirements established for a number to be Rational. Hence numbers whose decimal representation is nonterminating, nonrepeating are *nonRational Numbers.*

Actually, Euclid, in approximately 355 B.C. proved that there was no Rational Number $\dfrac{a}{b}$ such that $\left(\dfrac{a}{b}\right)\left(\dfrac{a}{b}\right) = \left(\dfrac{a}{b}\right)^2 = 2$. His proof is presented below.

Theorem 20.1   There is no Rational Number, (a/b), such that $(a/b)^2$ $= 2$.

The method of proof is to assume that there is a Rational Number $\left(\dfrac{a}{b}\right)$ whose square is   2. We then find this assumption to be incorrect, which forces us to assume there is no Rational Number whose square is   2.

Proof.

1. Assume there is a Rational Number, a/b, such that

$$\left(\frac{a}{b}\right)^2 = 2.$$

2. If a is not relatively prime to b, then a and b contain a highest common factor, c.
Then

$$\frac{a}{b} = \frac{cp}{cq} = \frac{p}{q},$$

thereby establishing that p and q are relatively prime [hcf(p, q) $= 1$].

3. Therefore,

$$\left(\frac{p}{q}\right)^2 = 2,$$

$$\frac{p^2}{q^2} = 2,$$

$$p^2 = 2q^2.$$

4. Since $2q^2$ is even, it follows that p^2 is even, and because p^2 is even, it follows that p is even.

5. If p is even, then p can be expressed in the form:

$$p = 2(n), \quad n \text{ is an Integer.}$$

6. From (3) above, $p^2 = 2q^2$, and by substitution:

$$(2n)^2 = 2q^2,$$
$$4n^2 = 2q^2,$$
$$2n^2 = q^2.$$

7. Using an argument similar to that in (4) above, we find that q is *also even.*

8. If p is even and if q is even, then they each contain a common factor of 2. But p is relatively prime to q from (2) above. Therefore, the assumption that p and q are relatively prime is false. We must then conclude that there is no Rational Number whose square is 2.

The particular set of numbers whose decimal representation is non-terminating, nonrepeating is the set of Irrational Numbers.

Definition 20.1—Irrational Numbers Any number whose decimal approximation is a nonterminating, nonrepeating decimal is defined as an *Irrational Number.*

Other familiar numbers are Irrational Numbers. One such number is π. The value of π is approximately 3.14159265..., which is a nonterminating, nonrepeating decimal. We frequently use the Rational approximation for π, $\frac{22}{7}$. However, the value of π is not $\frac{22}{7}$, for

$$\tfrac{22}{7} = 3.142857\overline{142857},$$

a nonterminating, repeating decimal.

Hence we have illustrated that a new kind of numbers exist—numbers whose decimal representation is nonterminating, nonrepeating. This new number does not belong to any set of numbers previously studied, therefore, we must define a new set of numbers called the Real Numbers.

Definition 20.2—The Real Numbers If n is a number and if the decimal representation of n follows one of the categories below:

(a) Terminating, (Rational Number).
(b) Nonterminating repeating, (Rational Number).
(c) Non-terminating, nonrepeating, (Irrational Number),

then n is a Real Number.

The set of Real Numbers is generally referred to as the set of *Reals.*

One recalls that three criteria were established for defining a new system of numbers. These criteria were:

1. That the new system of numbers retain all properties of previously defined systems.
2. Retention of all number operations of previously defined systems so these operations are still true within the new system; and
3. The new system contained a new kind of number.

Since we wish the system of *Reals* to adhere to the rules established above, we declare all properties for equality, inequality, and properties relating to the four basic operations previously studied directly transferred to the system of Reals. Since the system of Reals contains a new kind of number, the irrationals, we must define slight modifications to accommodate these new numbers. Also, new properties and new algorithms must be studied.

From the above, it is assumed that the Reals satisfy all basic properties for Rationals—closure, commutativity, associativity, and properties of equality and inequality. However, there is one exception—The Property of Denseness. This property is discussed in the following section.

20.3　SQUARE ROOT; RULER AND COMPASS CONSTRUCTIONS

In the previous section, we were trying to find a number c so that

$$c(c) = 2.$$

We were unable to find this number c, but were able to find the number c for some particular numbers:

$$1(1) = 1,$$
$$2(2) = 4,$$
$$3(3) = 9,$$
$$4(4) = 16,$$
$$5(5) = 25.$$
$$\vdots \qquad \vdots$$

From this, we can define a square root.

Definition 20.3—Square Root If each of c and n is a positive number* and $c(c) = n$, then c is the square root of n. The notation

$$\sqrt{n}$$

means "the square root of n."

(a) $\sqrt{25} = 5$　because　$5(5) = 25,$
(b) $\sqrt{64} = 8$　because　$8(8) = 64,$
(c) $\sqrt{2} = \sqrt{2}$　because　$\sqrt{2}(\sqrt{2}) = 2,$
(d) $\sqrt{3} = \sqrt{3}$　because　$\sqrt{3}(\sqrt{3}) = 3.$

* We will not discuss negative square roots.

We can state that the length of the hypotenuse of a right-angled triangle with sides   1   unit in length is $\sqrt{2}$ since $\sqrt{2}(\sqrt{2}) = 2$. Geometrically, this is interpreted below.

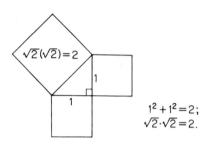

Figure 20.11

We have previously shown that the set of Rational Numbers could be matched in a complete one-to-one correspondence with a subset of points on the number line. Similarly, we can match the set of Irrationals with a subset of points on the number line. This may be illustrated by using a ruler and compass construction.

On the number line at the point associated with   1, construct a perpendicular line segment   1   unit in length. Denote this line $\overline{1B}$. Using a ruler, complete the right triangle by drawing a line segment from the point associated with   0   to   B. Denote this segment by $\overline{0B}$. From the Pythagorean Theorem, the length of $\overline{0B}$ is $\sqrt{2}$.

Using a compass, draw a circle with center at   0   and radius $\overline{0B}$. The circle intersects the number line at the point associated with $\sqrt{2}$.

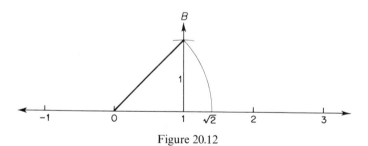

Figure 20.12

Similarly, the point associated with the irrational number $\sqrt{3}$ may be determined. Construct a perpendicular to $\overline{0B}$ at   B   that is   1   unit in length. Label this line segment $\overline{BC}$. Using   0   as center, construct a circle with radius $\overline{0C}$. The intersection of this circle and the number line is the point associated with $\sqrt{3}$. This point and other points associated with Irrational Numbers are shown below.

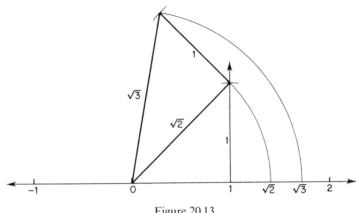

Figure 20.13

Now we must consider this question: "How do we know that the points matched with $\sqrt{2}$, $\sqrt{3}$, $\sqrt{5}$, etc. are not previously associated with a Rational Number?" In order to answer this question, one recalls the following.

(a) We proved that $\sqrt{2}$ was Irrational. (Similarly we can prove $\sqrt{3}$, $\sqrt{5}$, $\sqrt{6}$, $\sqrt{7}$, etc. to be Irrational.)

(b) We matched, by a complete one-to-one correspondence, each Rational Number with a subset of points on the number line, but *we did not match each point with a Rational Number.*

(c) Since we matched all numbers of the form $\frac{a}{b}$ with a point on the number line, *no point was matched with* $\sqrt{2}$, *because* $\sqrt{2}$ *cannot be expressed in the form* $\frac{a}{b}$.

Similarly, each of $\sqrt{3}$, $\sqrt{5}$, $\sqrt{6}$, $\sqrt{7}$ can be associated with a point on the number line, for each of these is an Irrational Number.

As in the case of Integers and Rationals, for every Real Number n, there is one and only one Real Number, $-n$, such that $n + (-n) = 0$. For example:

$$\pi \longleftrightarrow -\pi,$$

$$\sqrt{2} \longleftrightarrow -\sqrt{2},$$

$$\sqrt{3} \longleftrightarrow -\sqrt{3},$$

$$\frac{1}{2} \longleftrightarrow \frac{-1}{2},$$

$$2 \longleftrightarrow -2.$$

A few of these numbers are represented on the drawing of the number line in the following manner.

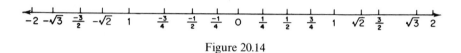

Figure 20.14

We are again confronted with the idea of density on the Real Number line, for we have proven that between any two Rationals, there are infinitely many Rationals. Similarly between any two Irrationals there will be infinitely many Irrationals. For example:

Figure 20.15

This illustrates the following two important concepts regarding *denseness* on the Real Number line *between any two Rational Numbers.*

(a) There are infinitely many Rationals, and
(b) There are infinitely many Irrationals.

Similarly *between any two Irrationals*, two possibilities exist.

(a) There are infinitely many Rationals, and
(b) There are infinitely many Irrationals.

Using the properties of order, we say that there is a unique Real Number corresponding to each point on the number line. This is defined as the property of completeness. *It is this property that distinguishes the Real Numbers from the Rational Numbers.*

Property of Completeness   There exists a complete one-to-one correspondence between Real Numbers and the points on the number line.

We shall accept the basic properties of the Reals without proof, for these are beyond the scope of this text. In general, the properties of the Reals parallel those of the Rationals with the one exception as noted above.

PROBLEM SET 20.1

1. The ancient Greeks discovered in approximately 500 B.C. a method to determine Pythagorean triples (a, b, c):

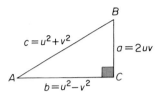

where u and v are relatively prime, u and v are not both odd numbers, and $u > v$. If $u = 2$ and $v = 1$, then we obtain

$$a = 2uv = 2(2)(1) = 4,$$
$$b = u^2 - v^2 = 2^2 - 1^2 = 4 - 1 = 3,$$
$$c = u^2 + v^2 = 2^2 + 1^2 = 4 + 1 = 5.$$

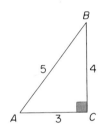

Find the Pythagorean triples (a, b, c) if (u, v) are:

(a) $(3, 2)$.   (b) $(13, 2)$.

(c) $(14, 3)$.   (d) $(8, 5)$.

2. Is the set of Irrational Numbers closed under multiplication? (*Hint*: investigate $(\sqrt{2})(\sqrt{2})$.

3. Which of the following can be represented by a terminating decimal, or a non-terminating, repeating decimal?

(a) $\dfrac{-7}{3}$.   (b) $\sqrt{64}$.   (c) $\sqrt{3}$.

(d) $\sqrt{12}$.   (e) $\sqrt{18}$.   (f) $\sqrt{6}$.

4. Which of the following sentences are true?

(a) $3 > \sqrt{8}$.   (b) $2 > 2\sqrt{2}$.   (c) $4 < 2\sqrt{8}$.

(d) $5 + \sqrt{2} > 4 + \sqrt{3}$.   (e) $\dfrac{\sqrt{2}}{2} < 1$.   (f) $2\sqrt{2} > 9$.

5. Using an argument similar to that within this chapter, show that $\sqrt{3}$ is irrational.

6. Construct triangles with hypotenuse $\sqrt{17}$, $\sqrt{8}$. Locate these points on the number line.

7. Using the idea discussed regarding *the largest number that is too little and the smallest number that is too big*, evaluate to two decimal places:

(a) $\sqrt{3}$. (b) $\sqrt{5}$.

(c) $\sqrt{8}$. (d) $\sqrt{17}$.

20.4   CALCULATIONS WITH REAL NUMBERS

We previously discussed the four basic operations within the set of Rational Numbers and found that in some cases we were forced to deal with approximations:

$$\tfrac{2}{3} \approx 0.6,$$

$$\tfrac{2}{3} \approx 0.66,$$

$$\tfrac{2}{3} \approx 0.666.$$

Calculations using Irrationals deal entirely with approximations in most cases. This is particularly true, if we desire to find an approximation for a particular measure. This is so because each Irrational Number has a decimal approximation that is nonterminating, nonrepeating:

$$\pi \approx 3,$$

$$\pi \approx 3.1,$$

$$\pi \approx 3.14.$$

$$2\sqrt{2} \approx 2 \times 1.414 = 2.824,$$

$$\frac{\sqrt{2}}{2} \approx \frac{1.414}{2} = 0.707.$$

$$\sqrt{2} + \sqrt{2} \approx 1.414 + 1.414 = 2.824,$$

$$\sqrt{3} - \sqrt{2} \approx 1.733 - 1.414 = 0.319.$$

Each of the above is an approximation for some Irrational Number. When using Irrational Numbers within the four basic operations, we generally resort to using an approximation to obtain an estimate of the true value.

EXAMPLE
The circumference of a circle is determined by the formula $C = \pi d$, where C is the circumference and d is the diameter of the circle. Find the circumference of a circle, if the diameter of the circle is   2 units.

From the above, the *actual* circumference of the circle is

$$C = \pi(2),$$
$$= 2\pi.$$

If we desire a decimal approximation for the value of C, then we resort to the following Rational approximations for π:

$$C \approx 2(3.1) = 6.2;$$
$$C \approx 2(3.14) = 6.28;$$
$$C \approx 2(3.141) = 6.282;$$
$$C \approx 2(3.1414) = 6.2828; \text{ etc.}$$

However, these are only Rational approximations for C. It follows that the more precise approximation for π, the more precise the approximation for C. In fact, we can never obtain the exact value of C unless we express C as $C = 2\pi$.

Many instances require division involving Irrational Numbers. Consider the problem of finding n if:

$$n = \frac{2}{\sqrt{2}}.$$

If we use successively more precise approximations for $\sqrt{2}$, then

$$n \approx \frac{2}{1.4} \approx 1.42857,$$

$$n \approx \frac{2}{1.41} \approx 1.41843,$$

$$n \approx \frac{2}{1.414} \approx 1.41442,$$

$$n \approx \frac{2}{1.4142} \approx 1.41422.$$

In each of the above instances, the quotient will be a nonterminating, repeating decimal. In many cases, the algorithm for division will require a considerable number of steps before determining the digits that repeat. This involves a great deal of work on the part of the reader to find an approximate value for n, above.

In order to alleviate the work encountered in problems such as the above, one recalls from division which involves Rational Numbers that it was much easier to divide, if the divisor was some small Whole Number, say of magnitude   2   or   3. If we perform an operation known as *Rationalizing the Denominator* (expressing the denominator as a Rational Number), division can be performed much easier because the divisor is a Rational Number.

EXAMPLE

Find a four-place decimal approximation for n if:

$$n = \frac{2}{\sqrt{2}}.$$

One recalls that if n is any number, Rational or Irrational, then $(\sqrt{n})(\sqrt{n}) = n$ by definition. Therefore, $(\sqrt{2})(\sqrt{2}) = 2$. To express the *divisor* of the above as a Rational Number, multiply both divisor and dividend by $\sqrt{2}$:

$$n = \left(\frac{2}{\sqrt{2}}\right)\left(\frac{\sqrt{2}}{\sqrt{2}}\right),$$

$$= \frac{2 \times \sqrt{2}}{\sqrt{2} \times \sqrt{2}},$$

$$= \frac{2\sqrt{2}}{2}$$

$$= \sqrt{2}.$$

Hence, the exact value of n is $\sqrt{2}$. This can be approximated by using any desired number of decimals in the value $1.414213\ldots$. Specifically, if we desire a four-place approximation for n, then

$$n \approx 1.4142.$$

The product of two Irrational Numbers of the form $\sqrt{a}$ and $\sqrt{b}$ is

$$(\sqrt{a})(\sqrt{b}) = \sqrt{ab}.$$

For example:

(a) $\sqrt{2} \times \sqrt{3} = \sqrt{6}.$
(b) $\sqrt{4} \times \sqrt{2} = \sqrt{8}.$
(c) $\sqrt{5} \times \sqrt{a} = \sqrt{5a}.$

If the product of two Irrationals is a Rational, each factor is called a rationalizing factor of the other:

(a) $\sqrt{2} \times \sqrt{2} = \sqrt{4} = 2.$
(b) $\sqrt{8} \times \sqrt{2} = \sqrt{16} = 4.$
(c) $\sqrt{3} \times 2\sqrt{3} = 2\sqrt{3 \times 3} = 2\sqrt{9} = 2(3) = 6.$

The rationalizing factor for numbers expressed in the form $a + \sqrt{b}$ is $a - \sqrt{b}$. By using the distributive property of multiplication over addition:

$$
\begin{aligned}
(a + \sqrt{b})(a - \sqrt{b}) &= (a + \sqrt{b})[a + (-\sqrt{b})], \\
&= (a + \sqrt{b})a + (a + \sqrt{b})(-\sqrt{b}), \\
&= a(a) + a\sqrt{b} + a(-\sqrt{b}) + (\sqrt{b})(-\sqrt{b}), \\
&= a^2 + a\sqrt{b} + (-a\sqrt{b}) + (-b), \\
&= a^2 - b.
\end{aligned}
$$

Since $(a^2 - b)$ is an Integer, $(a - \sqrt{b})$ is a rationalizing factor for $(a + \sqrt{b})$,

EXAMPLES

(a) $(2 + \sqrt{3})(2 - \sqrt{3}) = 2^2 - 3 = 4 - 3 = 1,$
(b) $(3 + 2\sqrt{3})(3 - 2\sqrt{3}) = 3^2 - 4(3) = 9 - 12 = -3,$
(c) $(2 - \sqrt{5})(2 + \sqrt{5}) = 2^2 - 5 = 4 - 5 = -1.$

In order to obtain a decimal approximation for numbers of the form:

$$
\frac{a}{b + \sqrt{c}}
$$

we again express the denominator as a Rational Number and proceed as before:

(a) $\dfrac{2}{3 - \sqrt{2}} = \left(\dfrac{2}{3 - \sqrt{2}}\right)\left(\dfrac{3 + \sqrt{2}}{3 + \sqrt{2}}\right) = \dfrac{2(3 + \sqrt{2})}{9 - 2},$

$\qquad\qquad = \dfrac{6 + 2\sqrt{2}}{7} \approx \dfrac{6 + 2.828}{7} = 1.261.$

(b) $\dfrac{2 + \sqrt{2}}{\sqrt{3} + \sqrt{2}} \times \left(\dfrac{2 + \sqrt{2}}{\sqrt{3} - \sqrt{2}}\right) = \dfrac{4 + 4\sqrt{2} + 2}{3 - 2}$,

$$= \dfrac{6 + 4\sqrt{2}}{1} \approx 11.565.$$

PROBLEM SET 20.2

The three-place decimal approximations for $\sqrt{2}$ and $\sqrt{3}$ are 1.414 and 1.732, respectively. Use these values where needed in the following problems. The three-place decimal approximation for π is 3.142.

1. Find a one-place, a two-place, and a three-place decimal approximation for c if $c = \pi d$ and $d = 5$ units.

2. Find a three-place decimal approximation for n if $n = \pi r^2$ and $r = 2$ units.

3. Is the set of Irrational Numbers closed under the following conditions.

(a) Addition?
(b) Subtraction?
(c) Multiplication?
(d) Division?

Using $\sqrt{2}$ and/or $\sqrt{3}$, cite examples to justify your answers.

4. Find, by rationalizing the denominator, a two-place decimal approximation for n if:

(a) $n = \dfrac{3}{\sqrt{2}}$.

(b) $n = \dfrac{5}{\sqrt{\pi}}$.

(c) $n \times \dfrac{\sqrt{3}}{\sqrt{2}}$.

(d) $n \times \dfrac{(\sqrt{2})(\sqrt{3})}{2\sqrt{2}}$.

(e) $n = \dfrac{2}{1 \times \sqrt{2}}$.

(f) $n = \dfrac{3}{2 - \sqrt{3}}$.

(g) $n = \dfrac{1}{\sqrt{3} - \sqrt{2}}$.

(h) $n = \dfrac{2}{2 \times 2\sqrt{2}}$.

(i) $n = \dfrac{1}{2\sqrt{3} - 1}$.

(j) $n = \dfrac{\sqrt{3} + \sqrt{2}}{\sqrt{3} - \sqrt{2}}$.

20.5 FIELD AXIOMS

School children usually study about six number systems—the system of Whole Numbers, Integers, Rational Numbers of Arithmetic (non-Negative Rationals), Rationals, Irrationals, and Reals. In order to more clearly define the differences between these systems, we shall define some abstract systems called *Groups*, *Rings*, and *Fields*. The simplest of these three systems is a Group.

Definition 20.4—Group Under Addition A set of elements forms a *Group* with respect to addition, if the following characteristics are obeyed.

Property I: The set is closed under addition.

Property II: The associative property for addition holds.

Property III: The Identity Element for addition is an element of the set.

Property IV: Each element of the set has its Additive Inverse within the set.

Using this definition, an investigation of the five different number systems we have studied will reveal that some of these systems satisfy the properties that define a Group under addition.

Groups With Respect to Addition

Property	Whole Numbers	Integers	Rationals	Irrationals	Reals
Closed (+)	✓	✓	✓	No	✓
Associative (+)	✓	✓	✓	✓	✓
Additive Identity	✓	✓	✓	No	✓
Additive Inverse	No	✓	✓	✓	✓
Group?	No	Yes	Yes	No	Yes

Figure 20.16

From the above, we see that Whole Numbers and Irrationals do not form a group under addition. One recalls that when studying Whole Numbers, we found that a solution to problems of the type $n = 8 - 10$ did not exist within these sets. This was one reason for defining Integers and Rationals.

A group is an *Abelian Group* with respect to addition, if the commutative property is also true. We can extend the above and determine, if each set of numbers is an Abelian Group under addition. This is done in Figure 20.17.

Abelian Groups With Respect to Addition

Property	Whole Numbers	Integers	Rationals	Irrationals	Reals
Closed (+)	√	√	√	No	√
Associative (+)	√	√	√	√	√
Additive Identity	√	√	√	No	√
Additive Inverse	No	√	√	No	√
Group	No	Yes	Yes	No	Yes
Commutative (+)	√	√	√	√	√
Abelian Group	No	Yes	Yes	No	Yes

Figure 20.17

By referring to the illustration above, we see that the set of Whole Numbers and the Irrationals do not form an Abelian Group under addition, even though the commutative property for addition is true for each set of numbers. This is so, for the first requisite to being an Abelian Group is for each set to be a Group.

Similarly, certain sets of numbers are Groups under multiplication. In order for a set of numbers to be a Group under multiplication, the set must satisfy the following properties.

Definition 20.5—Group Under Multiplication   A set of elements forms a group with respect to multiplication, if the following conditions are met.

Property I: The set is closed under multiplication.

Property II: The associative property for multiplication holds.

Property III: The Identity Element for multiplication is within the set.

Property IV: Each element of the set has its Multiplicative Inverse within the set.

A Group with respect to multiplication is said to be an Abelian Group under multiplication if Properties I-IV are satisfied and if the commutative property for multiplication is true. Sets of numbers that are Abelian Groups under multiplication are given in Figure 20.18.

From Figures 20.17–18 we see that no sets of numbers are Abelian Groups under both addition and multiplication. The next extension is that of a *Ring.* For a set of elements to be a Ring, the following properties must be satisfied.

Abelian Groups With Respect to Multiplication

Properties	Whole Numbers	Integers	Rationals	Irrationals	Reals
Closed (×)	√	√	√	No	√
Associative (×)	√	√	√	√	√
Multiplicative Identity	√	√	√	Yes	√
Multiplicative Inverse	No	No	No*	Yes	No*
Group?	No	No	No	No	No
Commutative (×)	√	√	√	√	√
Abelian Group?	No	No	No	No	No

Figure 20.18

* It should be noted that   0   does not have a Multiplicative Inverse.

Definition 20.6—A Ring   A set of elements forms a Ring if the following are met.

Property I :   The elements of the set form an Abelian Group with respect to addition.

Property II :   The set is closed with respect to multiplication.

Property III :   The elements of the set satisfy the associative property for multiplication.

Property IV: The elements of the set satisfy the distributive property of multiplication over addition   (× , +).

Figure 20.19 reveals which sets of numbers satisfy the properties of a Ring.

Rings

Properties	Whole Numbers	Integers	Rationals	Irrationals	Reals
Abelian Group?	No	Yes	Yes	No	Yes
Closed (×)	√	√	√	No	√
Associative (×)	√	√	√	√	√
Distributive (× , +)	√	√	√	√	√
Ring?	No	Yes	Yes	No	Yes

Figure 20.19

The last extension is that for a Field. In order to be a Field, each of the following properties must be satisfied.

Definition 20.7—A Field A set of elements forms a field if they meet the requirements.

Property I: The set forms a Ring.

Property II: The multiplicative Identity is an element of the set.

Property III: The commutative property for multiplication is satisfied.

Property IV: Each element of the set *except   0, the Additive Identity,* has a multiplicative Inverse.

We can now determine which of the sets of numbers studied satisfy the requirements for a Field. This is done in Figure 20.20.

Property	Whole Numbers	Integers	Rationals	Irrationals	Reals
Closed (+)	✓	✓	✓	No	✓
Associative (+)	✓	✓	✓	✓	✓
Additive Identity	✓	✓	✓	No	✓
Additive Inverse	No	✓	✓	No	✓
Group?	No	Yes	Yes	No	Yes
Commutative (+)	✓	✓	✓	✓	✓
Abelian Group?	No	Yes	Yes	No	Yes
Closed (×)	✓	✓	✓	No	✓
Associative (×)	✓	✓	✓	✓	✓
Distributive (×, +)	✓	✓	✓	✓	✓
Ring?	No	Yes	Yes	No	Yes
Multiplicative Identity	✓	✓	✓	No	✓
Commutative (×)	✓	✓	✓	✓	✓
Multiplicative Inverse	No	No	✓	Yes	✓
Field?	No	No	Yes	No	Yes

Field (heading above Whole Numbers column group)

Figure 20.20

Hence we see that only the Rationals and the Reals satisfy the Field Properties, properties that are generally established at the elementary or junior high school level. Any continuation in the study of mathematics almost invariably reflects upon the ideas of groups, rings, and fields. Teachers of mathematics can use these concepts to challenge and interest their pupils, particularly those preparing for college entrance.

We have attempted a study of the Real Number System, with particular emphasis upon its structure, and have shown how each of the subsystems of the real number system can be built upon a previously developed system. When we satisfy the properties of a field, we do not have to worry about properties such as closure, as encountered in cases of subtraction and division of Whole Numbers. Instead, we know that the closure property is true for all operations—addition, multiplication, and division. A further study of these systems is made in the following chapter.

PROBLEM SET 20.3

1. Does the set $\{1, 3, 5, 7, \ldots\}$ form a Group with respect to addition? to multiplication? A Ring? A Field?

2. Does the set $\{0, 2, 4, 6, \ldots\}$ form a Group with respect to addition? to multiplication? A Ring? A Field?

CHAPTER 21

Elementary
Number Theory

21.1 INTRODUCTION

In Chapter 5, an introductory unit on number theory was studied. Topics considered were odd numbers, even numbers, prime numbers, composite numbers, and various properties dealing with factorization. These topics were limited in scope because we had studied only the Whole Numbers. With the study of the set of Integers completed, we can now return to some of these topics and illustrate that they are also applicable to the set of Integers.

This chapter will also deal with finite number systems and the properties associated with these systems. Illustrations of "parallels" between Infinite number systems and finite number systems will be studied.

21.2 HISTORICAL ASPECTS OF NUMBER THEORY

Pythagoras and his students are generally credited with distinguishing between the computational aspects of numbers and the study of abstract relationships among numbers. The computational aspect has developed into arithmetic and the abstract relationships between numbers have developed into the number theory.

One of the first studies conducted by the Pythagoreans was made into *figurate numbers*. These numbers are represented by geometrical patterns, and are thought to be one of the first links between arithmetic and geometry. Some of these configurations are presented below.

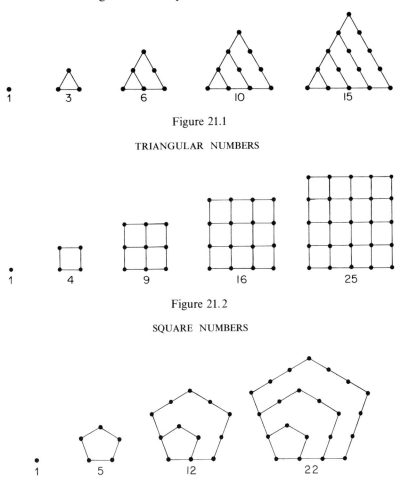

Figure 21.1

TRIANGULAR NUMBERS

Figure 21.2

SQUARE NUMBERS

Figure 21.3

PENTAGONAL NUMBERS

Note that the sum of any two triangular numbers is a square number. This is illustrated in the following configuration:

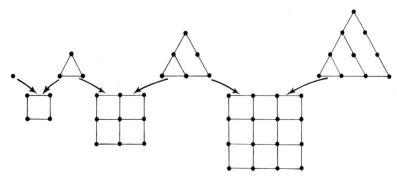

Figure 21.4

Similarly; other pertinent facts can be gleaned from a study of configurate numbers. Most of these are beyond the scope of this text. However, one of these is very interesting:

Theorem: If n consecutive odd numbers, starting with 1, are added together, then their sum is n^2.

We will not prove this Theorem but will give illustrations to show that it is true.

(a) If $n = 2$, $1 + 3 = 2^2 = 4$,

            1   ②

(b) If $n = 4$, $1 + 3 + 5 + 7 = 4^2 = 16$,

            1   2   3   ④

(c) If $n = 6$, $1 + 3 + 5 + 7 + 9 + 11 = 6^2 = 36$,

            1   2   3   4   5   ⑥.

By investigating configurations, we see that the sum of these odd numbers is also a square number, which follows the pattern above.

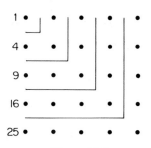

Figure 21.5

The Pythagoreans were also interested in finding *perfect, deficient,* and *abundant* numbers. If the sum of the proper divisors* of the number *was* the number, then the number was said to be a perfect number. For example, the proper divisors of   6   are   1,   2, and   3:

$$1 + 2 + 3 = 6.$$

Therefore,   6   is a perfect number. Approximately   12   perfect numbers have been discovered to date.

A number is deficient if it exceeds the sum of its proper divisors and is abundant if the sum of its proper divisors exceeds the number.

(a) 10 is deficient. $1 + 2 + 5 = 8.$
(b) 12 is abundant. $1 + 2 + 3 + 4 + 6 = 16.$

The Pythagoreans also studied *amicable* or *friendly* numbers. Two numbers were amicable numbers, if each was the sum of the proper divisors of the other.

(a) The proper divisors of   284   are   1,   2,   4,   71, and 142,

$$1 + 2 + 4 + 71 + 142 = 220.$$

(b) The proper divisors of   220   are   1,   2,   4,   5,   10, 11,   20,   22,   44,   55, and   110.

$$1 + 2 + 4 + 5 + 10 + 11 + 20 + 22 + 44 + 55 + 110 = 284.$$

Therefore,   (220, 284)   are amicable numbers.

The Pythagoreans were very interested in magic, horoscopes, sorcery, and astrology and by studying the properties of numbers attempted to influence their society and the society of people under their control. It is said that one Pythagorean was put to death for disclosing to the general public the discovery of Irrational Numbers, for the Pythagoreans had announced they knew all there was to know about numbers. The influence of the Pythagoreans in mathematics is still felt today, for they were among the first to investigate Irrational Numbers, triangles, circles, and other numbers and their applications to geometry. With these foundations, other people were able to continue their investigations into mathematics.

21.3   FINITE NUMBER SYSTEMS

Almost all of our previous work has been done in infinite sets of numbers— Whole Numbers, Integers, Rationals, and Reals. However, many physical

* The proper divisors of n include   1   but not n.

situations lend themselves to systems with a finite number of elements. For example, the months of the year form a finite system, for we can associate the number   1   with January,   2   with February, through   12 with December. After progressing through the twelfth month (December), we return to the first one, January, and begin the association all over again. Thus we need only the set of numbers   1,   2,   3,...,   12 to describe mathematically the months of the year.

Telling time on a twelve-hour clock is another example of an application of a finite mathematical system to a model established in the physical world. We can describe any hour of the day by using one of the elements of the finite set   {1, 2, 3, ..., 12}. To aid in the study of finite number systems, let us first investigate a clock that registers time according to the following pattern.

Figure 21.6

To "tell time" on this clock, we do it in the same manner as on a regular twelve-hour time piece. If the present time is   1, then in   3   hours the time is   4.

Figure 21.7

In terms of mathematics, we can denote *time in the future* using the numerals   0, +1, +2, +3,..., and denote *time that has passed* by −1, −2, −3,....

Hence   3   hours from now will be denoted by +3;   8   hours from now will be denoted by +8;   10   hours from now will be denoted by +10. As in the case for Integers, the "+" is generally dropped:

$$+n = n, \quad n \text{ any Integer.}$$

Similarly,   2   hours ago will be denoted by −2;   6   hours ago will be denoted by −6;   12   hours ago will be denoted by −12. This method of denoting numbers in clock arithmetic now "parallels" that of denoting numbers in the set of Integers. Hence we shall be able to find sums and differences by using some of the properties of Integers. This is explained in the following paragraphs.

Addition on the clock can be thought of as "jumps" in a clockwise direction, and subtraction can be thought of as "jumps" in a counterclockwise direction. To the sentence "If the present time is   *1*, in   *5*   hours the time will be   *0*" is related to the mathematical sentence

$$1 + (+5) = 1 + 5 = 0.$$

This is determined by starting on the dial of the clock at   *1*   and then "jumping"   *5*   times, landing each time on the next numeral.

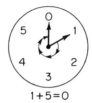

$$1+5=0$$

Figure 21.8

"If the present time is   *2*, then   *5*   hours ago the time was   *3*" is related to the sentence

$$2 + (-5) = 3,$$

and is pictured below by "jumping" in the counterclockwise direction.

$$2-5=3$$

Figure 21.9

We see immediately that certain Integers may denote the same hour on the clock. By starting at   *0*, and jumping in the clockwise or counterclockwise direction as outlined above, we can partition the set of Integers into the following six classes.

Starting at 0, Jumps of This Magnitude Terminate at		This Clock Hour
$\{\ldots, -18, -12, -6, 0, 6, 12, 18, \ldots\}$	$\longrightarrow$	0
$\{\ldots, -17, -11, -5, 1, 7, 13, 19, \ldots\}$	$\longrightarrow$	1
$\{\ldots, -16, -10, -4, 2, 8, 14, 20, \ldots\}$	$\longrightarrow$	2
$\{\ldots, -15, -9, -3, 3, 9, 15, 21, \ldots\}$	$\longrightarrow$	3
$\{\ldots, -14, -8, -2, 4, 10, 16, 22, \ldots\}$	$\longrightarrow$	4
$\{\ldots, -13, -7, -1, 5, 11, 17, 23, \ldots\}$	$\longrightarrow$	5

Figure 21.10

RESIDUE CLASSES OF INTEGERS

Each set of Integers in Figure 21.10 is called a Residue Class of Integers. The name Residue Class stems from the term Remainder. If each element of $\{\ldots, -18, -12, -6, 0, 6, 12, 18, \ldots\}$ is expressed as a product $6(n) + R \ (R \geq 0)$, we see that R is 0.

$$R$$

(a) $-18 = 6(-3) + 0.$
(b) $-6 = 6(-1) + 0.$
(c) $6 = 6(1) + 0.$
(d) $18 = 6(3) + 0.$

Similarly, if each element of $\{\ldots, -17, -11, -5, 1, 7, 13, 19, \ldots\}$ is expressed in the form $6(n) + R$, we see that R is 1:

(a) $-11 = 6(-2) + 1.$
(b) $-5 = 6(-1) + 1.$
(c) $7 = 6(1) + 1.$
(d) $19 = 6(3) + 1.$

Hence we have a method by which we can determine to which Residue Class any Integer will belong.

(a) -19 is an element of $\{\ldots, -13, -7, -1, 5, 11, 17, 23, \ldots\}$ because $-19 = 6(-4) + 5$:
(b) 28 is an element of $\{\ldots, -14, -8, -2, 4, 10, 16, 22, \ldots\}$ because $28 = 6(4) + 4.$
(c) -76 is an element of $\{\ldots, -14, -18, -2, 4, 10, 16, 22, \ldots\}$ because $-76 = 6(-13) + 4.$

As in the case for Rational Numbers, we shall use special symbols to denote the Residual Classes:

$\{\ldots, -18, -12, -6, 0, 6, 12, 18, \ldots\}$ is denoted by $\boxed{0}$,

$\{\ldots, -17, -11, -5, 1, 7, 13, 19, \ldots\}$ is denoted by $\boxed{1}$,

$\{\ldots, -16, -10, -4, 2, 8, 14, 20, \ldots\}$ is denoted by $\boxed{2}$,

$\{\ldots, -15, -9, -3, 3, 9, 15, 21, \ldots\}$ is denoted by $\boxed{3}$,

$\{\ldots, -14, -8, -2, 4, 10, 16, 22, \ldots\}$ is denoted by $\boxed{4}$,

$\{\ldots, -13, -7, -1, 5, 11, 15, 23, \ldots\}$ is denoted by $\boxed{5}$,

Similarly, any element from $\boxed{0}$ may be used to denote $\boxed{0}$; any element from $\boxed{1}$ may be used to denote $\boxed{1}$; etc.

EXAMPLES

$\boxed{4}$ may be denoted by 10 or -8 or 22 or ....

$\boxed{0}$ may be denoted by -18 or 6 or -12 or ....

$\boxed{5}$ may be denoted by -13 or 17 or 5 or ....

Several things should be noted about these Residue Classes of Integers. The first observation is that for any given Residue Class, the difference between any two *consecutive* Integers in this class is   6.

The second observation is a most important one—for any given Residue Class, the difference between *any* two Integers in this class is a member of $\boxed{0}$:

(a) For $\boxed{1}$,

$-17 - 13 = -30,$ $-30 \in \boxed{0}$,

$-19 - (-13) = 36,$ $36 \in \boxed{0}$,

$13 - (1) = 12,$ $12 \in \boxed{0}$.

(b) For $\boxed{5}$,

$-13 - 11 = -24,$ $-24 \in \boxed{0}$,

$$-19 - (-13) = -6, \qquad -6 \in \boxed{0},$$

$$23 - (-13) = 36, \qquad 36 \in \boxed{0}.$$

(c) For $\boxed{3}$,

$$9 - (-15) = 24, \qquad 24 \in \boxed{0},$$

$$(-9) - 21 = -30, \qquad -30 \in \boxed{0},$$

$$3 - 3 = 0, \qquad 0 \in \boxed{0}.$$

The third observation is that if two Integers are selected from two *different* Residue Classes, their difference is *never* a member of $\boxed{0}$.

(a) $0 - 1 = -1, \qquad -1 \in \boxed{5},$

(b) $13 - 2 = 11, \qquad 11 \in \boxed{5},$

(c) $15 - (-13) = 28, \qquad 28 \in \boxed{4}.$

The second observation, which states that for any given Residue Class the difference between *any* two Integers in this class is a member of $\boxed{0}$, also means that this difference is *evenly* divisible by 6. For example:

(a) For $\boxed{1}$,

$$-17 - 13 = -30, \qquad -30 \in \boxed{0} \quad \text{and} \quad -30 = 6(-5) + 0.$$

(b) For $\boxed{2}$,

$$15 - (-15) = 30, \qquad 30 \in \boxed{0} \quad \text{and} \quad 30 = 6(5) + 0.$$

(c) For $\boxed{5}$

$$-13 - (-37) = 24, \qquad 24 \in \boxed{0} \quad \text{and} \quad 24 = 6(4) + 0.$$

The observation above provides a basis that can be used to determine membership within a particular Residue Class. In each case, if the Integers a and b belonged to the same class, then $(a - b)$ or $(b - a)$ was divisible by 6. Such a system is defined as a Congruence Relation Modulo 6. In order to determine membership within the Residue Classes, the following definition is given.

Definition 21.1—A Congruence Relation Modulo n   The Integer a is said to be congruent to the Integer b, Modulo the Integer n, if and only if n is a factor of $(a - b)$.

The above is shortened to $a \equiv b(mod\ n)$, if and only if n is a factor of $a - b$. "$a \equiv b(mod\ n)$" is read "the Integer a is congruent to the Integer b, modulo n" or "a is congruent to b, mod n."

The symbol "$a \mid b$" means that a is a factor of b. To indicate that a is not a factor of b, the notation "$a \nmid b$" is used.

(a) $7 \mid 14$ because $14 = 2(7)$.
(b) $a \mid (ax + ay)$ because $ax + ay = a(x + y)$.
(c) $7 \mid (17 - 10)$ because $(17 - 10) = 7(1)$.
(d) $8 \nmid 10$ because there is no Integer n such that $10 = 8n$.
(e) $6 \nmid (17 - 13)$ because there is no Integer n such that $(17 - 13) = 6n$.
(f) $7 \nmid (21 - 18)$ because there is no Integer n such that $(21 - 18) = 7n$.

We use the above in the following manner.

(a) $3 \equiv 0(mod\ 3)$ because $3 \mid (3 - 0)$.
(b) $4 \equiv 1(mod\ 3)$ because $3 \mid (4 - 1)$.
(c) $5 \equiv 2(mod\ 3)$ because $3 \mid (5 - 2)$.
(d) $6 \equiv 0(mod\ 3)$ because $3 \mid (6 - 0)$.
(e) $7 \equiv 1(mod\ 3)$ because $3 \mid (7 - 1)$.
(f) $8 \not\equiv 1(mod\ 4)$ because $4 \nmid (8 - 1)$.
(g) $9 \not\equiv 2(mod\ 5)$ because $5 \nmid (9 - 2)$.
(h) $12 \not\equiv 4(mod\ 6)$ because $6 \nmid (12 - 4)$.

Frequently, tables are presented which present basic addition or multiplication facts modulo n. If we consider addition and multiplication as defined in the set of Integers then we can exhibit the tables as in arithmetic. Use is made of the Remainder idea to complete the tables.

Addition Table

Mod 3

+	0	1	2
0	0	1	2
1	1	2	0
2	2	0	1

R

$0 + 0 = 0, 0 = 3(0) + 0.$
$0 + 1 = 1, 1 = 3(0) + 1.$
$0 + 2 = 2, 2 = 3(0) + 2.$
$1 + 0 = 0, 1 = 3(0) + 1.$
$1 + 1 = 2, 2 = 3(0) + 2.$
$1 + 2 = 3, 3 = 3(1) + 0.$
$2 + 0 = 2, 2 = 3(0) + 2.$
$2 + 1 = 3, 3 = 3(1) + 0.$
$2 + 2 = 4, 4 = 3(1) + 1.$

Figure 21.11

Similarly, the Multiplication table, Modulo 3 is given.

Multiplication Table

Mod 3

×	0	1	2
0	0	0	0
1	0	1	2
2	0	2	1

R

$0(0) = 0, 0 = 3(0) + 0.$
$0(1) = 0, 0 = 3(0) + 0.$
$0(2) = 0, 0 = 3(0) + 0.$
$1(0) = 0, 0 = 3(0) + 0.$
$1(1) = 1, 1 = 3(0) + 1.$
$1(2) = 2, 2 = 3(0) + 2.$
$2(0) = 0, 0 = 3(0) + 0.$
$2(1) = 2, 2 = 3(0) + 2.$
$2(2) = 4, 4 = 3(1) + 1.$

Figure 21.12

Each fact can be verified by using Definition 21.1 Some examples are presented below. Each shows that   3   is a factor of $a - b$.

(a) $2 + 1 = 3$, $3 = 0 \pmod 3$ because $\dfrac{3 - 0}{3} = 1.$

(b) $2(2) = 4$, $4 = 1 \pmod 3$ because $\dfrac{4 - 1}{3} = 1.$

(c) $1(2) = 2$, $2 = 2 \pmod 3$ because $\dfrac{2 - 2}{3} = 0.$

PROBLEM SET 21.1

1. Illustrate, using the methods devised by the Pythagoreans that the square number   4   is the sum of two triangular numbers and that   9   is the sum of two triangular numbers.

2. Starting with   1, find the sum of the first   25   consecutive odd numbers, using the theorem of section 21.2. Find the sum of the first   125   consecutive odd numbers.

3. One perfect number lies between   25   and   30. Find this perfect number.

4. If the configuration of a number has one more column than rows, the number is an oblong number.

$$2 \quad \bullet\!\!-\!\!\bullet$$

$$6 \quad \begin{array}{c} \bullet\!-\!\bullet \\ \bullet\!-\!\bullet \end{array}$$

Find the next oblong number.

5. Figure 21.10 illustrates the set of Integers when partitioned into   6   Residue Classes. Find, if x is an Integer the sets:

$$A = \{x| \quad x = 0(\text{mod } 3)\}.$$
$$B = \{x| \quad x = 1(\text{mod } 3)\}.$$
$$C = \{x| \quad x = 2(\text{mod } 3)\}.$$

6. Refer to Figures 21.11–12 to answer the following questions:

(a) What is the Additive Identity for $\{0, 1, 2\}$, (mod 3)?
(b) What is the Multiplicative Identity for $\{0, 1, 2\}$, (mod 3)?
(c) What is the Additive Inverse for   1(mod 3)? for   2(mod 3)? for   0(mod 3)?
(d) What is the Multiplicative Inverse for   1(mod 3)? for   2(mod 3)? for   0(mod 3)?
(e) Is the set $\{0, 1, 2\}$ closed under Addition,   mod 3?
(f) Is the set $\{0, 1, 2\}$ closed under Multiplication,   mod 3?
(g) Illustrate that $(2 + 1)(\text{mod } 3) = (1 + 2)(\text{mod } 3)$. This is an illustration of what property?
(h) Illustrate that $[2(2 + 1)](\text{mod } 3) = [2(2) + 2(1)](\text{mod } 3)$.
(i) Using the Definition for a field, established in Chapter 20, does $\{0, 1, 2\}$mod 3, satisfy the properties of a field?

7. Answer the following true or false. All letters represent Positive Integers.

(a) $18 \equiv 4(\text{mod } 5)$.   (b) $(21 + 17) \equiv (2 + 1)(\text{mod } 8)$.
(c) $(35) \equiv [5(2)](\text{mod } 5)$.   (d) $2a \equiv a(\text{mod } a)$.
(e) $6b \equiv 3(\text{mod } 3)$.   (f) $ac \equiv ad(\text{mod } a)$.

8. Complete the following Addition Table, modulo 7, and the Multiplication Table, modulo 7.

(a)   Modulo 7 $\underline{R}$

+	0	1	2	3	4	5	6
0							
1							
2							
3							2
4					1		
5							
6						4	

$6 + 5 = 11, \quad 11 = 7(1) + 4.$
$4 + 4 = 8, \quad\; 8 = 7(1) + 1.$
$3 + 6 = 9, \quad\; 9 = 7(1) + 2.$

(b)

×	0	1	2	3	4	5	6
0							
1							
2							
3							
4						6	
5			3				
6						2	

$\underline{R}$

$6(5) = 30, \quad 30 = 4(7) + 2.$
$4(5) = 20, \quad 20 = 2(7) + 6.$
$5(2) = 10, \quad 10 = 1(7) + 3.$

9. Find the smallest Positive Integer, x, so that:

(a) $37 \equiv x(\bmod 7)$.   (b) $26 \equiv x(\bmod 9)$.
(c) $86 \equiv x(\bmod 5)$.   (d) $34 \equiv x(\bmod 5)$.
(e) $31 \equiv x(\bmod 2)$.   (f) $72 \equiv x(\bmod 13)$.
(g) $17 \equiv x(\bmod 4)$.   (h) $23 \equiv x(\bmod 14)$.

10.   The statement $a \equiv b(\bmod n)$ if and only if n divides (evenly) $a - b$
can also be restated: "If n divides (evenly) $a - b$, then $a \equiv b(\bmod n)$."
Hence

(a) $\dfrac{8 - 5}{3} = 1, \quad \therefore\ 8 \equiv 5(\bmod 3)$.

(b) $\dfrac{a(b - c)}{a} = b - c. \quad \therefore\ ab \equiv ac(\bmod a)$.

Restate each of the following in terms of $a \equiv b \pmod n$:

(c) $\dfrac{24 - 17}{7} = 1.$

(d) $\dfrac{16 - 3}{13} = 1.$

(e) $\dfrac{18 - 4}{7} = 2.$

(f) $\dfrac{ax - ay}{a} = x - y.$

(g) $\dfrac{2n - n}{n} = 1.$

(h) $\dfrac{7(x - y)}{7} = x - y.$

21.4 PROPERTIES OF EQUALITY

Many properties of finite number systems parallel those properties of infinite number systems. The first of these "parallel" properties deals with equality. In order to investigate these properties, we must prove the following.

Theorem 21.1 For every Integer a, for every Integer b, and for every Integer c, if $a|b$ and $a|c$, then we have the following.

(a) $a|(b + c)$.
(b) $a|(b - c)$.
(c) $a|(c - b)$.

We shall prove only part (a) above. Parts (b) and (c) will be left as an exercise for the reader.

Proof: Assume that each of a, b, and c is an Integer so that $a|b$ and $a|c$. If $a|b$, there exists a number k so that $b = a(k)$; if $a|c$ there exists a number d, so that $c = a(d)$;

$$b + c = a(k) + a(d),$$

$$= a(k + d).$$

Therefore, $a|(b + c)$.

This completes the proof that if $a|b$ and $a|c$, then $a|(b + c)$ because there is an Integer $(k + d)$, so that $(b + c) = a(k + d)$. Parts (b) and (c) are stated as Exercises in Problem Set 21.2.

By using Theorem 21.1 and the definition for the Congruence Relation, we can prove that the relation $\equiv$ is an Equivalence Relation.

Theorem 21.2—The Relation $\equiv$ is an Equivalence Relation For every Integer a, for every Integer b, for every Integer c, and for every Integer $n > 0$, the following can be considered.

(a) Reflexivity: $a \equiv a(\text{mod } n)$.
(b) Symmetry: If $a \equiv b(\text{mod } n)$ then $b \equiv a(\text{mod } n)$.
(c) Transitivity: If $a \equiv b(\text{mod } n)$ and $b \equiv c(\text{mod } n)$,   then $a \equiv c(\text{mod } n)$.

Reflexivity: If a is   an   Integer,   then $n|(a - a)$. Therefore,   if $n|(a - a)$, then $a \equiv a(\text{mod } n)$.
Symmetry: If $a \equiv b(\text{mod } n)$ then $n|(a - b)$ by the definition of congruence.
   If $n|(a - b)$, then $n|(b - a)$ by Theorem 21.1.
   If $n|(b - a)$, then $b \equiv a(\text{mod } n)$ by the definition of the Congruence Relation.
Transitivity: If $a \equiv b(\text{mod } n)$ and $b \equiv c(\text{mod } n)$,   then $n|(a - b)$ and $n|(b - c)$.
   By Theorem 21.1, if $n|(a - b)$ and $n|(b - c)$, then

$$n|[(a - b) + (b - c)],$$

$$n|[a + (-b + b) - c],$$

$$n|[a - c].$$

   If $n|[a - c]$, then $a \equiv c(\text{mod } n)$, by the definition of the Congruence Relation.
   The next two Theorems are commonly called the Addition Property and Multiplication Property. These two properties are used extensively in applications for modulo n systems.

Theorem 21.3—Addition Property   For   every   Integer a, for   every Integer b, and for every Integer $n > 0$, if $a \equiv b(\text{mod } n)$ and if c is any Integer, then

$$(a + c) \equiv (b + c)(\text{mod } n).$$

Proof: Let $a \equiv b(\text{mod } n)$ and c be any Integer.
If $a \equiv b(\text{mod } n)$, then $n|a - b$.
Now $a - b \equiv (a + c) - (b + c)$, c any Integer. Therefore,

$$n|[(a + c) - (b + c)],$$

and $(a + c) \equiv (b + c)(\text{mod } n)$.

Theorem 21.4—Multiplication Property   For   every   Integer a, for every Integer b, and for   every Integer $n > 0$, if $a \equiv b(\text{mod } n)$, then for every Integer c,

$$a(c) \equiv b(c)(\text{mod } n).$$

Proof: Let $a \equiv b(\text{mod } n)$ and c be any Integer.
Then $n|(a - b)$. If $n|(a-b)$, then $n|c(a - b)$.
  If $n|c(a - b)$, then $n|ca - cb$, from which we can conclude that

$$ca \equiv cb(\text{mod } n).$$

It should be noted that finite number systems,   mod n, do not retain properties which are total similarities when compared to the set of Integers. For example:

The Cancellation Property for Multiplication is Not True. We *cannot* conclude that if $ac \equiv ab(\text{mod } n)$, then $a \equiv b(\text{mod } n)$. This is illustrated by:

$$6(3) \equiv 6(2)(\text{mod } 6), \quad [6|(18 - 12)].$$

$$3 \not\equiv 2(\text{mod } 6), \quad [6\nmid(3 - 2)].$$

However, the Additive Cancellation Property is true.

Theorem 21.5—The Additive Cancellation Property   For every Integer a, for every Integer b, for every Integer $n > 0$, if

$$(a + b) \equiv (a + c)(\text{mod } n), \text{ then } \quad b \equiv c(\text{mod } n).$$

Proof: The proof is left as an exercise.
  These Theorems denote methods to form sums or products,   mod n. The ability to do this is most important in developing an understanding for applications of finite systems,   mod n. Illustrations of these Theorems and some of their uses are given below.

(a) If $6 \equiv 1(\text{mod } 5)$ and $7 \equiv 2(\text{mod } 5)$, then $(6 + 7) \equiv (1 + 2)(\text{mod } 5)$. $[5|(13 - 3)]$.
(b) If $6 \equiv 1(\text{mod } 5)$ and $7 \equiv 2(\text{mod } 5)$, then $6(7) \equiv 1(2)$ (mod 5). $[5|(42 - 2)]$.
(c) If $30 \equiv 40(\text{mod } 5)$, then $3(10) \equiv 4(10)(\text{mod } 5)$ and $3 \not\equiv 4(\text{mod } 5)$. $[5\nmid(3 - 4)]$.
(d) If $(11 \times 7) \equiv (5 \times 7)(\text{mod } 6)$, then $11 \equiv 5(\text{mod } 6)$. $[6|(11 - 5)]$.
(e) For every Integer n, $(2 + 7n) \equiv 2(\text{mod } 7)$.

Proof:

$$2 \equiv 2(\text{mod } 7), \quad [7|(2 - 2)].$$

$$7 \equiv 0(\bmod 7), \qquad [7|(7 - 0)].$$

$$n \equiv n(\bmod 7), \qquad [7|(n - n)].$$

$$7(n) \equiv 0(n)(\bmod 7), \qquad \text{Multiplication property.}$$

$$(2 + 7n) = (2 + 0)(\bmod 7) \quad \text{Addition property.}$$

$$(2 + 7n) \equiv 2(\bmod 7).$$

PROBLEM SET 21.2

1. Cite the property that justifies each of the following sentences. All letters represent Positive Integers:

(a) If $(7 + n) \equiv 7(\bmod 5)$, then $n \equiv 0(\bmod 5)$.
(b) If $7x \equiv y(\bmod 3)$, then $35x \equiv 5y(\bmod 3)$.
(c) If $21 \equiv 5(\bmod 8)$ and $17 \equiv 1(\bmod 8)$ then $38 \equiv 6(\bmod 8)$.
(d) If $5 \equiv 2(\bmod 3)$ and $7 \equiv 1(\bmod 3)$ then $35 \equiv 2(\bmod 3)$.

2. Prove parts (b) and (c) of Theorem 21.1.

3. Complete the proof for Theorem 21.5.

4. Prove, as illustrated in Section 21.3 above, that for every Integer n, the following is valid.

(a) $4 + 6n \equiv 4(\bmod 6)$.   (b) $7(-n) \equiv 0(\bmod 7)$.
(c) $8n \equiv 0(\bmod 8)$.   (d) $4(-n) \equiv 0(\bmod 4)$.
(e) $(3 + 5n) \equiv 3(\bmod 5)$.   (f) $(x + 4n) \equiv x(\bmod 4)$.
(g) $(3 + 6n) \equiv 3(\bmod 6)$.

21.5   IDENTITIES; INVERSES

For every set of numbers studied throughout this text (except for the Irrationals), there existed two unique elements, zero and one, that had the following property:

$$a + 0 = a,$$

$$a(1) = a,$$

where a was any number. The number 0 was defined as the Additive Identity and the number 1 was defined the Multiplicative Identity.

It is easily demonstrated that the Residue Class $\boxed{0}$ serves as an Additive Identity,   mod 6:

$$(4 + 0) = 4(\bmod 6), \qquad [6|(4 - 4)].$$

$$(4 + 6) \equiv 4(\text{mod } 6), \quad [6|(10 - 4)].$$
$$[4 + (-6)] \equiv 4(\text{mod } 6), \quad [6|(-2 - 4)].$$
$$[4 + (-18)] \equiv 4(\text{mod } 6), \quad [6|(-14 - 4)].$$

Similarly, for the Residue Class $\boxed{1}$, mod 6, that retains the parallel property of a Multiplicative Identity Element:

$$1(5) = 5(\text{mod } 6), \quad [6|(5 - 5)].$$
$$7(5) \equiv 1(5)(\text{mod } 6), \quad [6|(35 - 5)].$$
$$-5(5) \equiv 5(\text{mod } 6), \quad [6|(-25 - 5)].$$
$$13(5) \equiv 5(\text{mod } 6), \quad [6|(65 - 5)].$$

From these examples of number systems,   modulo n we then define $\boxed{0}$ to be the Additive Identity and $\boxed{1}$ to be the Multiplicative Identity,   modulo n. This parallels properties for infinite number systems.

It should be noted that number systems,   modulo n do not retain all properties related to 0. One recalls that in the system of Reals, if $a(b) = 0$, then,

(a) $a = 0$,
(b) $b = 0$, or
(c) both a and b equal 0.

However, this may or may not be true in a mathematical system, modulo n:

(a) If $a = 0$ or $b = 0$, then $a(b) \equiv 0(\text{mod } n)$:

$$4 \equiv 4(\text{mod } 32),$$
$$8 \equiv 8(\text{mod } 32).$$

But $4(8) \equiv 32(\text{mod } 32) \equiv 0(\text{mod } 32).$

Therefore, it is *not true in all cases* that if $a(b) \equiv 0(\text{mod } n)$, then $a = 0$, or $b = 0$, or both a and b are 0.

One recalls that for any Real Number $a \neq 0$ and for any Real Number $x \neq 0$, if

$$a(x) = 1,$$

the Multiplicative Identity, then a was the Multiplicative Inverse of x and x was the Multiplicative Inverse of a. In arithmetic, the number x was generally denoted as "$\frac{1}{a}$", and

$$a\left(\frac{1}{a}\right) = 1.$$

Each number, except   0, had a Multiplicative Inverse within the Real Number system. However, for finite systems,   modulo n, each element may or may not have an element that acts as a Multiplicative Inverse. In the following system, each element has a Multiplicative Inverse.

Modulo 5

×	0	1	2	3	4
0	0	0	0	0	0
1	0	1	2	3	4
2	0	2	4	1	3
3	0	3	1	4	2
4	0	4	3	2	1

Figure 21.13

The Multiplicative Identity,   mod 5, is $\boxed{1}$, because for any Integer a,   mod 5,

$$1(a) \equiv a(\text{mod } 5).$$

Similarly, for each Integer $a \not\equiv 0$,   mod 5, there is an Integer b, mod 5, so that

$$a(b) \equiv 1(\text{mod } 5).$$

From the table of Figure 21.13 we have:

(a) $1(1) \equiv 1(\text{mod } 5)$. Therefore the Multiplicative Inverse of   1   is 1.

(b) $2(3) \equiv 1(\text{mod } 5)$. Therefore the Multiplicative Inverse of   2   is 3.

(c) $3(2) \equiv 1(\text{mod } 5)$. Therefore the Multiplicative Inverse of   3   is 2.

(d) $4(4) \equiv 1(\text{mod } 5)$. Therefore the Multiplicative Inverse of   4   is 4.

From this, we determine that each Integer $a \not\equiv 0$,   mod 5, has a Multiplicative Inverse,   mod 5.

However, the same cannot be said for every Integer $a \not\equiv 0$,   mod 4.

Modulo 4

×	0	1	2	3
0	0	0	0	0
1	0	1	2	3
2	0	2	0	2
3	0	3	2	1

Figure 21.14

From the above, we see that   2,   mod 4 had no Multiplicative Inverse, for there is no Integer b such that

$$2(b) \equiv 1(\bmod 4).$$

Hence we see that in some cases, every element $a \not\equiv 0$ mod n has a Multiplicative Inverse and in other cases some elements do not have a Multiplicative Inverse. Particularly, if n is prime, then every element $a \not\equiv 0$,   mod n, will have a Multiplicative Inverse. This is so because, if n is prime, there are no two nonzero Integers a and b so that $a(b) \equiv 0(\bmod n)$, provided $|a|, |b| < n$. (This will be assumed and not proven.)

However, if n is *composite*, then there *may be* two nonzero integers a and b such that

$$a(b) \equiv 0(\bmod n).$$

Consider the multiplication,   mod 4, above. In this case, we see that

$$2(2) \equiv 0(\bmod 4).$$

From this we see that the Integer   2,   mod 4, has no Additive Inverse. This is summarized by the following definition.

Definition 21.2 If n is any prime number, and a is an element of $\{1, 2, 3, \ldots, (n - 1)\}$,   mod n, then there exists a unique Positive Integer $b < n$, so that

$$a(b) \equiv 1(\bmod n).$$

Hence only in certain instances will each element,   mod n have a Multiplicative Inverse.

Each element, mod n, will have an Additive Inverse, regardless of the conditions placed on n (prime or a composite number). Consider the tables below.

Modulo 4

+	0	1	2	3
0	0	1	2	3
1	1	2	3	0
2	2	3	0	1
3	3	0	1	2

Modulo 5

+	0	1	2	3	4
0	0	1	2	3	4
1	1	2	3	4	0
2	2	3	4	0	1
3	3	4	0	1	2
4	4	0	1	2	3

Figure 21.15

Note that each element above has an Additive Inverse, that is for any a, mod n, there is a b, mod n so that

$$(a + b) \equiv 0 \pmod{n}.$$

We see that consideration regarding primeness or compositeness need not be considered when discussing Additive Inverses. This is stated in the following manner.

Definition 21.3 If n is an Integer, and a is an element of $\{0, 1, 2, 3, \ldots, (n - 1)\}$, mod n, then there exists a unique Integer $b < n$, so that

$$(a + b) \equiv 0 \pmod{n}.$$

PROBLEM SET 21.3

1. Find $\boxed{a}$ so that $a \equiv 1 \pmod 4$.

2. Find $\boxed{a}$ so that $a \equiv 0 \pmod 4$.

3. Find two Integers, $a \neq 0$ and $b \neq 0$, whose product is congruent to the following.

(a) $0 \pmod 6$.
(c) $0 \pmod{15}$.

(b) $0 \pmod{12}$.
(d) $0 \pmod{16}$.

4. If possible, find two Integers, $a, b \neq 0$, whose product is congruent to 0 (mod 7). Investigate elements of the set $\{0, 1, 2, 3, 4, 5, 6\}$.

5. If possible, find two Integers, $a, b \neq 0$, whose product is congruent to 0 (mod 11). Investigate elements of the set $\{0, 1, 2, 3, \ldots, 10\}$.

6. Let $b \in \{0, 1, 2, 3, 4\}$. Find the unique positive Integer b so that

(a) $1(b) \equiv 1 \pmod 5$.   (b) $2(b) \equiv 1 \pmod 5$.
(c) $3(b) \equiv 1 \pmod 5$.   (d) $4(b) \equiv 1 \pmod 5$.

7. Let $b \in \{0, 1, 2, \ldots, 10\}$. Find the unique Positive Integer b so that

(a) $2(b) \equiv 1 \pmod{11}$.   (b) $8(b) \equiv 1 \pmod{11}$.
(c) $9(b) \equiv 1 \pmod{11}$.

8. Let $b \in \{0, 1, 2, \ldots, 8\}$. Find the unique Positive Integer b so that

(a) $6 + b \equiv 0 \pmod 9$.   (b) $7 + b \equiv 0 \pmod 9$.
(c) $1 + b \equiv 0 \pmod 9$.

9. Let $b \in \{0, 1, 2, \ldots, 12\}$. Find the unique Positive Integer b so that

(a) $6 + b \equiv 0 \pmod{13}$.   (b) $5 + 13b \equiv 0 \pmod{13}$.
(c) $9 + 12b \equiv 0 \pmod{13}$.

10. Given the set $\{a, b, c\}$, mod n and the binary (two at a time) operation $*$. Find:

(a) The Identity Element.
(b) The Inverse for each element, if it exists.

*	a	b	c
a	a	b	c
b	b	c	a
c	c	a	b

11. Using the addition and multiplication tables, mod 5, find the element x so that each of the following mathematical sentences is true:

(a) $x + 4 = 1$.   (b) $3 + x = 0$.
(c) $4 + x = 4$.   (d) $3(x) = 1$.
(e) $4(x) = 3$.   (f) $2(x) = 3$.

12. Using the table of Problem 10, find the element x so that

(a) $b * x = a$.   (b) $b * x = c$.
(c) $c * x = a$.   (d) $c * x = b$.

21.6 DISTRIBUTIVITY: FIELD PROPERTIES

One recalls that a set has the Distributive Property under the operations
$+$ and $\times$ if and only if for each element $a,$ $b,$ and c of the set,

$$a \times (b + c) = (a \times b) + (a \times c).$$

In this case, the operation $\times$ is said to distribute over the operation $+$.
We found this property to be true for each set of numbers when considering
the operations of multiplication and addition.

For   modulo n systems, we find that for any set $F,$ modulo n
and the operations $\oplus$ and $\otimes$, that this same property will be true. Consider
the tables below, for addition and multiplication,   mod 3.

Modulo 3

$\oplus$	0	1	2
0	0	1	2
1	1	2	0
2	2	0	1

Modulo 3

$\otimes$	0	1	2
0	0	0	0
1	0	1	2
2	0	2	1

Figure 21.16

EXAMPLES

(a) $2 \otimes (2 \oplus 1) = 2 \otimes 0 = 0,$
$(2 \otimes 2) \oplus (2 \otimes 1) = 1 \oplus 2 = 0.$
(b) $2 \otimes (1 \oplus 1) = 2 \otimes 2 = 1,$
$(2 \otimes 1) \oplus (2 \otimes 1) = 2 \oplus 2 = 1.$

Similarly, for the set $\{a, b, c, d, e\}$ and the two operations $\circledast$ and
$\boxtimes$ defined on this set, the Distributive Property of $\circledast$ over $\boxtimes$ holds.

$\circledast$	a	b	c	d	e
a	a	b	c	d	e
b	b	c	d	e	a
c	c	d	e	a	b
d	d	e	a	b	c
e	e	a	b	c	d

$\boxtimes$	a	b	c	d	e
a	a	a	a	a	a
b	a	b	c	d	e
c	a	c	e	b	d
d	a	d	b	e	c
e	a	e	d	c	b

Figure 21.17

EXAMPLES

(a) $c \boxtimes (d \circledast e) = c \boxtimes c = e$,
  $(c \boxtimes d) \circledast (c \boxtimes e) = b \circledast d = e$.
(b) $b \boxtimes (c \circledast d) = b \boxtimes a = a$,
  $(b \boxtimes c) \circledast (b \boxtimes d) = c \circledast d = a$.

One recalls that for a system to be defined as a Field, a set $F = \{a, b, c, \ldots\}$ must satisfy the following properties under the two operations $+$ and $\times$.

F1: Closure: $a + b \in F$ and $a \in b$ F.

F2: Commutativity: $a + b = b + a$ and $a \times b = b \times a$.

F3: Associativity: $a + (b + c) = (a + b) + c$ and $a \times (b + c) = (a \times b) + (a \times c)$.

F4: Additive Identity: There exists an element $0 \in F$ such that if $a \in F$, $a + 0 = 0 + a = a$.

F5: Additive Inverses: For every element $a \in F$, there exists an element $i \in F$ such that $a + i = 0$, the Additive Identity.

F6: Multiplicative Identity: There exists an element $e \in F$ such that if $a \in F$, $a \times e = e \times a = a$.

F7: Multiplicative Inverses: For every element $a \in F$, $(a \neq 0)$ there exists an element $a' \in F$ such that $a \times a' = a' \times a = e$, the Multiplicative Identity.

F8: Distributivity: For every $a, b, c \in F$, $a \times (b + c) = (a \times b) + (a \times c)$.

The set $\{a, b, c, d, e\}$ under the operations $\circledast$ and $\boxtimes$ as illustrated in Figure 21.17 is an example of a Field, for each property F1–F8 is satisfied.

PROBLEM SET 21.4

1. Given the set $F = \{0, 1, 2, 3, 4\}$ and the operations $\oplus$ and $\boxtimes$ as illustrated in Figures 21.14 and 21.15. Copy these tables and show if F is a Field.

2. Given the set $\{a, b, c, d\}$ and the operations $\circledast$ and $\boxtimes$ as defined below. Find, if this set under these two operations defines a Field.

⊛	a	b	c	d
a	a	b	c	d
b	b	c	d	a
c	c	d	a	b
d	d	a	b	c

⊠	a	b	c	d
a	a	a	a	a
b	a	b	c	d
c	a	c	a	c
d	a	d	c	b

3. Construct addition and multiplication tables for $\{0, 1, 2, 3, 4, 5\}$, modulo 6. Determine if this set is a Field under + and ×.

4. Construct addition and multiplication tables for $\{0, 1, 2, 3, 4, 5, 6\}$, modulo 7. Determine if this set is a Field under + and ×.

21.7 APPLICATIONS FOR MODULO–SYSTEMS

An investigation of divisibility properties for the Positive Integers shall be made in order to introduce some applications for modulo n systems. Some of these divisibility properties are listed below.

Divisibility by 2: An Integer is divisible by 2 if and only if the digit in the units position is one of 0, 2, 4, 6, or 8.

Divisibility by 3: If n is an Integer, then n is divisible by 3 if and only if the sum of the digits of n is divisible by 3.
 Before stating other Divisibility tests, it is appropriate that we study Divisibility by 3, for this test reveals an excellent way to apply a modulo n system. This is so, because if n is divisible by 3 and the sum of the digits of n is divisible by 3, then it follows that

$$n \equiv 0 (\text{mod } 3),$$

and (sum of digits) $\equiv 0 (\text{mod } 3),$

from which we can conclude that

$$[3|(n - 0)] \Rightarrow [3|n];$$

and $[3|(\text{sum of digits} - 0)] \Rightarrow [3|(\text{sum of digits})].$

This is the basis for the rule stated in Divisibility by 3 above.
 To illustrate the rule for Divisibility by 3, consider the following table. Each Integer that is divisible by 3 is circled and the sum of the digits is illustrated immediately below these particular numbers.

1	2	③	4	5	⑥	7	8	⑨	10
11	⑫	13	14	⑮	16	17	⑱	19	20
	(1 + 2 = 3)			(1 + 5 = 6)			(1 + 8 = 9)		
㉑	22	23	㉔	25	26	㉗	28	29	㉚
(2 + 1 = 3)			(2 + 4 = 6)			(2 + 7 = 9)			(3 + 0 = 3)
31	32	㉝	34	35	㊱	37	38	㊳	40
		(3 + 3 = 6)			(3 + 6 = 9)			(3 + 9 = 12 = 1 + 2 = 3)	

Figure 21.18

The method of attack to illustrate the rule of divisibility by 3 is to show that $n = 0 \pmod 3$ and (sum of the digits of n) $= 0 \pmod 3$.

EXAMPLE

The sum of the digits of 21 is congruent to $0 \pmod 3$:

$$2 \equiv 2 \pmod 3,$$
$$1 \equiv 1 \pmod 3,$$
$$(2 + 1) \equiv (2 + 1) \pmod 3,$$
$$3 \equiv 0 \pmod 3.$$

Twenty-one is also congruent to $0 \pmod 3$:

$$20 \equiv 2 \pmod 3,$$
$$1 \equiv 1 \pmod 3,$$
$$21 \equiv (2 + 1) \pmod 3,$$
$$21 \equiv 0 \pmod 3.$$

Therefore, we can conclude, by the definition of congruence that

[3|(sum of digits of 21)] and [3|21].

EXAMPLE

The sum of the digits of 123 is congruent to $0 \pmod 3$:

$$1 \equiv 1 \pmod 3,$$
$$2 \equiv 2 \pmod 3,$$
$$3 \equiv 0 \pmod 3,$$
$$(1 + 2 + 3) \equiv (1 + 2 + 0) \pmod 3,$$
$$6 \equiv 0 \pmod 3.$$

One hundred twenty-three is also congruent to 0(mod 3):

$$100 \equiv 1(\text{mod } 3),$$
$$20 \equiv 2(\text{mod } 3),$$
$$3 \equiv 0(\text{mod } 3),$$
$$(100 + 20 + 3) \equiv (1 + 2 + 0)(\text{mod } 3),$$
$$123 \equiv 3(\text{mod } 3),$$
$$123 \equiv 0(\text{mod } 3).$$

Again, we can conclude by the definition of congruence that

[3|(sum of digits of 123)]   and   [3|123].

This illustrates the rule established in Divisibility by   3. Since the sum of the digits of n is congruent to   0(mod 3)   then $n \equiv 0$(mod 3), we need investigate only the sum of the digits to determine if n is divisible by   3.

Other tests for divisibility are stated below. Some tests are easily applied to the   modulo n test as above. Some tests are not as easily adapted to this   modulo n criteria.

Divisibility by 9: If n is an Integer, then n is divisible by   9 if and only if the sum of the digits of n is divisible by   9.

EXAMPLE

297   is divisible by   9   because $2 + 9 + 7 = 18$.   18   is divisible by   9.

Divisibility by   10: If n is an Integer, then n is divisible by   10   if and only if the digit in the units position of n is   0.

Divisibility by   5: If n is an Integer, then n is divisible by 5   if and only if the digit in the units position of n is   0   or 5.

Divisibility by   4: If n is an Integer, then n is divisible by   4   if and only if the number denoted by the digits in the tens and units positions of n is divisible by   4.

EXAMPLE

42164   is divisible because   64   is divisible by   4.

Divisibility by   6: If n is an Integer, then n is divisible by 6   if and only if n is divisible by   2   and   3. [Comment: One recalls $6 = \text{lcm}(2, 3)$.]

Divisibility by   *8 :* If   *n*   is an Integer, then   *n*   is divisible by 8   if and only if the number denoted in the hundreds, tens, and ones positions is divisible by   8.

EXAMPLE

40064   is divisible by   8   because   064   is divisible by   8.

Divisibility by   *11 :* If   *n*   is an Integer, then   *n*   is divisible by 11   if and only if the difference of the sum of the digits in the odd-numbered position (from the right) and the sum of the digits in the even numbered positions (from the right) of   *n*   is divisible by   11.

EXAMPLE

84,557   is divisible by   11   because $(7 + 5 + 8) - (5 + 4) = 11$.   11 is divisible by   11.

Casting out Nines.   The next application for a   modulo *n* system is that of "casting out nines." The "casting out nines" process is a process to check a sum when adding two or more Integers. One recalls that if a number   *n* is divisible by   9, then the sum of the digits of   *n*   is divisible by   9. This is stated as

$$[9|n] \quad \text{and} \quad [9|(\text{sum of digits of } n)].$$

The reader should also note that if   *n*   is an Integer, when the sum of the digits of   *n*   is divided by   9, the *remainder* is the same as when *n*   is divided by   9.

EXAMPLE

$\frac{598}{9} = 66R4.$ $(5 + 9 + 8)/9 = 22/9 = 2\,R4.$

The Remainder is called the excess of nines and is the basis for the definition of the rule of casting out nines.

Therefore, if we investigate the sum of the digits,   mod 9, we should investigate the *excess of nines*.

(a) $87 \equiv 6 \pmod 9$. The excess of nines in   87   is   6.

(b) $8 + 7 = 15$, $15 \equiv 6 \pmod 9$. The excess of nines in the sum of the digits of   15   is   6.

(c) Therefore, the excess of nines in   87   is the same as the excess of nines in the sum of the digits of   87.

(d) $797 \equiv 5 \pmod 9$. The excess of nines in   797   is   5.

(e) $7 + 9 + 7 = 23$, $23 \equiv 5 \pmod 9$. The excess of nines in the sum of the digits of   797   is   5.

(f) Therefore, the excess of nines in   797   is the same as the excess
of nines in the sum of the digits of   797.

To apply this concept in checking column addition, the excess of nines
in the sum should be equal to the excess of nines in the sum of the digits of
the total. Since $9 \equiv 0 \pmod 9$, to "cast out nine" does not affect the
excess of nines for any Integer n. This is also illustrated in the following.

(a) $39 \equiv 3 \pmod 9$. The excess of nines in   39   is   3.
(b) $3 + 9 = 12$, $12 \equiv 3 \pmod 9$. The excess of nines in the sum of the
digits of   39   is   3.
(c) By casting out the "9" in $3 + 9$, we find that the excess of nines is
the same

$$3 + \not{9} = 3 \equiv 3 \pmod 9.$$

The method of casting out nines is illustrated in the following sum.

N	Excess of Nines in N	Cast Out	Excess of Nines in Digits of N
39	$39 \equiv 3 \pmod 9$	$\Longleftrightarrow$	$3 + \not{9} \equiv 3 \pmod 9$
76	$76 \equiv 4 \pmod 9$	$\Longleftrightarrow$	$4 + \not{9} \equiv 4 \pmod 9$
28	$28 \equiv 1 \pmod 9$	$\Longleftrightarrow$	$1 + \not{9} \equiv 1 \pmod 9$
143	$143 \equiv 8 \pmod 9$		$8 \pmod 9$

Excess of Nines in Sum	—Equals—	Excess of Nines in Sum of Digits of Addends

The reader should note that the sum of the digits in n above had
sometimes to be restated to "cast out nines." For example:

$$7 + 6 = 13 = 4 + 9.$$

$$2 + 8 = 10 = 1 + 9.$$

PROBLEM SET 21.5

1. Is   792   divisible by   2?   3?   4?   5?   6?   7?   8?   9? Use
the tests described in this section to answer these questions.

2. Show that   189   is divisible by   9, by illustrating that   [9|189]   and
that   [9|(sum of digits of 189)].

3. Show that   189   is also divisible by   3, by illustrating that   [3|189]
and   [3|(sum of digits of 189)].

4. Add and check the sum of casting out nines.

(a) 49   (b) 63   (c) 119
   37   42   27
   62   88   46
   ——   ——   ——

Index